COLLINS

EUROPEAN MAMMALS

EVOLUTION AND BEHAVIOUR

Collins European Mammals: Evolution and Behaviour is the companion volume to *Collins Field Guide to Mammals of Britain and Europe* by David Macdonald and Priscilla Barrett (ISBN 0 00 219779 0)

COLLINS

EUROPEAN MAMMALS

EVOLUTION AND BEHAVIOUR

written by
DAVID MACDONALD

illustrated by
PRISCILLA BARRETT

HarperCollins*Publishers*

For Ewan, Fiona and Isobel

HarperCollins*Publishers* Ltd 1995
77-85 Fulham Palace Road
London W6 8JB

Printed and bound in the UK by The Bath Press

Contents

Part three MAMMAL REPRODUCTION

Preface

This book is part of a brace on European mammals: the first volume is a *Field Guide* and the second *Evolution and Behaviour*. While each volume can stand alone, I hope they function best as a partnership. In the *Field Guide* readers can discover what they have seen and, in condensed form, ·delve into the vital statistics of each of the over 200 species they may encounter in western Europe. In this book they can learn something of the patterns that bring order to the enthralling variation of mammalian lives. To facilitate that link between the specific and the general, I have been at pains to discuss in this book the species that the reader may have identified while using the *Field Guide*. Familiarity, the axiom tells us, breeds contempt, which may be why it is all too common for European naturalists to assume that the really interesting species are confined to far off tropical lands. By selecting examples almost exclusively from European mammals I hope to have exposed fascination lurking in the familiar.

Modern mammals have changed radically since the days of their ancestors, and so too these books have evolved along an unexpected route to an end point that is dramatically different from the one envisaged at the outset. They are born as a complementary pair, but at the outset our sights were not set so high, with the modest aim of a single volume. However, a field guide alone treats each species in isolation, and thus ignores the patterns that make sense of biological diversity. On the other hand, while one might write about the principles that unite mammals with reference to only a few selected examples, not to introduce all the actors personally runs the risk of making abstract and tidy a story that is actually enthrallingly unfinished. Perversely, one of the most important lessons to be learned from flipping through the pages of the *Field Guide* is just how little is known about most species. All too many general rules in biology rest on all too few particular species. Therefore, realising that we could not achieve both aims within one book, Priscilla Barrett and I have collaborated to produce these two volumes.

Amongst the many debts of gratitude to record here we should begin with those who got us into this in the first place. The six-year gestation of these two books has had its share of authorial morning sickness, not to mention high blood pressure; but now that the birth pains are over, and the offspring healthy, we thank heartily Sir David Attenborough and Professor Christopher Perrins for their role in the conception.

This project has been a partnership. The books are illustrated by Priscilla Barrett. Her contribution extends far beyond the excellence of her artistry: she has attended to every facet of design and research with the result that every picture is not only beautiful but also subtly, and ingeniously, packed with accurate information. Furthermore, she has been a painstaking critic of the innumerable drafts I have produced of the text. Priscilla Barrett's commitment and friendship are almost the only things that have remained unchanged since the inception of this project.

Predictably, but honestly, I thank my wife, Jenny, and my children for adapting to the impact of these books on our lives. I hope Ewan, Fiona and Isobel will one day take some pride in these pages that were traded for too many sunny weekends, but I realise that the swap was tough at the time.

In writing these two books I have sought, whenever possible, to draw on primary sources of information. In a more technical book it would be conventional to acknowledge these sources by citing their authors' names in the text. However, that protocol is not accepted in books of this ilk and so the authors of hundreds of technical papers that are synthesised here will go unnamed. Their anonymity should not disguise the contribution of their publications to these pages.

Nobody knows enough about the mammalian fauna of a continent to portray it knowledgeably single-handedly. Priscilla Barrett and I have relied heavily upon colleagues around Europe who have given their time unstintingly to comment helpfully upon our efforts. So many people have helped over so long a time that we must begin by apologising to those we fail to acknowledge individually. Our thanks go not only to all those who have helped us excise errors from the *Field Guide* (they are listed by name in that volume). The following have waded through all or part of endless drafts of this book: S. Barker, C.J. Barnard, E.L. Bradshaw, P. Chanin, S. Creel, K. Daly, C.R. Dickman, A. Harcourt, C.E. Hawkins, P. Hersteinsson, A. Inamdar, M. Jennions, R. Kidman-Cox, P. Lievesly, E. Lindström, S. Lovari, J.M. Macdonald, S. Plesner-Jensen, S. Randolph, J. Reynolds, A.R. Sinclair, W. Sutherland, G. Stevens, P. Stockley, P.D. Stewart, P. Waser, R.B. Woodroffe and Y. Yom-Tov. Believing that, alongside its general readership, this book might help school pupils with their biology courses, the text was improved by comments from three teachers: K. Krebs, J. Townsend and A. Watkins. Laura Handoca helped me make countless corrections to the evolving manuscript. My sincere gratitude to each of these people is not diminished by singling out, for especial thanks, Drs Carolyn King and Rory Putman whose painstaking efforts saved me from many errors, and Clare Hawkins for her unrelenting determination to unearth intriguing facts.

The accounts in the *Field Guide* inevitably expose only the tips of many icebergs. For example, the reader who discovers that delayed implantation is characteristic of reproduction in stoats but not in weasels may guess that this distinction is overwhelmingly important, but the full story could not possibly be compressed into a field guide, and nor would one want it there. This, of course, is why I wrote *European Mammals*. For those wishing to follow up more detail there is an annotated bibliography. The bibliography deals only with books, whereas in fact most of the detailed information can only be found in technical papers published in scientific journals. In compiling the *Field Guide* and *European Mammals* I have drawn on the wisdom of a thousand or more original papers; to cite them here would not be appropriate, but I cannot repeat too often my gratitude to their authors.

One irksome area that bedevils the quest for consistency is the use of capital letters. This seemingly trifling matter of usage arises because the Red Fox is the name of a species which may or may not be red in colour (some Red Foxes are black). With maximum clarity as the goal, I have capitalised the names of individual species but not those of collections of species. Thus, the Red Fox is one of two foxes found in Europe (the other fox being the Arctic Fox). This rule leads to some odd, but informative styles: e.g. predators such as Eurasian Badgers, mink, martens and Red Foxes rarely eat red-toothed shrews but prefer Rabbits and hares. In this case Eurasian Badgers and Red Foxes are capitalised because each is a species, whereas mink might mean European Mink or American Mink and martens embraces Pine and Beech Martens. The red-toothed shrews are a collection of species sharing this dental trait. Similarly, Rabbits must refer to one species (in Europe) whereas there are two species of hares (the same rather flimsy logic would justify capitalising Badgers on the grounds that only one of their several species exists in Europe). Where it is not overly cumbersome I have tended to leave capitalised the secondary references to a particular species e.g. 'the Red Fox can tolerate extreme cold, and when the Fox trots in deep snow it regularly uses the same footholes to save energy – a trait that applies to European foxes in general'. To follow any such rules slavishly can mutilate the usage of language, but in general the foregoing rule seems to be an effective compromise.

In an often arbitrary manner, I have applied similar logic to capitalising some higher level taxonomic nouns. Because not all carnivorous (flesh-eating) mammals are Carnivores (members of the order Carnivora) and not all insectivorous mammals (insect-eaters) are Insectivores (members of the Insectivora), I have capitalised Insectivores and Carnivores, and for consistency, all other orders too. However, because it did not seem helpful to do so, I have followed the more normal convention of using lower case letters for the anglicised names of other taxonomic categories (e.g. the family Canidae is sometimes referred to as the canids). The main oddity thus arising is that I refer to Cetaceans and Chiropterans but to whales and bats or, more perplexingly, one might find that Insectivores and bats share a common ancestry as do Artiodactyls and whales.

The best way to use this book is as one of a pair. The *Field Guide* will tell you what you have seen, and then you can find out from this book how that species, its ecology and behaviour, fit into the mammalian scheme of things. In the *Field Guide* the 64 colour plates illustrate every wild mammal species that you can reasonably expect to find and identify on sight in western Europe. Even though there are over 200 European mammal species, the private lives of most remain remarkably unknown. Hopefully this text will convince you that whatever remains to be discovered is likely to be well worth the effort.

David W. Macdonald
Wildlife Conservation Research Unit
and Lady Margaret Hall
Oxford

MAMMAL EVOLUTION

Chapter one

What is a mammal?

The question 'what is a mammal?' takes on a personal and preoccupying significance when you realise that one answer is 'you are'. Humans are but one of the 4,150 or so species of mammal alive today. What we understand about the others will help us to understand ourselves. Considering the records that they hold (the largest creature on earth is a mammal), we might expect that ancestral mammals burst upon the world, launched by some dramatic evolutionary gimmick that made obsolete all that had gone before. Yet, searching the fossil bones of our ancestors, the reptiles, for some clue as to what innovation presaged the splendour of their descendants, we find only that a few bones around the ear and jaw of mammals have been reorganised. Each side of the lower jaw is made of one, not several, bones, and this single bone articulates directly with the skull. In addition, mammalian teeth are generally replaced once, and only once, in a lifetime.

Turning to the soft parts of modern bodies for some mammalian claim to uniqueness, we find only three crucial common denominators. First, a set of skin glands modified to produce milk on which young are nourished. Second, a covering of hair (and that is largely replaced by scales on armadillos, and in whales confined to vestigial whiskers on the muzzles of the newborn). Third, mammals are unique in having a diaphragm, the muscular curtain that partitions the guts from the rib cage – this was probably an anatomical prerequisite to the evolution of the galloping gait (see p. 18). And that is it – a dismayingly short list of seemingly unremarkable differences between mammals and the rest.

There is one feature, the organ of Corti (part of the inner ear), which probably deserves to be on the list of mammalian inventions, although we appear to share it with the extinct Ruling Reptiles (see p. 41). This auditory innovation was probably invented independently by the two groups. Similarly, mammalian skulls articulate with the backbone via two knobbly joints (the occipital condyles), whereas reptiles have only one such joint (but amphibians also have two).

Yet small changes in design can have enormous consequences. These few truly mammalian traits are the tangible signs of innovations that have underpinned a revolution in the animal kingdom. The modified skin glands, called mammary glands, secrete milk, and this food-on-tap buffers the suckling mammal from the vagaries of a fluctuating food supply. What is more, milk has revolutionised the relationship between parent and offspring and between male and female (because only females can lactate – see p. 75). The protection from the adversity of the adult world that is afforded to infant mammals by the opportunity to nurse at their mothers' teats opens the door to intricate social relationships (see p. 147).

The hair, which is made of dead skin (epidermal) cells strengthened by tough horny keratin, is unique among contemporary animals. However, some ancient reptiles were probably hairy too, and hair-like material is common in many invertebrates (think of 'furry' bumble bees). Mammalian hair serves, primarily, to insulate the body; it is a tangible symbol of the physiological processes whereby mammals control their body temperatures through their own central heating system. It is that mammals (and birds too) are 'warm-blooded' that unshackles their body chemistry from direct dependence on climate, thereby opening a world of opportunities beyond the grasp of 'cold-blooded' reptiles, amphibians and fish. Which came first, the central heating system or the insulation? Probably the central heating evolved first, and hair followed as a way of making it more effective. Although widely used, the term 'warm-blooded' is very confusing, because mammalian bodies are often cooler than those of so-called cold-blooded animals. A much better term for the mammalian central heating system is endothermy (see p. 57).

The changed arrangement of bones in the lower jaw represents an improvement in efficiency of both hearing and chewing. The design is clearly descended from a lumbering reptilian prototype, but the mammalian model is altogether slicker – a racy build that facilitates the life in the fast lane made possible by endothermy (but, as we shall see on p. 57, also made

Polar Bear and nursing cubs: marvellous adaptations of form and behaviour enable mammals to inhabit environmental extremes. This family embodies mammalian successes: the mother's milk buffers her young from the extremes of environment and allows complex relationships to develop during a prolonged infancy. Polar Bears are insulated from the cold by their hair, retaining the heat generated by their endothermic bodies.

more 'expensive'). The mammalian diaphragm is an integral feature of this sporty design. This does not mean that we should denigrate the reptiles that once ruled the earth (see p. 41) nor their modern descendants – some bipedal dinosaurs could probably run at 50 km per hour (and the 22 cm long Collared Lizard of North America can sprint at 25 km per hour). Nonetheless, it seems that reptiles cannot, and never could, breathe effectively while running, whereas mammals can do so through the most amazing mechanical interplay, mediated by the diaphragm, between their lungs and viscera.

The tireless trotting movements of the Arctic Fox traversing seemingly endless tundra might seem a breathtaking example of stamina. Yet breathtaking is an inappropriate adjective because, remarkably, the very act of trotting is breath giving, thanks to the diaphragm. As the fox trots along, opposite pairs of fore- and hind limbs strike the ground together to provide support and propulsion. Each leg movement is associated with a host of bodily forces and distortions. As a pair of paws strikes the ground the body sinks downwards, decelerating, but during the second half of the stride the body rises upwards and accelerates. This bodily oscillation occurs twice in every stride-cycle, once when the first diagonal fore- and hind limb pair is on the ground, and again when the other pair of legs strikes the ground. The viscera constitute a swaying pendulous mass, and as the trunk decelerates the guts sway forward, pushing the diaphragm towards the fox's head; as the trunk accelerates during the second half of each stride the viscera, like a wobbling jelly, move tailward. Thus, in the manner of a piston, the movements of the guts help pump air in to and out of the lungs.

The fox's breathing is synchronised with its stride. The trotting fox does not have to expend energy separately on both breathing and moving, rather, with a mechanical intricacy that boggles the mind, breathing in moving mammals is inextricably linked to locomotion. Indeed, the inertial swaying of the viscera, induced by movement, does not merely pump the diaphragm forwards and rearwards, with resulting exhalation and inhalation. Rather, because the striking of the paws on the ground shifts the mammals weight in a way that distorts the forces on its ribcage, the oscillations of the diaphragm take on an orbital pattern. The interaction of this orbital force on the lungs together with forces from the heart and the chest wall, result in some lobes of the lung filling while others empty, making the trotting fox's breathing much more than a simple in and out movement of air. The result is even greater efficiency, as even while breathing out, some air is being utilised.

Even the division of the lungs into lobes is itself an adaptation to the complicated forces exerted on the lungs during movement, the lobes being divided along the shear zones created by these forces. Different types of mammal move in different ways. These different ways exert different anatomical stresses and, correspondingly, the mammals' lungs are divided into different patterns of lobes. The fox pattern, with three lobes in the left lung and four in the right, is common to all carnivores, some rodents, rabbits and hares, cloven-hoofed ungulates and non-human primates. However, the left lung of small rodents and bats is not divided into lobes, and neither seals nor whales have any lobes because their chest walls are no longer buffeted by the forces of footfalls. The lungs of members of the horse family similarly have minimal subdivisions, presumably because their rib cage is so rigid that it is not deformed while running. The diaphragm may, at first mention seem no more than an unglamorous slab of muscle, but on closer inspection the linkage it establishes between respiration and locomotion illustrates the exhilarating elegance of the mammalian design.

Pared down to these few essentials, such as milk, endothermy, a diaphragm and jaw bones, and with a further nod of acknowledgement to social odours (see p. 185), the mammalian success story may sound undramatic, even bland. On the contrary, these fundamental characteristics have underpinned the evolution of an astounding diversity of adaptations to life on land, sea and air. Above all, the fascination of mammals lies in the intricacy and flexibility of their behaviour. The largest mammal, the Blue Whale, is not only among the largest creatures ever, it is also 100 million times heavier than the smallest living mammal, Kitti's Hog-nosed Bat (1.5 g). The Cheetah can sprint at 115 km per hour, and as such is probably the fastest terrestrial animal ever. At the other extreme, while the Sloth is not the slowest animal ever (plenty of invertebrates never move), its upside-down arboreal lifestyle is certainly different from that of the Cheetah. Elephants, like man, can

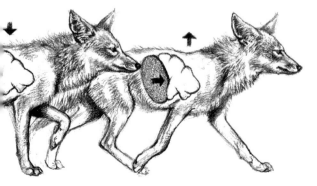

As this Golden Jackal trots along, the labour of breathing is eased as the movements of its viscera act like a piston on the lungs. This is an important economy of effort for a creature that must travel long distances.

clock up their three score years and ten, whereas male Australian marsupial mice succumb as yearlings, invariably predeceasing the birth of their first and only litter (see p. 244). The Virginia Opossum, also a marsupial, may bear 25 young or more per litter, and the House Mouse may have five to ten litters each year. By contrast, the Harbour Porpoise produces only three or four young in a lifetime of ten years. This seemingly inexhaustible diversity in form and function is a hallmark of mammals, whereas the excitement of studying them comes from tracing themes and patterns through that diversity.

Classification

Out of this diversity we seek order. This is partly because it is there already, reflecting evolutionary relationships, and partly because we need to reduce the kaleidoscope of variation to manageable categories so that we can understand it. One such search for order is the business of taxonomy or systematics. Systematics is the branch of biology whereby organisms are classified into a hierarchy of categories, depending on how closely they are related to each other. Species are defined as members of actually or potentially interbreeding natural populations which are reproductively isolated from other such groups. The more closely two species are linked through descent from a common ancestor, the more closely they are said to be related. Closely related species such as the Black and Brown Rats (known to science as *Rattus rattus* and *Rattus norvegicus*) are lumped within the same genus (*Rattus*). Closely related genera (e.g. *Rattus*, the rats and *Mus*, the mice) are classified within the same family (Muridae); families (e.g. Muridae and Gliridae, the dormice) within an order (Rodentia); and orders (e.g. Rodentia and Carnivora) within the class Mammalia. Classes (e.g. Mammalia and Aves – the birds) are then combined within the phylum Chordata (the animals with backbones) and phyla (e.g. Chordata and Mollusca) within the kingdom Animalia.

The specific, generic and familial names are more than pedantic terms in dead languages; they are internationally consistent labels which permit unambiguous communication between biologists the world over. They not only identify species but also, we hope, reflect their relationships: members of the same family share a common ancestor, those of different families are less closely related through a common ancestor at the level of the order. In nature the distinction between species is explicit only when two of them meet – whether a European Beaver and a North American Beaver are the same species is interesting to us, because we are interested in the timescale of their separation, but of no consequence to them if they live on opposite sides of the world. As it happens, these two species have met in Europe due

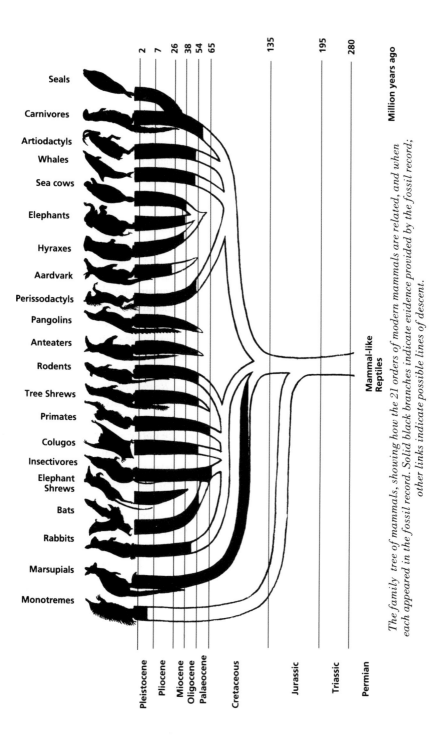

The family tree of mammals, showing how the 21 orders of modern mammals are related, and when each appeared in the fossil record. Solid black branches indicate evidence provided by the fossil record; other links indicate possible lines of descent.

Seals
Carnivores
Artiodactyls
Whales
Sea cows
Elephants
Hyraxes
Aardvark
Perissodactyls
Pangolins
Anteaters
Rodents
Tree Shrews
Primates
Colugos
Insectivores
Elephant Shrews
Bats
Rabbits
Marsupials
Monotremes

Mammal-like Reptiles

2 7 26 38 54 65   135   195   280

Million years ago

Pleistocene
Pliocene
Miocene
Oligocene
Palaeocene
Cretaceous
Jurassic
Triassic
Permian

to the meddling of people (see p. 290). Of course, where two species do meet their differences are crucially important: by definition, if they are different species, they cannot interbreed to produce fertile offspring.

The commonest way for mammalian species to form is when the descendants of one species become geographically separated so that, thereafter, their evolution follows different courses. This could easily happen, for example, if a few individuals of a mainland species drifted onto an offshore island. Similarly, on a geological timescale a new mountain range, or sea, might isolate segments of a formerly contiguous population. If the isolated colony stems from just a few founders it is inevitable that their genetic make-up will represent only a small part of the genetic variation that characterised their parent population. Natural selection operating on this restricted variety will soon yield a descendent population whose genetic make-up is different to that of their ancestors. This founder effect will accelerate the process of speciation that will occur anyway, if the circumstances of the ancestral and founding populations expose them to different pressures. Similarly, if a handful of colonists invade each of several islands, chance will dictate that the genetic make-up of each founding population will be a different subset of the ancestral mix, thereby launching each descendent population on a different trajectory towards speciation. Of course, if the ancestors and descendants never meet up again, there is no opportunity to find out whether they have diverged so greatly as to rule out successful reproduction, and thus qualify for status as distinct species. If they do form separate species then all the descendants of the single ancestral species are thereafter referred to as a clade. Modern taxonomy is based on cladistics: that is, the attempt to classify animals according to the inferred relative recency of their common ancestry. This differs from old-fashioned taxonomy, which often erected separate classes on the basis that their members appeared very different physically, irrespective of their origins. Thus, birds and dinosaurs look very different and, traditionally, are classified as separate classes. However, birds descend directly from the same ancestor as dinosaurs and therefore, cladistically, birds are dinosaurs, albeit miniaturised feathered ones. The notion of being two or more things at once by descent is not so unfamiliar: just as I am simultaneously Scottish, British and European, so I am simultaneously a hominid, a mammal and a mammal-like reptile.

In some cases, despite living in geographically distinct populations, the descendants of an ancestral species do not diverge sufficiently to become true species. For example, about two-and-a-half million years ago in the Pleistocene period of what is now Bavaria, a member of the weasel family, *Martes vetus* was adapted to agile hunting in trees. The fossil record shows that the descendants of *M. vetus* have taken up residence in different parts of the northern hemisphere and, today, include the Pine Marten and Sable, and that the latter gave rise to the Japanese Marten and, in turn, the American Marten. These four modern martens have been classified as different species largely because they live in different places (this separation is termed allopatry), and partly because there are minor differences between them. Of the four, the Pine Marten is the largest, the American Marten the smallest; the Pine Marten has the longest tail, the Sable has the shortest, and all four have creamy, orange or yellow throat patches and thickly furred soles to their feet. If they met they could probably all interbreed, in which case they could all be lumped together as one circumpolar species (if each of the four could interbreed with only some of the others then the whole complex would be termed a super-species). Certainly, where the ranges of Sable and Pine Marten overlap, in the Pechora Basin and trans-Urals, hybrids called Kidas occur. Kidas are smaller than the Pechora Sable and larger than the local Pine Marten, and can be fertile. In contrast, the Beech Marten's range overlaps widely with that of the Pine Marten (a geographical relationship termed sympatry), and they do not interbreed. Furthermore, there are lots of differences between the teeth, skulls and skeletons of Beech and Pine Martens, and they have different lifestyles. They are clearly separate species, but whether or not the Beech Marten also descends from

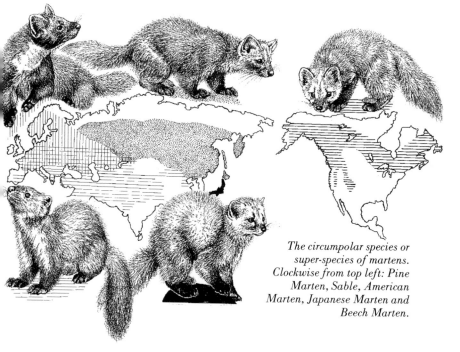

The circumpolar species or super-species of martens. Clockwise from top left: Pine Marten, Sable, American Marten, Japanese Marten and Beech Marten.

23

M. vetus is unknown because it appears in the fossil record (in Israel) only after the recent Ice Ages.

The mammals make up one of the five classes of living vertebrates (the others contain the fish, amphibians, reptiles and birds). Today's mammals comprise about 21 orders, of which nine are represented in the wild in Western Europe (it would be ten if we counted the feral horses of the Camargue). There are 16 additional orders of mammals known from fossils, but now extinct. Living mammals are classified into 130–140 families (37 of them represented in Western Europe, including ourselves in the Hominidae), and these are split into about 1,010 genera. One reason that these figures are approximate is that classification is, as a branch of science, open to debate, another is that evolution is still occurring. Sometimes it is hard to decide which species are related. For example, some people have classed Giant Pandas as relatives of raccoons. Others, studying the molecules in their blood, are probably more correct in concluding that they are a type of bear. Some authorities recognise separate species (or genera or families) which others lump together. Among mammals, one reason for being imprecise is that some people consider the seals and sea lions as a separate order, others as a suborder of the Carnivora (from which they are undoubtedly descended). Similarly, some would split the toothed and the baleen whales into separate orders.

New molecular techniques have elevated these debates to a previously undreamt-of level of sophistication. For example, over recent decades the same animal has been known successively as the Abyssinian Wolf, the Simien Fox and the Simien Jackal. Each name reflected new opinion on its ancestry, but studies of its DNA (deoxyribonucleic acid) have now unlocked the secret of its past: its immediate ancestors were wolves, and its new name is the Ethiopian Wolf. The genetic make-up of an individual is encoded in its genes, which are arranged in the famous double helix of DNA. The building blocks of the genes are called nucleotides, and each strand of DNA (a chromosome) may contain several thousand nucleotides, each comprising a sugar, a phosphate and one of four nitrogen-containing bases. The order in which triplets of these building blocks are arranged encodes the hereditary material of the gene, and determines the design on which the body's proteins will be built. The four nitrogen-containing bases can be arranged into 64 different triplets, and each of these codes for a specific amino acid from which body-building proteins are constructed. Furthermore, the order in which the triplets are arranged in the nucleic acid determines the order in which amino acids will be assembled into proteins. If you could visualise the order of all the nucleotides in an individual they could be read like a book, a complete instruction manual of how to assemble that individual, protein by protein. This is exactly what molecular biologists are now able to do. By comparing the instruction manuals for two species you would get a good idea of how similar they were. Some genes in modern mammalian bodies have remained unchanged since the days of our earliest ancestors, while others are recent innovations. If a gene mechanic trained millions of years ago on assembling a now long-extinct mammal read a contemporary nucleotide instruction manual for assembling a modern mammal he or she would still recognise the blueprints for many parts of its body, while other bits of the blueprint would seem new-fangled.

It is an astounding achievement of science that the pattern of nucleotides in each species can now be read, allowing the biologist to see how each successive edition of the genetic instruction manual has been updated over the eons. The idea behind the molecular analyses of evolution is that the pattern in which the nucleotides in a species' genome (or definition) are arranged will be more similar, biochemically, to the pattern shared with its direct ancestor, or with a species with which it shares a common direct ancestor, than to a pattern of molecules found in a more distantly related species. The more similar their biochemistry, the closer two species must be on their evolutionary family tree. For example, the molecules (or nucleotides) that make up the genes of Fin Whales and Blue Whales (both baleen whales) are arranged in such a similar sequence that these two species can sometimes produce fertile hybrids; such great similarity means they only just qualify as separate species. Equally, despite looking somewhat different, humans are startlingly close relatives to chimpanzees at a molecular level.

Molecular similarity is an appealing basis for classifying evolutionary relationships because whereas two completely unrelated species may look the same due to having converged on a similar lifestyle, only genuinely close relatives will have similar molecular characteristics, irrespective of their external appearances. Grey Whales look so different to the rorquals (e.g. Humpback, Fin, Sei Whales) that they are classified in a separate family. However, molecular studies reveal that Grey Whales are closely related to the rorquals but merely adapted to a very different lifestyle (undertaking marathon annual migrations, during which they fast, having built up fat reserves in the Arctic). In general, because of the hydrodynamic demands on their bodies, all whales have a pretty similar shape. This strong convergence in anatomy makes all whales sufficiently similar that it is hard to untangle how the species are related. Molecular studies have shed new light on this, but they have also illustrated that great hazards of interpretation remain in this thrilling but still immature branch of biology.

The fossil history of the whales is remarkable. Their ancestors were a catch-all group of rooters and browsers called condylarths, which eventually gave rise to all modern large herbivores, from deer to elephants. From their origins more than 65 million years ago, these ancient vegetarians gave rise to a highly predatory group of mammals known as mesonychids. Members of this family became dominant predators during the Eocene. They were rather like sheep in wolves' clothing, having a crushing bite and notches on their cheek teeth to hold flesh torn from bone, combined with heirlooms of their hoofed vegetarian ancestors – hooflets, albeit rather claw-like ones. One might think that a hoofed predator would be excellent at speeding after prey, but hopeless at bringing it down, lacking the crampons necessary to grab hold of it. However, for 20 million years hoofed prey were pursued and caught successfully by hoofed predators. Eventually, however, the mesonychids were replaced by two lineages of mammals – the Carnivora and the Creodonta (see p. 52) that independently hit upon a more efficient design for cheek teeth with which to slice flesh from bone.

Before becoming extinct as predators, the mesonychids set in train one of the most remarkable stories in mammalian history. About 53 million years ago a long-bodied, thinly furred mesonychid slipped into a tropical lagoon, bobbed beneath the surface and swerved in agile pursuit of a fish. This was *Hapalodectes*, which looked much like a modern Giant Otter except that its stocky limbs were hoofed. From nose to tail it was probably about 1.3 m long. Over time, its descendants became ever more adept at swimming and paid for their aquatic prowess with increasing cumbrousness on land. By 46 million years ago, this lineage had transformed to *Pakicetus*, a 2 m long creature with webbed feet. It looked much like a modern seal or sea lion, with nose and eyes high on its head to keep them above water, and limbs that were well on the way to becoming flippers. About two million years later, the 3 m long *Protocetus* had developed a massively muscled tail to provide the main propulsive force for swimming, and was probably fully aquatic. The process continued and by 35 million years ago all trace of hind limbs had gone. A line of wolf-sheep had become whales.

Thereafter, to judge by the fossil record, the ancestral whales split into two descendent branches, the echolocating toothed whales (Odontoceti) and the filter-feeding baleen or whalebone whales (Mysticeti), whose history is thought to have been separate for the last 35–40 million years.

The question arises, however, of where the two modern species of the sperm whale family fit into this scheme, and it was in an attempt to answer this that the molecular pundits entered the affray. The problem is that the answers that emerge do not only depend on the particular molecules selected for the analysis (in this case parts of genes from the mitochondria), which reveal very complicated biochemical patterns. They also depend upon the statistical method used to diagnose the extent of similarity of the patterns from each species of whale. An analysis of one group of molecules suggested that the sperm whales were more closely related to the rorquals, a group of baleen whales, than to the toothed whales (indeed, that sperm whales and rorquals had shared a common ancestor only 10–15 million years ago) (see tree A). As sperm whales are toothed, this was a revolutionary proposal, which suggested that the whole supposed 40 million year division between toothed and baleen whales had been in error. Furthermore the fact that all toothed whales, but no baleen whales, perform echolocation was also made

Molecular studies are revealing evolutionary relationships between species. However, such techniques are in their infancy and can be difficult to interpret. In the case of these three whales, the Sperm Whale (pointing down to the left) and Long-finned Pilot Whale (top) have teeth, whereas the Northern Right Whale (pointing up) is a rorqual and has baleen plates. Traditionally it was thought that all the toothed whales shared a common ancestry, which was distinct from that of all the baleen whales. However molecular studies have suggested that any of the three family trees may be correct.

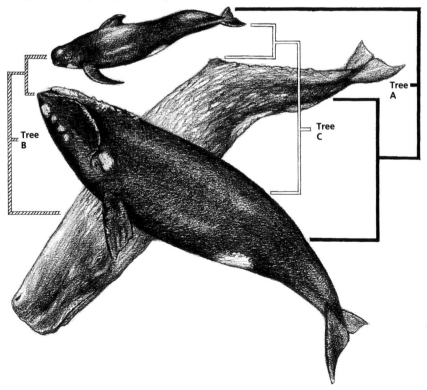

perplexing by the proposed sisterhood between sperm and baleen whales. A year later, however, another analysis using a different set of molecules suggested that the toothed and baleen whales were so-called sister groups, which had both descended from a shared common ancestor which had in turn shared its descent with sperm whales (see tree B).

The next scientific team into the arena used the molecular data provided by the first two teams, and subjected them to a more statistically sophisticated analytical technique to discover which of the possible relationships between the whales was most likely. They concluded that not only was neither of the foregoing options more likely than the other, but worse still, that neither could be distinguished, on statistical grounds, from a third option. This is that the sperm whales and toothed whales are sister groups (see tree C). The fact that three teams produced three different answers certainly does not ridicule their efforts. Rather, it points out that classifying mammals on the basis of their molecules is an amazing stride forward in biology, but one that involves such biochemical and statistical sophistication that it may be some time before a consensus is reached. Incidentally, in this case, all three groups agreed that the molecules revealed all whales as more closely related to the even-toed ungulates than the odd-toed ungulates. The important point is that modern taxonomy is not merely a matter of lumping animals together on the basis of superficial similarities. Rather, the idea is to identify so called clades, that is groups of animals who all genuinely descend from a common ancestor. The more this cladistic search for the evolutionary truth prospers, the more faith we can have that evolutionary trees reflect genuine relationships rather than the coincidences of convergence and divergence.

Because evolution is a continuous process, the moment at which one species becomes two is hard to define, and there is an inevitable flavour of arbitrariness to some taxonomic decisions. However, one distinction that is far from arbitrary is the division of mammals into two subclasses: Prototheria and Theria. This division even predates the end of the Ruling Reptiles. The subclass Prototheria, which includes the egg-laying Platypus and echidnas, predated the origin of the live-bearing Theria by 200 million years. The Theria had also split before the Cretaceous period, 110 million years ago, into the marsupials (which give birth to extremely immature young that often develop to maturity in a pouch) and the placentals (whose young develop much further before birth). These three major divisions (Prototheria, marsupials and placentals) each with its reproductive peculiarities, have major implications for the lifestyles of their members.

Modern mammals descend from three stocks, distinguished by their reproductive biology. The subclass Prototheria includes egg-layers such as the echidna (left). The subclass Theria is divided into two infra-classes, the marsupials, such as wallabies (below left), which give birth to relatively premature young, and the placentals, such as the Roe Deer (below), which give birth to relatively developed young.

Echidna and egg

Wallaby and newborn

Roe Deer and newborn

Chapter two

Evolution and natural selection

Any encounter with mammals conjures up a horde of questions: what is the function of each trait? How is it adaptive? And how is it similar to, or different from, the traits of closely or more distantly related species? These are questions, in essence, about the natural function of every feature. Furthermore, when we ask how one group of mammals arose from another, or how all developed from reptiles, the answer can only be found through an understanding of evolution.

What is evolution?

Three dates, 1798, 1859 and 1865, are the touchstones of current understanding of the processes of evolution and the importance of natural selection. In 1798 Malthus published his *Essay on the Principles of Population*, in which he noted that although many breeding pairs produce litters totalling more than two offspring, many populations are stable in size. This Malthusian paradox implies that many of the young produced must die before breeding.

Darwin's classic *The Origin of Species*, published in 1859, emphasised both the minute precision with which animals are adapted to their environment, and the variation between individuals in the detail of these adaptations, that is, the variation in their fitness. Fitness, in the Darwinian sense, refers to being well fitted (i.e. adapted) to prevailing conditions, and does not necessarily imply athletic vigour (although this might be one important ingredient of an individual's adaptations).

Combining Malthus' observations on the inevitable wastage even in stable populations, and his own on individual variation, Darwin saw the enormous implications of selective death for allowing better adapted individuals to prosper. This natural selection means that as members of each generation run the gauntlet of prevailing circumstances, those that survive will, on balance, be better fitted to these conditions than those that flounder. It will be these well-adapted individuals that go forth and multiply. Darwin realised that over generations, traits that conferred survival (or, more specifically, higher reproductive success) would spread through the population if they were heritable. This spread occurs because individuals with traits promoting survival would be most likely to produce surviving young that inherit the same adaptations, whereas other individuals would perish (taking their less adequate traits with them into evolutionary oblivion). The mere achievement of improved survival is not the key to evolutionary success, nor even necessary for it. The ultimate yardstick of fitness is reproductive success and this is measured by the number of surviving descendants. However, Darwin did not know the mechanism whereby valuable characteristics were inherited. The mechanism of inheritance was Mendel's 1865 contribution to the theory of evolution by natural selection, although nobody took much notice of his findings until 1900.

Genes

Mendel, working on the inheritance of characteristics by his now famous peas, discovered that part of the variation between siblings arose at their conception as a result of sexual reproduction, during which there was an opportunity for mixing (recombining) the genetic material inherited from their parents. Additional heritable variation is very occasionally and very importantly provided by mutation; that is, permanent change in the genetic material that is passed to succeeding generations. Mutations represent copying errors as the genetic material is passed from parent to offspring. They accumulate at a rate of about 100 per lifetime in each individual. Of these 100 differences between the offspring's genetics and its parents, perhaps only one will make any difference. One important copying error, out of around 75,000 pairs of genes that make up an individual mammal, is not much. However, it is what leads to a steady accumulation of new 'ideas' for mammalian design as evolution progresses.

We now know that the characteristics passed from parent to offspring are encoded in the genes, and that each egg and each sperm that fuse during sexual reproduction contribute half of the full complement of genetic material. A loose analogy can be drawn by thinking of each parent's genes as a suit of cards. Imagine four players (would-be parents), whose hands of cards (i.e. genes) each comprises one suit. Diamonds pair with Hearts, Spades with Clubs; the game (sexual reproduction) is played by reshuffling each hand each time, and dealing a half set of cards to each offspring, the other half coming from the other parental pack. The merging of the two half hands ensures that each offspring will get half its cards (genes) from each parent, but each offspring's hand will be different because of the reshuffling before each deal. Offspring dealt by the Diamond and Hearts team have more in common with each other (brothers and sisters) and with their parents then they have with Spade or Club player's hands or their offspring. The rules of the game (natural selection) will determine which players drop out and, if their cards are then lost from the pack, the overall composition of the remaining hands will evolve: if high cards win then royal cards will come to predominate in successive rounds as winning hands survive to be dealt (to breed) again.

The changing environment

The result of natural selection is that the individuals that survive in successive generations are those with the characters that fit them more and more finely to their environment. They are unlikely to become perfectly adapted, however. This is partly because most environments are complicated, and because starting conditions limit the possibilities – in the words of the idiom, you must cut your clothes from the available cloth: if your lifestyle involves flying it might be better to lay eggs than to be burdened with a hefty pregnancy, but bats simply do not have that option (they are placental mammals). Animals are also unlikely to be perfectly adapted because they are beset by chance in the short-term, and because conditions change in the long-term. What was a tropical sea 300 million years ago in the Carboniferous might be a desert today; where ice covered Europe 15,000 years ago, temperate woods now stand; and the bark of a tree that was once silvered with lichens has become blackened with industrial pollution.

On timescales from generations to millennia, things are changing. In the long-term, mutation provides the variation (reshuffled by sexual reproduction) on which natural selection operates. Evolution is a race without a finishing line – for those competitors that stay the course there is always another lap. A good example is the eternal battle between predator and prey, an arms race in which each new adaptation to escape the predator will, eventually, be met with a new ruse to overwhelm the prey, which in turn will lead to yet further refinement on the behalf of prey. The fact that we still have foxes and hares, weasels and voles, wolves and deer shows that neither side has ever won these particular races. However, we might expect prey more often to be ahead, because selection to avoid being eaten is stronger than that to catch the prey – a prey cannot afford even one mistake, whereas a predator can, because losing one dinner is less disastrous than losing your life.

A less conspicuous, but highly pervasive evolutionary arms race occurs between mammals and their parasites. Indeed, it is increasingly clear that parasites have had a huge influence on many aspects of mammalian life (see p. 202), and the arms race between parasite and host has much in common with that between predator and prey. Hosts evolve ever better defence against pathogens, whereas parasites exploit their host's behaviour in ways that increase their chances of infecting new victims. For example, the gutworm *Heligmosomoides polygyrus* afflicts Wood Mice, and releases its eggs in mouse faeces according to a daily cycle. Most eggs are released in the mid-afternoon, when the nocturnal mice are tucked up snugly in their burrows. Wood Mice often share burrows, so by releasing eggs at this time of day the gutworm increases the chances of its larvae encountering a new host. More subtly, parasites actually manipulate the behaviour of their hosts to increase the chances of infection. This applies to all forms of life: for example, a fungus which infects House Flies causes the female fly's abdomen to swell up. This increases the chances of infecting male flies because they find swollen female abdomens irresistible and thus contract the infection in their eagerness to mate. An obvious mammalian example is the notorious 'furious' symptom of rabid foxes: the rabies virus causes a proportion of its victims to travel far and wide, fearlessly approaching creatures they would normally have shunned, and biting anything in its path. The bite wounds are injected with virus-laden saliva, so the disease is passed on (see p. 319). Brown Rats afflicted by the parasite *Toxoplasma gondii* provide another illustration. *Toxoplasma* is a single-celled creature whose life cycle is spent partly within the cells of rats and partly within those of cats. For the parasite to complete its life cycle, an infected rat must be eaten by a cat, so a

Toxoplasma whose rat dies without being eaten by a cat is doomed. It is commonplace for up to 35% of farmyard Brown Rats to be infected with *Toxoplasma*, with the parasite forming cysts in the brains of infected rats. It is to the advantage of the parasite, while residing in the rat's brain, to do anything it can to increase the chances of its host falling prey to a cat. Indeed, rats infected with *Toxoplasma* are more active than their uninfected contemporaries, scuttling about in ways that make them potentially conspicuous to predatory eyes. Furthermore, they lose their fear of unfamiliar odours. It seems probable that these behavioural changes increase the likelihood of infected rats being caught by cats, and thus that in the evolutionary war between this particular host–parasite pair, the parasite is currently doing well. Ironically, however, the loss of fear of novelty associated with *Toxoplasma* infection in rats, also renders them guileless when confronted with poison baits, with which modern farmyards are regularly peppered in the attempt to control rats. If this human intervention resulted in the infected rat succumbing to poison before being consumed by a cat, the parasite would be thwarted. If, on the other hand, the poisoned rat, while dying, was even more likely to lurch into a cat's clutches, then human intervention would have served the parasite well.

Evolutionary processes act over many generations to shape species to average environmental conditions. Conditions change, however, from year to year, so any one generation is only imperfectly fitted to its environment because it is designed for the average conditions its species has encountered in the past. Even within one generation, individuals will differ in how well their particular set of genes happens to match the precise conditions with which fate confronts them. This lottery is all the more testing for individuals of species, like Roe Deer or Red Foxes, that occupy a variety of widely contrasting habitats. Each such individual must rely upon devices, such as the capacity to learn and its own plasticity, to make the best of its personal evolutionary predicament.

Adaptations can be marvellous in their intricacy, but that is not to say that every trait is an adaptation. That panglossian view, that everything is for the best, ignores the fact that some traits may be neutral, functionless or even disadvantageous. Furthermore, we tend to look for perfection in one adaptation at a time, whereas animals must adapt to their total environment – including all the physical and living components – so their solutions must be compromises. One trait may have several functions, for example an Elk's antlers may serve to impress females and to fight males. Satisfying both functions may involve a trade-off in design with the result that animals pay a cost, in terms of survival, for a benefit, in terms of reproductive success.

However, disadvantageous traits can persist only if they are woven into a generally advantageous package. For instance, sometimes a single gene controls several seemingly unrelated effects. This state of affairs (called pleiotropy) could lead, in principle, to a species exhibiting a maladaptive trait which was linked to an overwhelmingly important adaptation. It is rather hard to prove the existence of such disadvantageous, or even neutral, traits in the wild, but the principle is illustrated by domestic cats and mice. One particular mutation gives laboratory mice grey fur and causes their teeth to fail to erupt. The result is that these grey mice starve. Similarly, the Manx mutation is lethal for kittens that inherit a double set of Manx genes (i.e. one from each parent), whereas it causes taillessness in kittens combining Manx from one parent with the normal gene from the other. Greyness itself does not provide sufficient advantage, if any, to overwhelm the disadvantage of toothlessness, but peoples' whimsical liking for tailless cats has proven sufficient selective pressure to keep the Manx mutation in business, despite its disadvantages. The same phenomenon underlies the resistance of rats to some poison (see p. 315).

Natural selection and the individual

A common but incorrect belief is that animals behave 'for the good of the species'. Natural selection acts on individuals, and thus, indirectly, on the traits conferred on them by the genes for which they are temporary vehicles. These genes programme individuals to behave to maximise their own fitness, which is to maximise the number of their offspring that survive to breed. This is generally equivalent to maximising the number of copies of their genes in the next generation. Essayist Samuel Butler's aphorism, that a hen is only an egg's way of making another egg, is very close to the mark. As you read this you are a staging post for a set of mind-bogglingly successful genes: some of your genes have been building unfailing winners in the race for survival in every generation not just from your grandparents, and their grandparents, but from the days the same genes were fashioning the bodies of mammal-like reptiles, back to creatures ancient beyond imagination. Others have arisen only recently. The realisation that natural selection ultimately works on genes has explained the apparent paradox of individuals acting in ways that are detrimental to themselves, but beneficial to their close relatives (for example, a worker bee committing suicide by stinging you in order to protect its relatives in the hive). The paradox is resolved when we remember that close kin share many genes in common (see p. 154).

Evolution today and speciation

Perhaps because it is so often associated with fossils, there is a tendency for people to think that evolution is confined to the distant past. On the contrary, natural selection may be operating every time you see a mammal succeed or fail in doing something – especially if that something is producing young. Evolution is happening all around us. For example, a boat trip from one Scottish island to the next, or a hike between Alpine valleys, might lead you to encounter mice that are well on their way to becoming separate species. The House Mice of the Rhaetian Alps, on the Swiss–Italian border, are a case in point. In at least six different valleys the mice differ markedly from each other, and from the 'normal' mice living in the surrounding districts. You cannot tell that these populations of mountain mice are different just by looking at them, but each is characterised by a different number of chromosomes. Furthermore, each population of mountain mice is fringed by a zone of hybrids – crossbreeds with the ocean of 'normal' mice that surrounds them. If the mountain mice can interbreed freely with the normal mice, as the crossbreeds of the hybrid zone prove they can, then why haven't hordes of normal mice swamped the isolated mountain populations, crossing with them until their peculiar chromosomal traits are diluted to genetic oblivion? The answer must be that the mountain mice have sufficient special adaptations to their isolated retreats to be at a selective advantage on their mountainous home ground.

Human history and culture have played a major part in the evolution and spread of House Mice.

House Mice probably invaded Italy in the company of prehistoric man, travelling from the East. For example, a people called the Camunes became Alpine farmers in about 3500 BC. These farmers settled in isolated Alpine valleys and since mice generally do not disperse far (see p. 264), except when carried unwittingly by people, the House Mice stayed put too. It just so happened that the mice founding each of the populations in these six Alpine valleys had mutations that made them a bit different, and subsequently natural selection has slowly been pushing each population towards its own separate destiny. Now it is too late for a reconciliation: their genetic differences are so great that if mice from these isolated communities meet, which under normal circumstances they never do, they mate but the offspring of their liaison are sterile (i.e. infertile hybrids, like the mules born of horse–donkey crosses). They have become, in effect, separate species.

However, there is one place where mice from two valleys do meet and that is in the cellar of a cheese factory in a village called Migiondo. There, tobacco-coloured mice with 26 chromosomes from the Swiss Val Poschiavo, meet 24–chromosome mice from the Italian Valtellina. They meet, but they do not mate, which shows that they have gone so far down their different roads that they see (or smell) each other as separate species. But how did these two types of mice ever become so estranged in the first place when there is no insurmountable geographical barrier to the movements of villagers between these two valleys? The answer may be that the people of the Val Poschiavo were Lutherans and traded with Switzerland, whereas the people of the Valtellina were Catholics and traded with the Duchy of Milan. To mice, dependent on the movements of 'their people', the religious barrier was as effective a block to dispersal as a mountain range would have been. It was only in the 1850s that new trade routes were opened, and the tobacco mouse moved to Italy. By then, as the segregated denizens of Migiondo's cheese factory have discovered, the die had been cast. How long will it be until the mice of all six valleys have become truly separate species, unable to breed at all with the normal mice around them? It has taken them 3,000 years, or 12,000 generations, to get this far towards independence. One forecast is that taxonomists have about another 1,000 years in which to think up names for six new species.

These subspecies of mice cannot be reliably distinguished on sight, but some mammals more blatantly wear their genes on their coats. In snowy regions it is probably an advantage for stoats and weasels to turn white in winter, thereby making themselves less conspicuous to predators. In the case of weasels, their winter coat is a subspecific badge. At about 60 °N, roughly on a level with Stockholm and Uppsala, a line no more than 100 km

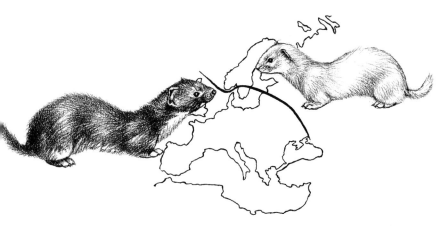

The line running from Scandinavia to the Caspian Sea divides two subspecies of weasel, the Common Weasel (to the southwest) which does not change to white in winter, and the Least Weasel (to the northeast) which does.

wide stretches across Sweden. To the south, weasels stay brown throughout the year; to the north they turn white in winter; along the line some are turncoats, others not. This is the meeting of two subspecies: to the north the Least Weasel, *Mustela nivalis nivalis*, to the south the Common Weasel, *M. n. vulgaris*. Nowadays the two meet along the Swedish strip (and along a frontier arching through Eastern Europe to the Caspian Sea), but the determined brownness of the common form, in the face of Scandinavian snow, may indicate that it evolved in a more clement climate and remains less adapted to snow.

The situation for stoats is quite different: they reliably turn white in winter at much milder (more southerly) temperatures than weasels, and their tendency to do so is not necessarily an emblem of their subspecies. Rather, the expression of the stoat's gene controlling winter whitening is temperature dependent. The critical temperature for going white not only varies from one place to another, but also from one part of the stoat's body to another. For example, where the flanks and rump turn white at 2 °C, the head and back turn at −1 °C. In general, the result is that stoats change to ermine where snow lies at a depth of more than 2 cm for more than 40–50 days annually. Where the climate hovers on the edge of this threshold, piebald stoats are common. The climatic sensitivity of stoats results in them often turning white in Scotland and Wales, but rarely doing so in England where they are warmed by the Gulf Stream. It seems that only those stoats living on the climatic borderline have winter-whitening genes with hair triggers that are temperature-sensitive: an individual moved from the Swiss

Alps (a stolidly white zone) to England (where stoats are unanimously brown) stubbornly turned white like its Alpine compatriots, and irrespective of its new surroundings. In the climatic borderline regions, where it may or may not snow in winter, more females than males tend to go white in any given year. Perhaps this is simply because females, being smaller, lose heat more easily and are therefore more sensitive to the cold. However, another possibility is that the gene controlling winter whitening is sex influenced, that is, dominant in one sex, recessive in the other. If so, this would be a neat mechanism for keeping options open (a situation called balanced polymorphism). The result would be that individual parents do not necessarily put all their eggs in either the white or brown basket, because the best bet varies with the weather: whether the stoats face a white Christmas, or merely a muddy one, some individuals will have the appropriate coat.

With new techniques at our disposal, taxonomy offers many more surprises. For example, the tiny Common Pipistrelle bat is a common species in Britain, but was recently discovered to exist as two so-called 'phonotypes'. That is, an analysis of their echolocation calls revealed that British Pipistrelles belonged to one of two distinct voice classes, both of which are widespread throughout Britain. Remarkably, when these two voice-prints were matched up with molecular fingerprints, the DNA analyses revealed that not only were their voices different, but there were two distinct types of bat. Indeed, despite being indistinguishable to the human eye, the two phonotypes of Pipistrelle are so genetically distinct that they are as different as is normally expected of members of different genera. This may mean that what has hitherto appeared to be obviously a single species is actually made up of two different species, from long-separated lineages, which have converged in appearance due to their similar lifestyles. With such astonishing revelations, biologists must expect that in the next decade or so molecular techniques will demolish many long-cherished taxonomies.

Chapter three

The origins of mammals

Reptiles: ancestors and oppressors

Before exploring the lives of modern mammals, let us consider their origins. The roots of mammalian ancestry trace back through geological time to the fossils of the Mammal-like Reptiles of the subclass Synapsida. The emergence of Mammal-like Reptiles from even earlier types of reptile began late in the Carboniferous period, 300 million years ago, when the world was hot and humid. With a spate of advances on classic reptilian design, the increasingly agile and mammal-like Synapsids dominated the Permian and early Triassic periods 280–210 million years ago. Then the Ruling Reptiles (subclass Archosauria, including dinosaurs, crocodiles and later, birds) burst upon the evolutionary scene, launching a body plan that allowed them to subjugate the competition for 80 million years or more. Most famous of the Ruling Reptiles were two orders, the Saurischia and Ornithischia, collectively known as the dinosaurs. Eclipsed, but not annihilated, the Mammal-like Reptiles maintained a low profile while the Ruling Reptiles adapted to ways of life ranging from that of the docile browser to that of the

Cynognathus was one of the Mammal-like Reptiles, the group from which mammals evolved. Their gait still had a reptilian waddle, but they were beginning to develop mammal-like skeletons.

fearsome predatory giant. They rampaged triumphantly through the Triassic world, dominating land, water and even air. Dinosaurs eventually gave rise to birds which, along with contemporary crocodiles, are their only descendants.

It was from the usurped Mammal-like Reptile stock that, in the Triassic, 225–195 million years ago, the first mammals arose. Forced by the dinosaurs into unobtrusive niches, these 5 cm long refugees were probably nocturnal and partly arboreal. Considering the significance of the occasion, defining the instant of mammalian emergence is unsatisfactorily arbitrary. As we know, the diagnostic characters of mammals lie in the soft parts of their bodies, i.e. in their endothermy, milk and hair, yet none of these is preserved in fossils. There are, however, clues available: for example, today the turbinal bones of the nose are part of a counter-current heat exchange system used by mammals to warm up cold inhaled air, so the presence of these bones in fossil skulls may hint that their owners were endothermic too.

We have to recognise the first mammals from fragments of their skeletons. The moment of transition is defined largely, and arbitrarily, by the development of a hinge whereby the lower jaw is articulated with the skull. The lower jaws of the early Mammal-like Reptiles contained seven bones, one of which, the articular, formed a link to the quadrate bone of the skull. Among the Therapsids, the order that eventually spawned true mammals, some of these lower jawbones were repositioned in the skull. In modern mammals, bones that were once part of the ancestral lower jaw have been reshuffled into the inner ear. This leaves only one bone in the lower jaw, the dentary, which articulates with the squamosal bone of the skull. In the meantime, the old articular bone has been recast as the malleus (or hammer) within the sound amplifying apparatus of the mammalian ear. There it maintains its old alliance with the quadrate, itself reformed as the incus (or anvil) of the ear. The third ossicle of the mammalian ear, the stapes (stirrup) is the only one present in reptiles and birds.

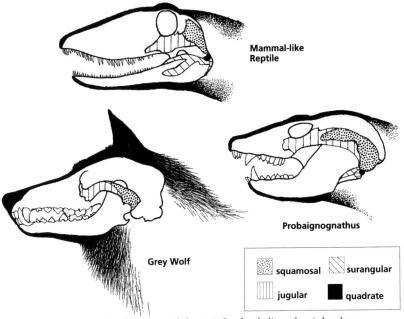

Bone seems such inflexible material that it is hard to believe that it has been reshaped and moved about in the body during evolution. The lower jaws of the Mammal-like Reptile (top), of the intermediate Probaignognathus (centre), and of a modern mammal, a Wolf (bottom), show just how malleable bones are in evolutionary time. Originally the lower jaw of the Mammal-like Reptile was composed of several bones, including the articular, angular, surangular and dentary. The articular bone formed the hinge with the quadrate bone of the skull. In the mid-Triassic, 200 million years ago, the half-reptile, half-mammal Probaignognathus still used the ancient reptilian articular/quadrate joint, but also had a joint between the surangular and the squamosal bone of the skull. In fact, the surangular only came into play in the joint because the dentary bone had greatly expanded to make up almost all of the lower jaw. Another notable change is that Probaignognathus had a zygomatic arch at its cheeks, in order to anchor the powerful jaw muscles with which it was now equipped. Finally, in the Wolf the hinge only involved the dentary and squamosal. Although it is not visible in this exterior view of the skull, several of the bones of the reptilian jaw apparatus have been relocated as parts of the middle ear of modern mammals.

Chinese Water Deer. A dainty introduction from Asia (now spreading in Britain) with the elegant gait typical of the mammal: the consequence of streamlined pectoral and pelvic girdles.

To the undiscerning these changes are just a dreary list of archaic, unmemorable names. In fact, not only are we considering an astounding physical migration of bones, over millions of generations, but also structural redesign which underlies a functional revolution. The migration of reptilian jawbones to mammalian ear and cheek arch represents refinements of engineering comparable to those which were needed before a Model T Ford could be developed into a Lambourghini. That is not to say that modern reptiles, with their bones in archaic positions, are obsolete failures of weak hearing and slow on foot (try sneaking up on one). Considering that birds, which like reptiles have only one ear ossicle, can apparently hear just as well as mammals the obvious question is: why have mammals built their hearing apparatus with old jawbones?

The answer may be that the jaws of ancestral Mammal-like Reptiles articulated with their skulls in such a way that the lower jaw was the obvious place to receive sound, so lower jaw bones became part of the hearing apparatus before altered jaw articulation required their repositioning in the middle ear. Astoundingly, this history is recapitulated in the pouches of marsupials where infants have the would-be ear bones in their ancient position in the lower jaw. Only when the young marsupial leaves the pouch do the two bones detach and make their way up to become the malleus and incus in the middle ear. This is a case of the evolutionary history of the lineage (phylogeny) being replayed in the development of each individual (ontogeny), a phenomenon leading to a time-honoured biological aphorism that ontogeny recapitulates phylogeny.

The significance of the redesigned mammalian jaw is that it provided anchorage for more powerful muscles and allowed more complicated chewing. This, in turn, allowed the evolution of specialised teeth (heterodonty) to perform different functions within one mouth, whereas reptilian teeth are all rather similar and simple (homodonty). The significance of specialised teeth is that they permit more efficient food processing and may even (as in the case of the hyena's bone crushers) open the door to specialised diets and the diverse niches beyond. Similar changes were going on elsewhere. The pectoral and pelvic girdles were being streamlined to facilitate a more efficient gait; the angles on the heads of the limb bones were realigned to position the limbs beneath the body, thereby replacing the ancestral reptilian waddle with a mammalian stride which we perceive as elegant (but who knows what lizards think of it). A false palate formed a shelf of bone in the roof of the mouth separating the airway from the food passage and enabling the animal to breathe with its mouth full. This is an advantage not only to those wishing to abide by the mores of polite society, by eating with their

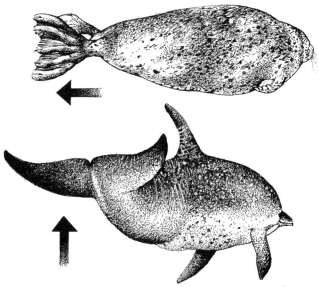

Modern mammals have modified their basic gait in various ways. For example, the slim mammalian pelvic girdle has been adapted for swimming by both seals (Order Pinnipedia) and whales (Order Cetacea). However, the seal (top) is propelled by lateral movements of the hind limbs, the dolphin by vertical movements of the tail.

mouths closed. It also facilitates the efficient fuelling of the high metabolic rates that keep the internal fires of endothermy burning (see p. 57). The palate permits the simultaneous consumption of lots of food and lots of oxygen, fuels demanded by the fast-running mammalian engine. Changes in the circulatory system, such as the evolution of the four-chambered heart, were also prompted by these high energy requirements. These innovations are not all unique to mammals, nor do they make the mammalian system intrinsically better; animals with lower metabolic rates do not require so much energy and therefore do not require such efficient physiologies, but they live a slower life. In other words, mammals are not better than reptiles, they are simply different.

All these changes were part of a web of design that together added up to a mammal. It was an infinitesimally slow progression, a continuum of change in which what we choose to call reptile blended into what we choose to call mammal. There was no switch to click from reptilian darkness to mammalian light, no reptilian father who sired a mammalian son. Indeed, far from shattering the previous evolutionary mould, reptile transformed to mammal at such an unimaginably slow pace that one creature, *Probaignognathus*, was both at once. *Probaignognathus* was one of a group of dog-like predators from the late Triassic known as Cynodonts, from which all modern mammals descend. Schizophrenically, *Probaignognathus* spans the divide, its lower jaw articulating with its skull at the same time in two places, once with the reptilian mechanism and once in the mammalian fashion – the evolutionary past and future chewing side by side.

The early mammals

How, then, did the early mammals overthrow the dinosaurs' repression? Perhaps they were simply in the right place at the right time. The time was the end of the Mesozoic era, when the earth's temperature was falling, and dragging down with it the 'cold blooded' dinosaurs' ability to function. A clue to the dinosaurs' demise may lie in the dust of iridium, a rare heavy metal, that is found in late Cretaceous sediments around the world. Iridium is generally confined to the molten core of the earth, or within meteorites, asteroids or comets. The worldwide dust of iridium probably arose as the result of a collision between the earth and either a shower of comets or a single huge meteorite (as large as 10–15 km diameter). These meteorites would have exploded on impact to produce an enormous cloud of dust and steam which would have shrouded the earth for weeks or months. Plants would have died in the darkness, and the food pyramids built upon them crumbled. The creatures most likely to survive such a nemesis would be

Zalambdalestes, *a small opportunistic scavenger, was one of the earliest mammals (whose fossils date back to the Cretaceous period about 145 million years ago).*

small, opportunistic scavengers – a description of the early mammals. Remarkably, a crater has now been found in Yucatan, Mexico, which has all the hallmarks of being the impact site of the meteorite that annihilated the dinosaurs.

It is a perplexing fact that the history of life on earth has involved a series of mass extinctions – periods when a large number of species suddenly (on a geological timescale) plummet out of existence. The Mammal-like Reptiles endured two or three such cataclysms. One explanation is that periods of severe climate caused some of these extinctions. During the evolution of the mammals, it was generally the large carnivores that were most prone to extinction. This was due, perhaps , to their low population density and slow rate of evolving new species, dictated by the long intervals between their generations. Overall, small carnivores were the most likely mammals to survive and radiate into a new generation of species because of their relatively high population density and relatively unspecialised lifestyle. Furthermore, if mass extinctions are caused by periods of adverse environmental conditions, then the bodily constancy provided by endothermy could be of great survival value at such times. Since small size favoured endothermy in mammals (because they lose heat, and therefore get chilled fast, see p. 60) one might speculate that it was, indirectly, their diminutive physiques that enabled the early mammals to outlast the dinosaurs – a case of the meek inheriting the earth.

Whatever has prompted previous mass extinctions, it has never been the influence of a single species on the fate of all others. It is a gruesome thought that we are now in the midst of a unique event in the morbid history of extinction, as mankind's influence rings changes on a scale which previously required major astronomical or geological events.

Mammals versus dinosaurs

After their initial good fortune (that the dinosaurs were devastated by a meteorite) two traits, endothermy and lactation, were doubtless crucial ingredients of the mammals' new-found competitive edge over their reptilian rivals. Solar heating panels are a great way to heat a house, as long as the sun is shining; endothermy allowed early mammals to forage by night, when the setting sun imposed lethargy upon the chilled metabolisms of similarly sized dinosaurs. Endothermy not only opened nocturnal niches, it freed mammals from the quirks of climate so that they could grow continuously and breed prolifically. The mammalian metabolism always runs strong, whereas reptilian bodies effectively 'switch off' in the cold. Not that 'cold blooded' animals have done so badly in this regard: insects and amphibians were the stuff of biblical plagues, and an alligator can produce 80 young in one season and quadruple its length in a year. Furthermore, the enormous size of some dinosaurs would have meant that they cooled slowly (see p. 60) and even modern reptiles can be active by night in the warm tropics. The difference is that the mammalian engine continues to fire, albeit expensively, under conditions in which the reptilian model idles.

Nonetheless, endothermy was probably also achieved by the Mammal-like Reptiles and yet mammals did not do well for another 100 million years. So the invention of milk (which itself depends on endothermy) may have been the trait which tipped the balance.

Lactation, and the other forms of parental care it encourages, protects the infant mammal from the vagaries of the environment, allowing it to depend on its parents' ability until it can be launched into the affray to compete on almost adult terms. The young dinosaur, in contrast, needed to occupy a succession of niches as it grew from hatchling to giant. Each of these niches had to be available on cue, a condition that may have become increasingly unlikely in the unpredictable deteriorating climate of the Mesozoic. It seems fair to assume that dinosaurs graduating between a succession of niches were worse off competitively than mammals onweaning.

Perhaps it all boils down to body size: the dinosaurs were mostly large, and throughout vertebrate history large animals have been more likely to become extinct than small ones. This is partly because larger animals are almost inevitably rarer than small ones (larger fleas have smaller fleas upon their backs to bite 'em ... and on *ad infinitum*). In the balance between birth and death which determines a species' abundance, the laws of chance dictate that, all else being equal, rare species are more prone to the disastrous effects of a run of bad luck. On this view the dinosaurs may have been annihilated, and

Lesser White-toothed Shrew (above) and Greater White-toothed Shrew (below).
The earliest ancestors of all modern mammals were small and probably lived
similar lives to these modern shrews.

thus the mammals unfettered from their stifling competition, by nothing more savage than a throw of the evolutionary dice or the path of a large comet.

The earliest fossil mammals come from the Triassic, 250 million years ago (or on about 10 December by analogy with an annual calendar running from the origin of the earth 4,500 million years ago to the present). The first three orders to arise were the Triconodonta, the Multituberculata and the Pantotheria. The first two are named after their teeth: Three-cones and Many-tubercles referring to the pattern of cutting or grinding cusps on each tooth. These two orders are members of the subclass Prototheria of which the modern Platypus and echidnas are the only survivors (both, as it happens are toothless). It is quite reasonable that the first mammals should be named after their teeth, not only because many are known only from their teeth (these being the best preserved fossil features), but also because their teeth were their interface with the outside world. The structure of mammals' teeth is determined by their lifestyle. Indeed, it seems that the teeth of the third Triassic order, the Pantotheria, were the key to their greater success: they too had three cones on each cheek tooth, but these were aligned in a triangular pattern rather than a straight line, and this pattern set the scene for the much more complicated feats of chewing, grinding and shearing that lay in the evolutionary future. Indeed, the pantotheres, members of the subclass Theria, were the ancestors of modern placental and marsupial mammals (see p. 21).

These early mammals were all small; their skulls were generally 1.5–2 cm long, about the same as those of a modern Common Shrew or Harvest Mouse.

Indeed, the multituberculates used their pimpled teeth to grind vegetation and evolved gnawing incisors giving their skulls a remarkable resemblance to those of modern rodents. The multituberculates were later usurped in the late Jurassic by an even more rodent-like order, the Tritylodonta, which in turn fell to the modern rodents in the late Palaeocene. With one order ousting another from a similar set of niches in the fossil record, we can see the continual refinement of design associated with evolutionary success. In this sense it is fair to think of modern rodents as being better designed for the job they do than were multituberculates.

However, we should be cautious about concluding that modern forms are invariably better designed than ancient ones, because the world has changed and therefore so too has the 'job description' for each niche. For example, we could not conclude that the modern lion is a more refined occupant of the top predatory niche than was the sabre-toothed cat. Conditions have changed, not least because the lumbering giant herbivores on which the sabre-tooths preyed have gone, possibly due to climatic change or the hunting or agriculture of early man, so the comparison is invalid. The sabre-tooths were a success in their niche just as the lions have been in theirs. They were not ousted from their niche, but simply had the historical misfortune that it disappeared (as, due to human intervention, may the lions' niche disappear).

The pantotheres were probably reminiscent of modern insectivores such as tree shrews. One can imagine them scuttling about the understorey or aloft in trees, using their versatile teeth to process nutritious insects and fruits. Late in the Jurassic two lineages emerged from these pantotheres to become the ancestors of the marsupials and of the placentals. So some 60 million years ago, or just before Christmas on our annual calendar of world history, modern mammals arrive on the stage.

Part of the success of early mammals may lie in another coup of dental engineering. It seems that during the early Palaeocene, at about the time other groups of mammals with adventurous new diets split off from the basic insectivore stock, an important improvement in the structure of tooth enamel evolved. The new design incorporated cross-struts in the enamel, running at right angles to the long axes of the tooth cusps, and strengthening the tooth against cracks that were liable to form parallel to the cusps in the old design (and still do in today's insectivores). The process of chewing on the kind of food eaten by large mammals involves mechanical stress on the teeth, so one might speculate that the invention of this reinforced enamel opened the door for the evolution of large body size in mammals. Whether or not this speculation is valid, few would argue with the French biologist

Lineages have come and gone throughout mammalian history as circumstances have changed. The sabre-toothed cats, such as Smilodon *(above), flourished as recently as two million years ago. It was lion-sized and its heavy frame and huge canine teeth were successful in hunting the slothful, thick-skinned herbivores of the day. As fleet-footed, modern antelopes replaced these ancient mega-herbivores, so too modern big cats replaced the sabre-tooths. Thus, just because* Smilodon *is extinct and modern lions are not, does not indicate that lions are better in absolute terms than was* Smilodon. *Rather, circumstances changed: modern lions would be as ill-equipped to deal with palaeolithic ungulates as* Smilodon *would be at dealing with modern ones.*

Georges Cuvier's remark (*c.* 1800) addressed to all mammals, 'Show me your teeth, and I will tell you what you are.'

The importance of the nuances of dental engineering to the evolution of modern mammals is illustrated by the success of the Carnivora (see p. 21). The evolution of the Carnivora followed the evolution of suitable prey. After the demise of the dinosaurs 65 million years ago, no large dinosaur herbivores were left to provide a niche for large predators. Then a group of hoofed, mammalian herbivores, the condylarths, arose. The first predators to respond to this new resource were from among their own kind, the mesonychids (in fact the ancestors of modern whales), leading to the unorthodox state of affairs where hoofed predators were pursuing hoofed prey. In the wake of the mesonychids, two carnivorous lineages sprang up to replace them about 58 million years ago. One of these lineages became the true Carnivora, distinguished principally by the evolution and positioning of carnassial teeth (i.e. teeth with a specialised shearing edge to slice meat as scissors would). The rival lineage was the Creodonta, and they too developed the carnassial shear. The only real difference between them was that the carnivores evolved their carnassial scissors out of their most rearward upper premolar cutting against their most forward lower molar, whereas the creodonts evolved theirs from their second and third upper molar and third and fourth lower molar.

Two great predatory lineages, the Creodonta and the Carnivora, differed principally in the location of their carnassial scissor teeth. Those of the Creodonta (left) were at the very back of the tooth row, whereas those of the Miacid – an ancestral Carnivore (right) – were further forward. This seemingly insignificant difference in design may explain the demise of the entire Creodonta lineage.

A puzzling question is why the creodonts lost the evolutionary race. There is little to distinguish the two orders in terms of the efficiency of their dental equipment, their senses, their brain size or their anatomy (although creodonts had somewhat less flexible backs). Yet, having proliferated far more than the carnivores at first, the tables began to turn in the Miocene. Although the last creodont, *Dessopsalis*, hung on in India until five million years ago, most declined to extinction some 38 million years ago. This was the very time when the carnivores began to prosper, a coincidence that hints strongly at cause and effect. One possibility is that the creodonts were too committed to obligate carnivory. By using their molars to make their meat-shearing carnassials, they were left with no teeth to specialise in grinding less amenable foods. The carnivores, having evolved more forward carnassials, could subsequently put their molars to other uses, such as grinding. This would leave them better equipped to adapt to other diets, such as omnivory or herbivory. If this explanation has any force, then, ironically, it was their ability to diversify from carnivory that secured the carnivores' success against the creodonts.

The demise of the creodonts raises the general question of what determines the life span, in geological terms, of groups of mammals? Probably, the answer is that it is, like most things in life, a game of chance. All else being equal, groups which are abundant and diverse are less likely to succumb to chance than those whose representatives are rare and uniform. Creodonts were limited to meat-eating by their dentition, and so could only produce as many species as it took to fill up the meat-eating niches of the early Tertiary. The carnivores, in contrast, produced a wider range of dietary specialisations, and a correspondingly larger number of species. So, in simple terms, QED: the carnivores had more throws of the dice than the creodonts, so they have lasted longer.

Chapter four

European mammals past and present

As it happens, this book was written towards the end of the 20th century but, had it been drafted earlier, the story could have been very different. Only 30,000 years ago, Reindeer, Bison, Musk Oxen and Brown Bear were far more widespread in western Europe than they are now, and part of a community containing wild horses, Woolly Rhinoceroses, Cave Lions and Spotted Hyenas. Further back in time (but still astonishingly recently), 130,000 years ago during the warm period between two glaciations, Europe was the stage for an even more unexpected cast which included Hippopotami, Narrow-nosed Rhinoceroses, Straight-tusked Elephants, and even another species of hominid, Neanderthal man. What is more, they abounded in places that now seem absurdly improbable: hippos wallowed in what is now London's Trafalgar Square!

About 30,000 years ago, by the time Cro-Magnon man had displaced Neanderthal man, artists published their work on cave walls. One region of western Europe, running between the Dordogne, the Pyrénées and the northern coast of Spain contains one of the richest libraries of cave paintings in the world. Particularly famous sites include the Lascaux Caves (approximately 27,000 years old) in France, the Altamira Caves (approximately 15,500 years old) in Spain and the Adolara Cave in Sicily. In each of these, images of bison, bear, wild horses and deer abound, not to mention Woolly Mammoths painted as recently as 10,000 years ago. Palaeolithic artists were mindful of detail: they show the mammoth with a high-domed head, humped shoulders and a steeply sloping back; they show its trunk ending in a pair of grasping lips, contrasting with the unequally-sized lips of modern elephants. Subsequently, the frozen mammoths found in Siberia have confirmed these details.

In addition to cave paintings there are carvings and ceramics of Ice Age mammals. From Dolni Vestonice in the former Czechoslovakia come rhinos fashioned in baked clay dating back 27,000 years. From the work of these artists we know how the Woolly Rhinoceros stood, we know that ibex (now confined to the Alps and the Pyrénées) once roamed across western Europe, and we know of at least two sorts of wild horse: those with long asinine necks, and those with stouter equine necks. The latter looked rather like modern Przewalski's Horses, and the artists emphasised the upright mane and the stripes on the shoulders and lower limbs. We know also that palaeolithic Red Deer were often in superb condition. Today, and presumably then too, the number of tines on their antlers is an indicator not merely of age, but also nutritional status. On the poor hill land of Scotland a 'royal' stag might be crowned with 12 tines, but the stags of the palaeolithic not uncommonly bore 15 or more tines (of course, the artists may have drawn only the grandest specimens). And unless they drew only lionesses, it seems that the European lion lacked a mane, perhaps like the contemporary cougar, although it did have a tuft on its tail.

Times have changed. Once Musk Oxen roamed in central France. The most recent Ice Age was at its frostiest some 18,000 years ago. It was then that the giant woollies (mammoths and rhinos) cohabited in southern Europe with Wolverines and Reindeer. As the ice retreated northwards, so too went these tundra species, and cave illustrations in southern and central Europe record such newcomers as Red Deer, Wild Boar and Wild Asses. Had there been an even earlier generation of artist in the warm period 120,000 years ago, between glaciations, he or she could have been drawing hippos as far north as the Yorkshire Moors.

In the story of the changes in fauna through history, Britain is of special interest. Britain lies at the edge of Europe and its climate has been on the one hand fiercely influenced by the comings and goings of the Polar front, and on the other hand, differentiated from the Continent by a corridor of residual warmth in the North Atlantic during the last interglacial period. The consequence is that changes in the British mammal fauna during the ice ages have been as spectacular as any in the world. The wolves, hyenas and cave lions that were hunting tropical prey 120,000 years ago, left descendants which, 20,000 years ago, hunted Collared Lemmings (an Arctic species) where previously hippos had roamed. Of course, western Europe was a different shape in those days: during the glaciations much water was locked up on land as ice, and the sea level was lowered by more than 100 m. Herds of mammoth and reindeer could have walked from England to Denmark on the exposed sea bed. These faunal changes have continued until very recent times: Elk lived in the north of England 9,000 years ago, as did the Giant Ox or Aurochs until the end of the neolithic (4,500 years ago). Indeed, on the Continent, 17th-century artists were still painting Aurochs (which became extinct in 1627). Brown Bears survived in England until the 10th century, beavers until the 12th, wolves until the 16th. The Scottish Wolf lasted until 1740 (see p. 279).

The cost of living

Much of the 230-million-year mammalian story hinges on their 'warm-blooded' central heating system. Today, this trait is shared only with birds (although various extinct reptiles, in addition to those ancestral to mammals, probably experimented with it). The body temperature of 'cold-blooded' creatures, such as the modern reptiles, is largely determined by outside conditions, although they do what they can to be in the right place at the right time (sitting in the warming sun or cooling breeze, for example). The body temperature of such creatures varies so that their blood may be colder or warmer than that of a mammal, depending on the outside temperature. Thus they may more aptly be called ectotherms than cold-blooded (ecto, meaning outside, describes the source of heat). Although their body temperature is not necessarily always the same as external temperatures, and they can exercise some considerable degree of control of their body temperature by behavioural means, the range of external temperatures over which reptiles can maintain a constant internal temperature is relatively limited. By contrast, mammals (and birds) regulate their internal body temperature from within; in other words they are endothermic. When it gets too cold they generate heat by the oxidation (equivalent to burning) of food to provide energy, and when it is too hot most of them dissipate heat through the cooling effect of the evaporation of their sweat (or saliva). The whole process, which is called homeostasis, is regulated by a 'thermostat', situated within a part of the brain called the hypothalamus.

The overwhelming significance of endothermy is that it frees mammals from direct subjugation by climate, thereby opening a world of different environments to them. The consequences are profound because life is a myriad of linked chemical reactions, and the rate of all chemical reactions depends on temperature (which is why fish are sluggish in colder water). Endothermy provides stable conditions in which these fundamental life processes can operate.

However, endothermy is both lifeline and burden to mammals; like any central heating system, it is expensive to run. In this case the bills come in the form of demands for food to fuel the system. The cost of endothermy is unending – when inactive some 80% of the energy used by a mammal is needed simply to maintain its temperature. Weight for weight, a resting lizard 'burns' energy at about a quarter of the rate at which a resting mammal does so.

Fluctuating body temperature

Not all mammals maintain the same body temperature. The echidna's temperature is about 28–30 °C. Man's temperature is maintained at 37 °C (98 °F), in rabbits and cats the temperature is 39 °C (101.5 °F), whereas in wallabies it is 35 °C (95 °F). These species regulate their temperature at a constant level (and are called homoiothermic – from Greek *homoios* = similar). Some others opt for a different strategy: they minimise their fuel consumption by sacrificing constancy in favour of a sort of 'off-peak' central heating. For example, hedgehogs cool from about 31 °C to 10 °C or less (but never less than 1 °C) while hibernating; and a hibernating echidna's temperature falls as low as 4 °C (see p. 272). Many bats have to opt for a similar economy because the huge area for heat loss from the skin of their wings makes it too costly to maintain a constant temperature while they rest. When they wake up, their body chemistry is so sluggish that they go through physical jerks (an exaggerated form of shivering) to raise their temperatures before takeoff.

Camels save water by 'storing' heat. If a camel drinks water every day, its core temperature varies by just over 2 °C per day, between 36 and 38 °C. When dehydrated, however, a camel's temperature varies between 34 and 41 °C. In other words, camels heat up rather than waste water as sweat. For example, a 500 kg camel stores the equivalent of 2,900 kcal per day during a hot day – this stored heat is lost during the night by conductance and radiation, without the use of water. This mechanism of heat storage can cut a dehydrated camel's water losses by two-thirds. Its tolerance of overheating saves water for the camel not only by allowing its temperature to rise, but also by reducing the heat gradient between camel and environment, slowing the rate of heat gain. Badgers face the opposite problem in the northern European winter: they burn so much fat to keep warm that they may lose half their autumn body weight by spring. One suggestion is that they combat this energy drain by lining their dens with grassy bedding, which ferments to generate heat – a sort of bacterial blanket.

Insulating mechanisms

It takes energy both to warm up and to cool down, just as it takes energy to run both a cooker and a refrigerator. Two crucial elements of both systems are derived from mammalian skin: hair and sweat glands. Hair is vital for insulation, which reduces the costs of any heating system. Mammalian hair can insulate the Arctic Fox from polar winds, the European Otter from freezing water, and the African Ground Squirrel from desert sun (the squirrels, like Giant Anteaters, use their fluffy tails as parasols).

Insulation by hair works in two ways. First, the volume of air trapped in the fur can be adjusted depending on the angle to which the hairs are erected by muscles in the skin, and second, species living in cold climates have much

Hair care is important to mammals as a way of keeping their thermal underwear effective. For aquatic mammals, like the European Beaver (above) spreading an oily secretion from the sebaceous glands over the fur provides vital waterproofing.

denser underfur. Arctic Foxes begin to shiver only when the temperature drops below −40 °C. Seals, unlike otters, cannot rely on air trapped in their fur for insulation, because during deep dives it is evicted by compression. Instead they use fat (blubber), which is a less efficient insulator (1 cm of air is equivalent to 4 cm of fat), but is unaffected by dives in deep water. Polar Bears appear black in ultraviolet photos, because their fur absorbs ultraviolet light − as does the fur of Harp Seal pups. The fur itself is hollow, and acts like a fibre-optic filament. Longer wave radiation is reflected, and just 16% of the total solar radiation hitting the bear is absorbed − but this absorbed radiation is all short wave, and includes ultraviolet. Such short-wave radiation is not reflected or absorbed by the cloud layer, so Polar Bears can take up heat even on overcast days. Transmission of this energy to the body is encouraged by a final refinement: their skin is black, which is the colour which best absorbs heat. Plagiarising bear design into modern solar panels has allowed a 50% increase in efficiency.

Hair is maintained in good condition by oil produced by sebaceous glands in the skin encouraged by grooming. Another type of gland, the coiled sweat gland, secretes a watery fluid which evaporates, thereby drawing heat from the skin. Primates, such as the Barbary Macaque, have these glands all over their bodies, whereas whales have none (water cannot evaporate under water). Sweating may not be an effective way of losing heat for very hairy mammals. For example, in carnivores such as wolves and lynx, sweat glands are confined to the pads of their feet, and when these prove inadequate 'air conditioning', panting enables more heat to be lost through evaporation of saliva. Panting is an all or nothing activity: a hot dog shifts its respiratory rate in one jump from 30–40 breaths per minute to 300–400. This is because these are the frequencies at which the lungs have a natural frequency of oscillation in the same way that a guitar string has. Panting at these frequencies reduces the energy used in panting and thus avoids generating further heat by movement of the respiratory tract. The heat lost by panting is controlled by the proportion of air breathed out via the mouth rather than the nose. The air exhaled from a dog's mouth is at 38 °C, that exhaled from its nose is 29 °C because the heat has been retained by the counter-current system of the nasal passages.

The cost of size

In comparison to smaller mammals, large ones have relatively more inside than outside. That is, their surface to volume ratio is lower. They have more surface, but even more volume, because of a simple mathematical law: the surface area

Mammals have different methods of keeping cool. Horses, like this Mongolian Wild Horse can sweat profusely from widely distributed sweat glands, whereas members of the dog family, such as the Arctic Fox, have no sweat glands on the body and pant to lose heat. For the Wild Pig, wallowing in a muddy puddle is a good way to cool down.

of a body increases with the square of its length, whereas its volume increases with the cube of its length. The demands of endothermy mean that this mathematical fact has repercussions which reverberate throughout the life histories of mammals. The reason is that a bigger mammal having less skin surface per unit volume loses heat more slowly in the cold than would a smaller mammal. The result is that the larger mammal needs relatively (not absolutely) less fuel. This is why the total energy costs of a horse are, per unit weight, one tenth those of a mouse. To compensate, the mouse must be ten-fold greedier in its energy consumption. A Common Shrew must spend almost half its time eating to fuel its tiny body; a person with a shrew's metabolism would have to eat 30 kg of food a day! The fact that smaller mammals are more expensive to run not only determines much about the size and shape of living species, but also has implications for traits as apparently distant from squares and cubes as litter size and parental care (see p. 241).

The pervasive influence of body size is revealed in an interesting distinction between two seemingly dusty academic terms: homoiothermy and endothermy. A homoiotherm is an animal that is able to maintain its body temperature within a narrow range, usually above that of its surroundings, despite large variations in the ambient temperature. An endotherm is one that achieves homoiothermy by means of burning its bodily fuels to produce more or less metabolic heat as required. A lizard, seeking out sunny spots, may keep its temperature both constant and high, but does not do so directly by burning internal energy. The extraordinary point is that it is possible to be homoiothermic without being endothermic, simply by being very large – a condition termed inertial homoiothermy. A huge reptile which warmed up in the midday sun might lose heat so slowly that it effectively retained a constant temperature throughout a chilly night – just as a large mug of coffee cools down more slowly than a dainty cupful. This may have applied to some dinosaurs, and it may even explain how endothermy arose in mammals (and birds) since some very large species featured in their ancestries. The idea is that, having evolved to a very large size, a 'cold-blooded' (ectothermic) animal's body temperature inevitably stabilises due to the slower rates of heat loss and gain imposed by a relatively small surface wrapped around a large volume. Physiological processes would thus evolve to become tuned to that relatively stable temperature. If these large 'inertial homoiotherms' then faced new circumstances in which small size was an asset it is unlikely that the physiology of their descendants could cope with a return to the violent temperature fluctuations that would be imposed by being small. In other words, if a niche opened up for small creatures, large homoiotherms would have great problems adapting to fit it. According to this argument, only the lineages that developed endothermy could subsequently evolve small descendants. In other words, endothermy may have become a prerequisite of small size.

The relationship between area and volume (i.e. varying together but at different rates) would apply whether we were contrasting the problems of centrally heating a pleasure dome compared to a ping-pong ball or a Blue Whale compared to a Common Dolphin. The whale is only 12 times longer, but 1,475 times heavier (Blue Whales are 27 m long, 118 tonnes in weight, and 186 m^2 in surface area, which gives 634 kg of body weight per m^2 of skin. Common Dolphins are 2.2 m long, 80 kg in weight, and 12.7 m^2 in surface area, which gives 6.3 kg of body weight per m^2 of skin). The result is that the whale has about 100 times less surface area per kilogram body weight

The size of a mammal's body has repercussions for almost every aspect of its life. There are many reasons for this, for example, smaller prey species are likely to have more predators, whereas larger predators, isolated at the top of the food chain, are likely to need huge hunting ranges. But the most pervasive effect of a mammal's size can be traced back to a simple physical law, which relates the volume inside a body to the surface outside it. Bigger bodies have less outside relative to inside, in comparison to smaller bodies. This means that heat is lost from bigger bodies relatively slowly, which in turn means they need to eat relatively less energy. You can see this fundamental truth of geometry if you make a little stack of sugar cubes, here representing the volumes of a Wolverine and a Least Weasel (the smallest carnivore on earth), both of which are members of the weasel family. The Weasel contains one cube, which loses heat through six surfaces. The Wolverine contains a super-cube of 3 x 3 x 3 = 27 little cubes. However, although the volume of the super-cube is 27-fold larger, it does not have 27 x 6 = 162 outside surfaces (it has 54 little cube outside surfaces, which is only ninefold larger than the Weasel). In short, trebling the length of the cube results in squaring the area of its outside and cubing the volume of its inside. The inner warmth of a Weasel will therefore be able to waste away far faster than that of a Wolverine. Small mammals are, thus, more expensive to run than larger ones. The Weasel is particularly prone to lose heat because it is long and tubular – which means it has even more outside relative to inside. To minimise this lack of energetic thrift (necessitated by the need to squeeze down rodent burrows) the Weasel rolls into a heat-conserving ball to relax. However, its fuel bills are so high that it seldom has time to rest. The Wolverine, in contrast, with its dense fur and larger body, may often have to sprawl out and pant to lose heat.

than the dolphin. Furthermore, the whale's blubber weighs 27% of its total body weight, while the dolphin's blubber is 30–45%. These differences add up to a huge thermal advantage to the whale in cold water. In consequence the dolphin eats 11.3% of its weight in food each day, while the whale eats less than 1%. Indeed, cetaceans – the whales and dolphins – whether large or small, are much worse off than ping-pong balls or terrestrial mammals not only in terms of keeping warm but also because water is a better conductor than air and therefore drains heat from them even faster than air. For this reason smaller cetaceans (along with seals, sea lions and otters) have even higher fuel demands than comparably sized terrestrial mammals. Commonly, mammals that live largely in burrows need much less fuel, as heat dissipates slowly from their burrows because their underground homes tend to be both humid and buffered against changes in temperature.

The Water Shrew faces exacting challenges in heat conservation: its tiny body loses heat fast, and in the water the rate of loss is even greater.

Within any one taxonomic group, energy costs escalate with diminishing size. There comes a point when a yet smaller mammal simply could not eat enough to sustain its racing metabolism. This is the evolutionary precipice upon which teeters the Pygmy White-toothed Shrew, which weighs between 2–3.5 g. This frenetic creature must eat highly nutritious food almost incessantly. Yet even the Pygmy White-toothed Shrew is not the smallest of all mammals: at 1.5 g, Kitti's Hog-nosed Bat does not defy the laws of physics, but rather opts out of its impossible quest for food by periodically going into torpor, effectively decelerating its racing engine. This solution to the energy crisis precipitated by the area:volume law has a cost – the tiny

The Pygmy White-toothed Shrew eats voraciously to stave off its daily energy crisis.

bats are forced to return partially to ectothermy. Furthermore, infant Kitti's Hog-nosed Bats are so small that their survival would be an impossibility were it not for lactation.

The surface area:volume rule punishes larger mammals too, for while they are at a relative advantage when it comes to conserving heat, they suffer when it comes to losing it. One way to overcome their heating problem is to dissipate heat through radiators such as their large, thin ears. Incidentally, deep-frozen mammoths found in Siberia had small ears and, today, Arctic Foxes have relatively smaller ears than Red Foxes. In the case of dolphins, which have no option but to brave cold waters and need flippers for steering, the blood vessels in their flippers are arranged as a counter-current heat exchanger: vessels carrying warm blood towards the extremities pass close to, and give heat to, vessels carrying chilled blood back from the flippers.

If the punishing food requirements imposed by small size set the limit on the smallest mammal, what determines the size of the largest? The largest terrestrial mammal known is *Indricotherium*, a fossil herbivore about four times larger than the mightiest bull elephant (and who is to say that yet larger fossils have not slipped through the palaeontologist's net). It is possible that the largest land mammals (none of which survives today) pushed against the upper size limit for mammals with the same vigour with which Kitti's bat is challenging the lower limit. Giant mammals face serious architectural problems – the giraffe already defies the rules in pumping blood all the way up to its head (it manages this with the aid of a series of non-return valves in the blood-vessels of its neck). The most serious problem is that the strength of leg bones, like any other pillars, only increases with the square power of their diameter, whereas the weight of the body they support increases with the cube power of its length. Thus bigger animals require disproportionately stocky limbs. In design terms, a rhino is effectively a two-tonne version of a gazelle, the solid legs and massive neck being necessary to support the great weight. Huge animals are at risk of being too heavy to lift their own weight: an elephant's skin weighs 1,500 kg and if an elephant had the strength to jump (which it has not) its bones would shatter on the impact of landing. Even to cope with standing up, 27% of its body weight has to be bone (standing up is a task from which the even larger Blue Whale is excused, but their huge size explains why they die when stranded on land – their lungs are crushed by their bulk).

Gigantism has its ecological drawbacks too. Despite eating less weight for weight than smaller mammals, larger mammals require more food and therefore must travel larger distances to find it, all else being equal, so the difficulties of finding time and space in which to satisfy their requirements places a limit on body size. However, dinosaurs apparently overcame these problems, suggesting that the size of mammals is limited by something else (indeed, in purely engineering terms, it has been calculated that a land mammal the size of a jumbo jet could be built). The most likely reason why mammals are not bigger is that, because of endothermy, large mammals are seriously prone to heatstroke. Nowadays, they are also the most common victims of human interference.

Food quality

All else being equal we might expect the racing metabolism of, say, the 11 g Harvest Mouse to force it to eat relatively more than its 30 kg cousin the European Beaver (cousin in the sense that both are rodents). However, all else is not equal. In particular, as every weight watcher knows, foods differ in their energy and nutritious value. Smaller representatives of each mammalian lineage avoid the (unsustainable) prospect of perpetual gluttony by eating better food rather than more food. Conversely, large vegetarians cannot (and because of their slower metabolisms, need not) find sufficient high-quality food because fruits are inevitably scarcer than leaves. Thus the Harvest Mouse nibbles highly nutritious seeds while the beaver munches through relatively indigestible grasses, Roe Deer are selective feeders while Elk are less so, and Chinese Water Deer pick fruit and buds while the Reindeer mows lawns of lichen.

The problem is that high-quality foods tend to be scarcer than low-quality foods, which explains why large members of each lineage cannot feed on them (and do not need to) – a hedgehog the size of a horse simply could not find and catch beetles fast enough to sustain it. The largest insectivorous

The Common Vole is a grazer and thus, despite its small size, shares many problems in common with large grazers such as some antelope and deer. Many voles eat almost their body weight in wet weight of vegetation every day.

mammals, Giant Anteaters, Giant Armadillos, Pangolins and Aardwolves, eat prey that occurs in locally very abundant clumps. They could probably not evolve to any larger size without abandoning insectivory. In general, selectivity is an option for smaller species, because highly nutritious food tends to come in small parcels. How, then, does this generalisation square with the fact that many voles are both herbivorous grazers and small? One answer is that voles eat fungi, lichens, berries and seeds as well as leaves. In some northern Swedish forests, lichens make up 20–50% of their diet, and plentiful berries are eaten in season. Voles will also eat bark when other foods are rare. In English woodland, Bank Voles eat growing shoots in preference to the older parts of plants, and fungi often make up 10% of their diet. Furthermore, some voles eat mostly poor quality grass, but they process this food very rapidly. The grass goes through their system quickly so the voles can fill up their gut several times each day. These grasses may be relatively poor in quality, but so much passes through their system that they are able to meet their daily requirements. Many voles eat almost their body weight in wet weight of vegetation every day.

The gourmet subtly underlying mammalian food choice is illustrated by the finicky tastes of Wood Mice living in cereal fields. In early summer, amidst the oceans of dietetically boring unripe Wheat, the mice seek out delectable weeds, such as Chickweed, Sterile Brome, Blackgrass and Cleavers. Their particular favourites vary from month to month, presumably as the seeds of each species ripen, but some of these preferences vary between male and female mice. Thus male Wood Mice seek out Chickweed in May, whereas females focus on this weed in April. Perhaps these differences arise because the female must cater for the special nutritional demands of pregnancy and lactation, whereas males need high energy food to fuel their wide-ranging quest for females. By late autumn, both sexes favour ripe Wheat, Blackberries, Oilseed Rape, Wild Oats and Barley. At this time of the year the Wood Mice take a siesta for two to four hours in the middle of the night. Seeds of different species differ greatly in their content of carbohydrates and proteins. Remarkably, Wood Mice not only select a menu of seeds which balances their intake of carbohydrate and protein throughout the night, but they also select different types of seed during the active and lethargic parts of the night. While scampering actively hither and thither they choose seeds rich in both carbohydrates and proteins, whereas during midnight feasts between naps they nibble on seeds rich in sugar and water. Furthermore, during the first part of the night they seek out seeds whose carbohydrate content is high in sugars, but they do not favour sugars during the last part of the night. As sugar is more quickly digestible than other carbohydrates, the mice may be selecting for a quick source of energy at the beginning of the night's work.

Foods differ hugely in their extractable energy content and their digestibility. Plant cells are encased in tough walls of cellulose, and breaching these has been a major obstacle to mammalian digestive systems (see p. 88). Fruits, tubers and nuts are all nutritious and digestible, as is animal flesh. The consequence is that the conversion of grass into vole is some 26 times less efficient than the conversion of vole into weasel. However, although carnivory is more efficient (per mouthful of food eaten) than herbivory, energy is nonetheless lost at each stage of the food chain, so overall there is less of it available for species at the top of the chain. On average about 10% of the energy at one level passes on to the next level of the food chain. The remainder is lost through the burning of energy to fuel the processes involved in day-to-day living, and because animals at one level in the food chain are unable to find and eat all the animals or plants in the next level below them. This spillage of energy on the way up the food chain explains why the total biomass (weight of living matter) per unit area of carnivores is less than that of herbivores, which in turn is less than that of plants.

Chapter five

Reproduction and the impact of milk

Methods of reproduction

Monotreme reproduction

The major evolutionary divisions of mammals pivot on their reproductive systems. There are no members of the mammalian subclass Prototheria in Europe; neither have their fossils been found outside Australia and New Guinea. The three surviving Prototherians, the Platypus and two spiny anteaters or echidnas (all members of the order Monotremata) are largely confined to Australia. There, in the last sanctuary for reproductive anachronisms, these mammals lay eggs. In common with some contemporary Insectivora (see p. 21), the monotremes have a cloaca (an opening common to the urinary, digestive and reproductive tracts). Only the left ovary produces eggs (an asymmetry shared with birds), shedding them into an oviduct where they are coated with albumen and a shell. The eggs, measuring 14 x 18 mm, are laid 12–20 days later. The embryo is nourished from its yolk-sac while being incubated in a nest by the Platypus or in a pouch by the echidna. On hatching, the infant monotreme sucks milk that drains from its mother's mammary glands onto tufts of abdominal hair.

Members of the subclass Theria (that is, all living mammals except the relict monotremes) eschew egg-laying in favour of bearing live young. However, there is a fundamental division in how they go about this: the marsupials (infraclass Metatheria) essentially conduct their pregnancies in the pouch, whereas placental mammals (infraclass Eutheria) conduct theirs in the womb.

Marsupial reproduction

Marsupial eggs are shed by both ovaries into a double-horned uterus. They are exactly homologous with bird or reptile eggs in wrapping their contents within three membranes. The eggs of most placental mammals have two coats (rabbits spoil this generalisation by having three). From the partisan standpoint of a placental mammal, everything about marsupial reproduction is odd, starting from the moment at which a two-pronged penis inseminates each of the two branches of the female's uterus. Depending on the species, marsupial pregnancies last 12–28 days (aside from those, such as the endearingly named Dibbler, which store sperm – see p. 207). This variation in the length of pregnancies is minimal in comparison to the huge variation in adult body size amongst adult marsupials.

The key point is that the embryo feeds from a yolk-sac and on glandular secretions from the uterus ('uterine milk'). Nutrients diffusing into the abundant blood-vessels of the yolk-sac from the mother's bloodstream provide only a supplement to its diet. This dependence on the yolk-sac and diffused nutrients, however, is inefficient and cannot last long. Adherents to this mode of reproduction, represented in Europe only by the introduced Red-necked Wallaby, are born at what seems to be a hopelessly premature stage of development – weighing less than 1 g (equivalent to 0.003% of the mother's weight). As miniature distortions of their adult selves, with grossly exaggerated snouts to house the massive olfactory apparatus that guides them on their journey, they haul themselves along a trail of saliva with which their mother has marked the route to her nipples in the pouch. To accomplish this epic journey they have precociously developed forelimbs, in comparison to their skimpy hindquarters. In some marsupials, such as the Quokka, gravity is the youngster's only guide; this was demonstrated by a parturient Quokka being held upside down unceremoniously, which resulted in the newborn navigating enthusiastically up their mother's tail. Once the minuscule marsupial has latched on, the teat swells, plugging itself into the infant's mouth. There the young will stay, often within a pouch, until it detaches at approximately the same proportion of its mother's weight at which a placental mammal would have been born. Thereafter, it continues to suck from the outside. Alternatively, if food is short, the mother marsupial's milk dries up and the pouched young, albeit externally, is aborted.

Placental reproduction

The third method of mammalian reproduction hinges on the evolution of an organ whose various forms are collectively called the chorio-allantoic placenta. This innovation is so significant that it lends its name to the most modern and widespread of mammals – the placental mammals. The placenta frees the embryo from dependence on a limited supply of yolk for food, and forms a remarkable liaison between the blood systems of mother and infant. This liaison facilitates efficient exchange of respiratory, excretory and nutritional material. The early embryo, having adhered to the uterine wall, digs itself in by secreting hormones which dissolve the mother's tissue. The result is that the embryo's outer membrane, the chorion (equivalent to the inner lining of the shell of a bird's egg) abuts against maternal tissue. The chorion grows finger-like projections, called villi, which are richly supplied with blood-vessels and which anchor it to the mother's womb and protrude into a soup of degenerating maternal tissue. The villi absorb this nutritious broth.

Two facts about placentae emphasise the diversity of mammals. First, different types of mammal have different types of placenta: the number of layers between the parent and offspring bloodstreams varies. The more layers there are, the less damage is done to the uterus, but also, the less efficient the exchange of nutrients and gases between mother and growing infant. On the embryo's side of the divide there are always three layers. Among whales, dolphins, and non-ruminant ungulates (e.g. Wild Boar and other members of the pig family) there are also three on the maternal side (the inner surface of the uterine wall, the connective tissue below and the walls of her blood-vessels). In this system the foetal villi plug into pockets in maternal flesh: they simply pull out of these sockets at birth, sparing the mother much damage, but paying the cost of being less efficient than other designs. Among the ruminant artiodactyls such as the Chamois or Ibex the number of layers between mother and embryo is reduced to five (only two on the mother's side); in the carnivores it is four; while in bats, most rodents and insectivores and primates (e.g. the Barbary Macaque) it is only three. This three-layer design, shared by mice and Man, is reputedly 250-fold more efficient at transferring bodily salts than the Wild Boar's six-layer type of placenta. The pinnacle of this trend is illustrated by lagomorphs, such as the rabbit, and some rodents (e.g. porcupines and rats) in which not only are all uterine tissues eroded so that the embryo is bathed in maternal blood, but even the embryo's side of the fence is slightly pared away.

The more intimate the placental link, the more of the mother's tissue is discarded at birth (as 'afterbirth'), and such deciduous, throw-away placentae incur a heavy cost in bleeding. However, the benefit is measured in abbreviated gestations: the pregnancies of rats and mice proceed, in relation to body size, at threefold the rate of those of fox or lynx.

This Fallow Deer doe is eating the placenta (afterbirth), possibly to conceal signs of the birth from predators, but certainly also to recover some of the valuable nutrients she will need during the expensive phase of suckling her fawn.

The second fact about placentae is their partnership with milk. Milk and placentae are both routes through which the mother's antibodies are transferred to the young. Again, this varies between different types of mammal, and the variation suggests that milk was the original route for antibody transfer in groups. In species with archaic multi-layered placentae, milk still transports the bulk of antibodies (see colostrum, p. 78), but for species with few-layered placentae the milk's role in this is minimised.

One idea about the origin of milk is that it evolved as an disinfectant. All skin glands produce anti-microbial substances, and the survival of eggs laid by an ancestor to mammals might have been increased if such disinfectant secretions were especially copious from the patch of skin against which the eggs were brooded. The more copious the germ-killing secretion of the brood-patch, the greater its chances of killing the germs threatening eggs and hatchlings. Hence, natural selection would favour development of these proto-mammary glands, whose secretions eventually became a dietary supplement too.

Above all, however, the great significance of the chorio-allantoic placenta is that it prevents the mother's body rejecting the embryo as it would other foreign bodies, and as marsupial mothers do. The result is that, unlike marsupials, placental mammals can opt for relatively long pregnancies. This, among other things, opens the door to life histories in which young are born well-advanced (i.e. precocially). In effect, by postponing its birth, the infant can rely directly on its mother's abilities during the period of its own greatest incompetence.

With this system, the ultimate limit to the duration of pregnancy is the size of the infant skull which will fit through the mother's pelvis. This limit is partly affected by the athleticism and agility demanded by the way of life of the species. Both are compromised by long pregnancies and large litter weight because pregnant females would be disadvantaged if too heavily burdened by embryos. In general, gymnastic species tend to give birth early and prolong lactation. The Common Pipistrelle Bat has a 44-day pregnancy, and nurses for as long again. Variation between mammalian species in gestation is, however, less than that in size: the Blue Whale is pregnant for 12 months and nurses for 7 months, while the Harvest Mouse is pregnant for 19 days and nurses for 15 days.

Mating

While there are three mammalian approaches to bearing young, there is fundamentally only one way to conceive them. All mammals reproduce sexually, and although mating may take from 10 seconds in the Common Shrew to 4 hours in the Aardwolf, the end result is invariably that the male produces vast numbers of spermatozoa which compete to fertilise a relatively tiny number of the female's eggs. The maximum known litter size is the reputed 56 young produced by a Virginia Opossum; in Europe the record is probably held by the Raccoon Dog with 19 whelps. Furthermore, male mammals never become pregnant and never lactate. These inescapable inequalities have far-reaching consequences for mammalian life histories (see p. 211).

Each egg ends up with a half-set of maternal genes (alleles), and which half each egg gets is, largely, a matter of chance. Similarly each sperm has a half-set of paternal genetic material. The two half-sets of hereditary building blocks make a whole complement upon fertilisation. Because of the randomness of segregation of parental genes into each egg or sperm, and the randomness of the process whereby each half-set ends up wedded to another half-set, each mammalian offspring is different from all its siblings and from both its parents. However, because each individual has a one-in-two chance of sharing a given gene with its sibling, siblings are likely to share, on average, 50% of their genetic constitution (assuming the litter has only one sire, which is not always the case, see p. 230) and each is certain to share 50% with each of their parents. More distant relatives share fewer genes, but still have more in common than unrelated individuals, and these facts also have enormous implications for their life histories (see p. 154). Apart from the occasional pair of identical twins, the generalisation that mammalian brothers and sisters always differ is corrupted only by the Long-nosed Armadillo – which routinely produces identical quads from each fertilised egg – and by the Pink Fairy Armadillo which produces 12 identical embryos from a single egg, although only eight or nine of these survive pregnancy.

Mating poses some tricky timing problems. Males must be attracted to females at a time when the females are receptive to amorous advances (described as being on heat or in oestrus). A female must be on heat at the right time to ensure that a male is on hand exactly when her eggs are ripe for fertilisation. This process of ripening involves hair-trigger control by hormones, culminating in the egg drifting into the funnel-shaped opening of a tube adjoining the ovary, called the oviduct. In the oviduct, the egg is transported by myriads of tiny waving filaments (cilia) towards its hoped-for assignation in the womb with the thousands-to-one winner of the spermatozoon race. If no fertilisation occurs then the boat has been missed for the year in species with only one annual heat (monoestrus). However, in species which have several oestrous periods each year, the whole hormonal cycle begins again. Primates have a rather different system from other mammals in this regard and opt for a menstrual cycle in which, if fertilisation fails, part of the wall of the uterus (the endometrium) breaks down with resultant bleeding. It is not certain why primates opt, uniquely, for this system, but one idea is that it is part of a mechanism for accelerating pregnancies.

Mammals may trigger the shedding of their eggs, ovulation, in two different ways. Which of these ways a given species adopts will greatly affect its natural history. Ovulation may be spontaneous, which, in practice, often means it is triggered by some environmental cue indicating the season of the year, such as day length; or it is 'induced' by the act of mating. Deer, foxes, jackals, wolves, many rodents, and people are examples of spontaneous ovulators. Wildcats, stoats, mink and coypu are induced ovulators, in which the follicles (which nourish the egg) develop but do not shed the egg (ovulate) until after copulation. Among rabbits and hares both the ripening of follicles and subsequent ovulation are stimulated by mating. A variant common among species of mice and rats involves odours of the male triggering oestrus in the female (see p. 194).

Both sorts of ovulation are designed to maximise the chances of mating success under different social conditions. Spontaneous ovulation often starts in the season that ensures the young will be born when food is abundant. Induced ovulation ensures, indeed demands, that the male and female are in the right place at the right time. Often, several males are present, far from harmoniously, at the right time, and among mink, shrews, cats, badgers and doubtless others too, variations on the system lead to multiple paternity (see p. 230). In the case of the rabbit, the induced ovulation allows eggs and embryos to develop side by side, so the doe can ovulate immediately if she mates within 12 hours of giving birth. This *post partum* ovulation maximises productivity and justifies the adage 'breeding like rabbits'.

Spontaneous ovulators include bats (which ovulate on awakening from hibernation), mice and monkeys. Ovulation in Red Deer is spontaneous and basically controlled by day length, but influenced by body weight and condition. The sound of roaring stags can bring Red Deer hinds into oestrus sooner, which is an advantage to males because it reduces the time for which they must protect their harem from interloping males; it may also benefit females by ensuring that they come into oestrus when a male is present.

Lactation

The name Mammalia derives from the salient trait of the class, the milk-producing mammary glands with which females nurse their young. The conventional wisdom is that these glands evolved from sweat glands, but some modern evidence hints that they may instead have arisen from the same skin glands which gave rise to scent- and oil-producing glands (see p. 185). Either way, the story emphasises yet again how the special qualities of mammals stem from the remarkable attributes of their skin. The glands producing the milk should not be confused with the mammae or teats through which it is delivered. All mammals produce milk, but not all possess mammae; in female Platypus and echidnas (see p. 28) the fluid simply exudes through pores in the skin on the abdomen. The number of teats varies widely, from two in the Barbary Macaque for example, to a maximum average of 29 in hedgehog-like insectivores in Madagascar called tenrecs. Excluding the placental tenrec (one female has been recorded to rear 32 young successfully), most of the high scorers in the nipple stakes are marsupials. The Virginia Opossum has 25, the Koala 24 and the Pale-bellied Mouse Opossum has 19. Incidentally the odd-numbered teat in the opossums is sited between the two rows. The number of teats may also vary between individuals – between 12 and 16 in the Arctic Fox, and 8 to 10 in the Stoat.

When an infant placental mammal sucks on a teat it stimulates the mother to 'let down' milk – which is why, if you bottle-feed a lamb, it repeatedly butts the bottle at the start of each feed. After about half a minute of stimulation the maternal muscles squeeze milk out of the honeycomb of tubes and cavities in the mammae, and into the ducts leading into the teat from which it is sucked. The infant's sucking triggers nerve impulses which travel to the mother's pituitary gland in her brain. The gland responds by releasing two hormones (chemical messengers) that travel in the blood back to the mammae. One hormone, oxytocin, facilitates the ejection of milk already stored in the mammae. The other, prolactin, stimulates renewed secretion.

Milk is highly nutritious, and it can enable infants to grow at astounding speed. Infant elephant seals are the record-breakers; one was seen to put on 11 kg in one day. Even an averagely gluttonous infant elephant seal, born at 46 kg, doubles its weight in 11 days and quadruples it in three weeks. Meanwhile the mother loses weight at an equally astonishing weight. Furthermore, young male elephant seals 'steal' milk from unrelated mothers in an attempt to get bigger faster. The potency of pinniped milk is phenomenal: a Hooded Seal is suckled for four days – the same period as a House Mouse!

Milk contains fats, proteins and carbohydrates along with minerals, antibodies and water. Just as the shapes of tooth and claw have been variously fashioned by evolution for particular lifestyles, so too the nature of milk varies. The milk of the elephant seal is 55% fat, the Wolf's is 9.3% fat; the Cow's milk is 88% water, and the Reindeer's is 27% water. Rich, fatty milk is characteristic of species which must grow fast (e.g. marine mammals, as explained below) or which nurse infrequently (e.g. hares). The milk of pinnipeds is rich in fats, between 40–60% in the Hooded Seal. Young Hooded Seals have the shortest weaning period of any mammals. This haste in terminating the mother–infant relationship is probably an adaptation to an unstable home: the pack ice is likely to break up beneath them. Another virtue of this fatty milk is to foster rapid growth, before the infant takes the plunge into cold seas. Small mammals also grow fast because of their racing metabolisms, and to minimise the time for which they are fighting a horrendous surface area to volume ratio. The American Least Shrew is born at 1 g, has trebled its weight a week later, and reached its adult size of 4–7 g at two weeks old.

The composition of milk also changes as the suckling youngsters grow. For example, during the first three weeks of the elephant seal's four-week nursing period the milk's fat content rises from 15% to 55% and the water content falls from 75% to 35%. The Brown Hare suckles its newborn only once a day for three to four minutes, about an hour after sunset. This presumably diminishes the risk of the mother attracting the attention of predators to her offspring. In consequence, each drink must be potent: hare milk is 11–24% fat and 11–20% protein. The same anti-predation motive may explain the mother echidna's avoidance of her infant. Not surprisingly, once baby echidnas grow spines at about 50 days old they are no longer welcome in the pouch. Thereafter the mother nurses them only once every four days or so, but once again the milk is very rich (15–35% fat). The result of this sporadic maternal care is that the baby echidna grows in fits and starts – its growth-curve looks like the teeth of a saw. Incidentally, it is worth dispelling a couple of apocryphal tales concerning echidnas and Platypuses: it is not true that their babies lick milk from the hairs of the areola – they suck audibly. Neither is it true that male echidnas lactate: they do have mammary glands, but they are small (8 mm, versus 50 mm in the female) and non-functional.

The female wallaby has two teats, and nurses two offspring simultaneously. The older baby outside the pouch is provided with fatty milk, whereas in the pouch the younger infant receives fat-free milk.

Most remarkable of all is the mother wallaby's ability, when nursing two young of different ages, to deliver milk of different composition to each. The teat onto which an older offspring is plugged delivers milk with about 20% fat content and low in protein, whereas that from which its younger sibling drinks produces milk high in protein but fat free.

Milk also varies, of course, in volume: Red Deer may produce three to four litres daily; the Blue Whale a torrent of 292 litres per day – the infant whale downs 13 litres at each feed.

Milk is the substance of parental care in mammals. Its most important function is to provide for the young a specialised food, the supply of which is largely unaffected by short-term variations in the parent's feeding success. It is a buffer, allowing a useful postponement of the day when the infant must enter, directly, the competitive world of its parents. Birds also provision their young, but their ability to do so is more directly affected by environmental circumstances. The contrast with mammals is that if the food supply falters then a mammalian mother continues to nurse her infants, mobilising her own bodily tissues, minerals and trace elements to maintain the supply of dietetically balanced milk. Lactation is the linchpin of mammalian parental care, and it is parental care that permits mammals to bear small, heavily dependent young (litters are commonly about 10% of maternal body weight), which then grow fast and remain dependent until they reach an age and size at which they can operate independently on more or less adult terms. The biochemical reactions that give rise to their growth are speeded by the warmth of endothermy, and fuelled by milk.

Milk also functions in health care. It contains a number of anti-microbial agents (enzymes) which fight bacteria, fungi, viruses and protozoa. Furthermore, the first batch of milk, called colostrum, contains antibodies. In rabbits, for example, these antibodies remain in the gut and prevent germs sticking to the gut wall. The bacterial battlers are so important in the colostrum of ruminants that it may contain as much as 10 g of antibodies per 100 ml. This is why shepherds are at such pains to ensure that newborn lambs get adequate colostrum.

The cost of producing milk can be quite substantial. Producing the milk can double the daily energy requirement of the mother. The mother Blue Whale loses up to 25% of her weight while nursing her calf. The cost of milk production is so high that females of many species cannot conceive again until they have finished lactating. Indeed, in humans the use of wet nurses to cut short the period of breast-feeding by high status women was recorded as a means of speeding up their next conception as early as 1800 BC.

Teeth

As we have seen, the single most tell-tale clue to a mammal's lifestyle are its teeth (see p. 51). Teeth may be designed for chewing, grinding, slicing, nibbling, puncturing, pulping or gnawing, and in the jaws of no other class of vertebrates can such diverse evolutionary engineering be found. Once formed, mammalian teeth are encased in enamel and therefore cannot expand in girth. The complex interactions between teeth in the upper and lower jaw depend upon a perfect fit between the intricate pattern of their cusps when eating. Any such precise arrangement developed in the mouth of a baby mammal would be thrown out of alignment as the jaw grew whilst the teeth remained their original size (encased in their enamel strait-jacket). Therefore, the complexity of mammalian dentition relies upon a postponement of the time at which it comes into service, indeed until the jaws have stopped growing. This postponement is facilitated in part by lactation.

The sophistication of mammalian teeth in dealing with solids owes much to milk. The race to have effective dentition before weaning explains why mammalian skulls grow disproportionately fast after birth (beforehand their size is limited by the need to pass through their mother's pelvis). Furthermore, jaws grow at a pace that is remarkably unaffected by circumstances, keeping to schedule even when their owner is starving.

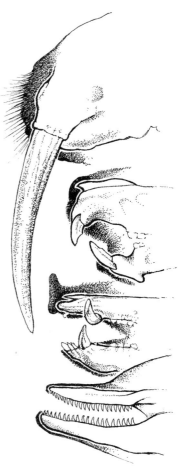

Mammalian teeth are diversely adapted. From top: the canine tusks of the walrus can be used as levers to hook into ice. The beaver's incisors, protruding outside their lips, can chew through wood. The Wild Boar's enlarged canines are useful for fighting and rooting for food. The dolphin's teeth grip slippery fish.

Another contribution to solving the problem of jaws outgrowing their teeth is provided by deciduous (or milk) teeth, a simplified set which are shed when they are outgrown. This two-stage system of teething is called diphyodonty, and is one of the hallmarks of mammals (see p. 15). However, there are exceptions: not all teeth are diphyodont, nor do all species of mammal have diphyodont teeth. Molar teeth are not replaced twice: they appear after the last of the deciduous teeth, at about the same time as the latter are replaced by the permanent dentition. In marsupials, only the premolars are always replaced between infancy and adulthood. The rule that mammals are diphyodont is also clearly broken by secondarily toothless forms such as anteaters, and by the Platypus which has teeth only as a juvenile.

The type of teeth in the second set can be different from those in the first. For example, among big herbivores the juveniles have low-crowned (brachydont) grinding teeth, which they swap for high-crowned (hypsodont) teeth as adults. Just as in the evolutionary history of ungulates, the high-crowned tooth is a modern innovation, replacing the old fashioned low-crowned form which wore out more quickly, so for the infant ungulate it may not be worth investing in a high-crowned tooth which will be discarded at maturity.

The Edible Dormouse has chisel-like incisor teeth for cutting into seeds and nuts. This abrasive task wears down the incisors, which grow throughout the animal's life.

Extremes of size pose dental problems. Elephants have to eat almost incessantly, wearing out teeth that must last a long lifetime. They have one or six sets of teeth, depending on how you look at it. Their molars and premolars are formed high up in the skull by the cementing together of up to 27 separate plates of dentine and enamel. These teeth are then used one at a time as six pairs; the first three teeth to be used are premolars which are worn out quickly. Next come three molars, each one rolling down the conveyor belt as its predecessor wears out. At the other extreme, miniaturisation also has its problems. Shrews also have an odd arrangement – they grow and shed their milk teeth before they are born with a full adult set. Perhaps this accelerated development gives them a racing start in their struggle to stay in credit energetically (see p. 57).

Lactation in males

Finally, the glaringly obvious question about lactation is why male mammals do not do it. At one level the answer is that, doubtless, it would be an exceedingly difficult evolutionary trick to do in terms of the hormones that control maleness and femaleness. The development of a female mammal's milk-producing apparatus involves hormones produced by her ovaries from puberty onwards – hormones that are largely incompatible with their male equivalents that can produce, for example, manes and musculature instead. However, although very difficult, it is not impossible for males to lactate. Prolonged treatment with female hormones has resulted in mammals including bulls and men producing milk. Indeed, the males of one species, the Dayak Fruit Bat in Malaysia, have recently been discovered to produce milk naturally. The key question is: would it pay males in general to lactate? Most mammalian species have polygynous sex lives, and under this system males would not rear more offspring if they lactated, because they hardly engage in paternal care at all, instead devoting their energies to mating with as many females as they can (see p. 211). It is plausible that for some species the flow of milk limits females' breeding success. For example, female Bank Voles and Field Voles increase their energy consumption by 250% when nursing infants and it seems quite likely that this huge energy demand is the limit on their maternal abilities. But in these species the idea of milk-producing males is a non-starter because they pursue the evolutionary goal of producing descendants by promiscuity, not by caring fatherhood.

The situation is different in monogamous species, where the father's care of the young is important to their survival (see p. 216). But is the survival of young born to monogamous pairs of, say, Red Foxes, limited by the mother's milk production? Probably not, and anyway monogamous fathers are busy doing other vital things (bringing food and standing guard, for example), and if they were to get involved in suckling, they would be distracted from these chores. If the male does provide paternal care, the male and female are thus better off each specialising in a certain type of care, rather than both parties compromising their abilities. So it seems likely that male mammals do not lactate partly because it would be extraordinarily difficult to reconcile maleness with the feminising properties of milk-producing hormones, and also because it would not pay them to do so, as they can better maximise their breeding success by other means. However, while they are caring for their offspring, the males of some species, such as wolves, do produce the hormone, prolactin, normally associated with milk production in females. Perhaps this hormone promotes the male's paternal care of his pups.

PART TWO

MAMMAL BEHAVIOUR

Chapter six

Brainpower and the quest for food

Mammals are commonly perceived as being brainy; most people would rank their dog's or cat's intelligence over that of their canary, terrapin or goldfish. But is this a fair assessment, and anyway, what is intelligence and when is it a valuable trait? It is true that many mammals have larger brains than most birds, reptiles or fish, but then mammals also tend to have larger bodies too. So in proportional terms the straightforward comparison is not fair. Just as larger telephone exchanges need larger computers to run them, so larger mammalian bodies need larger brains. To overcome this inequality, brain sizes are compared using the Encephalisation Quotient (EQ), which compares the size of a species' brain with the predicted brain size of an average animal of that body weight. On this measure of *relative* brain size, birds score similarly to mammals, whereas reptiles, amphibians and fish have lower scores. However, mammals were not the first group to evolve relatively large brains – this trait was first seen in some cartilaginous (i.e. shark-like) fishes in the Jurassic era, and again in the ostrich-like dinosaurs (Ornithomimidae) and some mammal-like reptiles. The fact that none of these groups were thereby saved from extinction shows that braininess is not everything. Similarly, small-brained dinosaurs suppressed the Mesozoic mammals for 150 million years.

Brain size does not get bigger in direct proportion to body size but, rather, smaller mammals have relatively larger brains. As a generalisation, a mammal with quadruple the body size of a smaller species would have only treble the brain size. There is a notable coincidence between this relationship and that between metabolic needs and body size (which also 'scale' to each other according to the same 3:4 power rule). This coincidence has prompted the suggestion that brain size varies with metabolic needs because mammals of different sizes all devote a constant proportion of their energy to growth and maintenance of their brains (exactly the same relationship applies to birds too). However, nobody has yet thought of a good reason why all mammalian species should allot the same proportional investment to their brains. Furthermore, within the mammals some taxonomic groups have relatively larger brains than others (i.e. higher EQs) as do adherents of some lifestyles. Among bats, the fruit bats tend to have relatively larger brains than the insect-eating bats of the family Vespertilionidae. Similarly, among primates (which, as an order, have the highest EQs of all), fruit-eaters, along with insectivorous and grain-eating representatives, have relatively larger brains than leaf-eaters. Among both opossums and squirrel-like rodents, arboreal species tend to have relatively larger brains than terrestrial ones.

Lactation and the parental contact it demands prolongs the opportunity for young to learn from adults. As a general rule, adults of species bearing helpless (i.e. altricial) young have larger brains for their body size than adults of those bearing advanced (i.e. precocial) young. The smallest relative brain sizes are found among certain marsupials (opossums of the family Didelphidae), and among shrews and hedgehogs.

Munching leaves may be less mentally demanding than lifestyles based on such unpredictable and patchily available resources as fruit; leaf-eaters certainly tend to have relatively small home ranges which demand limited orienteering brainwork (then again, they may have lower metabolic rates too, see p. 66). Similarly, the third dimension added to the lives of arboreal species may be associated with a need for increased sensory and perceptual abilities, demanding the processing of more elaborate spatial information than that utilised by terrestrial species. Since it is more difficult to catch moving prey than grass, one might expect carnivores to have higher EQs than their ungulate prey. In fact, this simplification ignores the fact that grazers face the mental challenge of avoiding being eaten, and this presumably partly explains why members of the order Carnivora and modern ungulates have similar-sized brains. However, modern carnivore families have higher EQs than extinct ones had, and within today's families modern canids and felids have relatively larger brains than their ancestors. Moreover, there is some evidence, albeit controversial, that relative brain size of predators and prey has leap-frogged through evolutionary time. It appears that the 'progressive' ungulates evolved larger brains (and presumably more adroit escape tactics to outwit archaic carnivores) only to prompt a surge of increased brain size in the next 'generation' of carnivore design (presumably indicative of yet craftier predatory tactics).

Mammals often behave in ways that appear so complicated that it is tempting to conclude they are very intelligent. However, while some mammals may solve some problems using their intelligence, others may not. When an Egyptian Mongoose, found feral in Spain or Portugal, opens an egg by throwing it backwards onto a rock it looks clever, but it may simply be following an instinct.

Modern carnivore and ungulate brains have been their current sizes for at least 35 million years, however, and today each order has its brainier representatives. Among ungulates, perissodactyls such as rhinos and tapirs have small brains compared to artiodactyls such as llamas, antelopes and deer. Similarly, relatively speaking, the brains of members of the dog family, the canids, are 8% larger than those of weasels, 38% larger than those of cats, and 45% larger than those of genets and mongooses. Explanations of these differences, often couched in terms of the relative complexity of the motor skills required by different families, tend to beg the question of how brain size and EQ relate to intelligence. Interpretation of relative brain sizes is further complicated by variations in the proportions of component parts. So, a large brain does not necessarily imply much thinking. For example, the part of the brain used for processing information from the nose is larger in the Eurasian Badger than in the Barbary Macaque, whereas the macaque has a larger cerebral component.

Intelligence is loosely understood as having something to do with the capacities to learn and to solve problems. However, the complexity of a task is no guarantee that it demands intelligence: for a human to build a spider's web would require great intelligence and mathematical acumen, for a spider it requires only instinct. Furthermore, different mammals may have been selected by evolution to excel at certain tasks but not others. Rats have a prodigious memory for networks of paths and can doubtless learn routes through mazes better than people, but we have the edge over them in solving quadratic equations. The difficulty of defining intelligence in mammals involves recognising that it (like talent in people) can be expressed differently, and may mean different things for different species.

Whatever intelligence may be, there is some evidence that the processing power of brains increases with their absolute size. Among mammals three orders have very large brains in absolute terms: the elephants (pachyderms); the whales and dolphins (cetaceans); and monkeys, apes and especially humans (primates). The elephants, however, are much less impressive when brain size is scaled according to body size. Whales and dolphins have big brains both in absolute terms and relative to their body size. Yet in linking size to intelligence we should ask what a given species' brain is used for. Dolphins use echolocation (see p. 170) and a lot of their brainpower may be devoted to deciphering these signals (although this argument is weakened by the relatively small brains of echolocating bats. Nonetheless, aside from Man, the most impressive brain of all is that of the Bottle-nosed Dolphin and it may be that their intelligence is as great as, but mysteriously different from, that of the great apes or even ourselves. However, we should be careful not to confuse great intelligence with greater evolutionary fitness. Curiosity may be a symptom of intelligence, but remember what it did to the proverbial cat.

Food and digestion

Energy for life comes ultimately from the sun, from which it is trapped by plants through the biochemical intricacies of photosynthesis. Mammals wanting to commandeer some of this energy have the options of intercepting it either at the plant stage, or after it has been converted to animal tissue by a herbivore. Unfortunately, energy is lost at each link in the food chain. The result is that less energy is available to carnivores than to herbivores, and thus animal communities are organised as pyramids, with small numbers of carnivores depending upon larger numbers of herbivores (see p. 107).

Eating plants has, in digestive terms, pros and cons. Plants contain abundant carbohydrates, such as sugars and starches. Yet they are low in proteins, which are essential for growth and repair of the mammalian body, and even lower in fats to the extent that many ungulates have lost the gall bladder, the organ responsible for producing the bile salts used to emulsify fats prior to their digestion. The scarcity of protein is particularly punishing for smaller ungulates since their higher metabolic rates impose relatively greater energy demands than those faced by large ungulates (see p. 66); yet this can be overcome by picking a menu of seeds and fruit, which are rich in protein. Nevertheless, equally serious is the fact that the apparent richness of plant carbohydrates is partly illusory.

The most nutritious plant carbohydrates can be found in two places. The first reserves are sugars or starches in readily digestible solution inside plant cells. Unfortunately, these are encapsulated by tough cell walls. These same walls contain the second supply of carbohydrate, cellulose, but it is bound chemically and indigestibly into their fabric. Grinding teeth can breach the cell walls and liberate the starches and sugars within. However, unless herbivores can rely upon an accomplice in their assault on the actual walls of the plant cell, the cellulose therein would shimmer elusively before their digestive systems like a mirage before a thirsting man. So it is fortunate that in their struggle to convert abundant carbohydrate to available carbohydrate, herbivores do have powerful allies in the form of bacteria and protozoa. Herbivores are able to digest the cellulose of which plant cell walls are made, and so release the energy stored in the fabric of the cellulose, only if somewhere in their guts they can harbour organisms capable of fermenting the plant tissue. The bacteria and their hosts both need each other, and such beneficial trysts in nature are called symbioses. All ungulates have formed symbiotic liaisons with bacteria, but different groups have gone about it in different ways.

Digestion in herbivores

Ungulates crop vegetation with their lips, tongues and teeth. Some even-toed ungulates, such as deer, have lost their upper incisors and so crop food using their lower incisors like a knife against the 'chopping board' horny plate of their upper gums, and grasp with their tongue and upper lip. The onslaught of herbivores on resilient plant cells is begun by grinding dentition: flat, square molars, with high crowns (hypsodont) which last a lifetime, and a musculature and jaw structure that permits sweeping, transverse grinding. Ancestral mammals used their canine teeth as daggers to pierce and grip prey. Modern predators do the same, but among ungulates, those that do not use them as weapons (Wild Boar and Muntjac, for instance) have either lost their canine teeth or incorporated them into their row of

Without taking time to chew the cud, the Bison would be unable to extract nutrients locked within the cell walls of its plant food.

mowing incisors (as in most deer and all other ruminants, for example). Among ruminants, that is all even-toed ungulates excepting the pig family, the masticated food passes immediately to a fermentation chamber, the rumen, which forms part of the multi-chambered stomach. The rumen is basically a storage chamber for newly eaten but only partially chewed food. Therein, bacterial action leads to some digestion of cellulose (and absorption of the products) and to the synthesis of vitamin B. Incidentally wallabies, although from a completely different lineage (being marsupials), have independently evolved a functionally similar stomach for dealing with grass. The food, now as cud, is then returned to the mouth for further chewing. The fermentation can take about 80 hours before the products of the bacterial action render the cellulose digestible, but it is an efficient process and results in ruminants absorbing about 60% of the carbohydrate they eat. What is more, they also digest the protein-rich bacteria that slop over from the fermentation chamber into the stomach chambers, the omasum and abomasum. Urea, a nitrogen-rich waste product of digested protein, also gets recycled via the stomach, thus further improving nitrogen retention.

A complex series of sieves prevents the mulch passing too swiftly through the system, and periodically the mulch is regurgitated for further grinding through chewing the cud. This is what cattle are doing when they lie in the shade after grazing. The chewed cud is swallowed, bypassing the rumen and entering the second chamber (the reticulum). One advantage of a slow passage of food is that it allows time to cope with the toxins with which the plant may have armed itself against herbivores. Sloths represent an extreme case: they have huge stomachs (comprising around 15% of their body weight when empty) where they use bacteria to ferment food. Bananas and citrus fruits remain in the sloth's stomach for up to 90 hours, and may take a week to pass all the way through the digestive system.

The perissodactyls (odd-toed ungulates such as horses), along with elephants, koalas, vegetarian rodents and primates, store their symbiotic bacteria towards the rear of their guts in the caecum and colon. There, the process is the same, but the speed at which food passes is faster (about 48 hours). The efficiency is lower (45% of carbohydrates eaten are absorbed), but more food can be processed. However, because of the rearward housing of the bacteria, the opportunity to digest their corpses, as a further source of nourishment, is missed. This loss is made good by lagomorphs and many rodents, which have invented a means of effectively digesting their food twice to circumvent the disadvantages of having the bacteria at the end of the intestinal tract. This necessitates the unendearing, but intensely thrifty, habit of eating their faeces – a practice known as coprophagy (from the Greek *copros* = excrement, and *phagein* = to eat). Food being passed through the gut for the first time is shaped in the caecum into larger, softer and lighter coloured pellets than the familiar droppings. The two types of faecal pellets are kept separate as they pass into the rectum: the soft ones being eaten directly from the anus. These re-ingested, membrane-coated faeces are neither chewed nor mixed with other food in the pyloric (forward) region of the stomach, but lodge separately in the fundus (rearward portion) of the stomach where they continue to ferment for many hours. One of the fermentation products is lactic acid, and so the stomach fundus of coprophagous species like rabbits and hares may fill the same role as the rumen (fermentation chamber in stomach) of artiodactyls. After passing through the intestine a second time, the food is excreted as the characteristic hard, dark droppings.

Another form of coprophagy is found in other mammal species, such as the koala, which lives on a diet of tough, toxic eucalyptus leaves. Towards

the end of suckling, a single young feeds on special, soft faecal material produced by the mother, which is quite different from the normal hard faecal pellets, and this apparently contains partially digested material. The young may eat this faecal mate-

Rabbits are amongst the herbivorous mammals that need to pass their food through their digestive systems twice to extract the necessary nourishment. After food has passed through once, the special faeces are eaten again, a behaviour called refection.

rial for up to six weeks and thereby also acquire all the right gut bacteria from its mother. The Afghan Pika, a relative of rabbits and hares, is fully weaned at the age of three weeks, but from about ten days after birth the young eat the mother's faecal pellets as well as milk, suggesting a system similar to that of the koala.

Neither the foregut nor hindgut system is superior, they are merely different. Ruminants can deal most efficiently with the young, growing parts of herbage, which are higher in protein, and can extract all their requisite nutrients, albeit in small doses. Ruminants prosper where the quality of vegetation is high even if its quantity is low (the Musk Oxen and Reindeer of tundra, for example). Hindgut fermenters do better where the nutrient quality of vegetation is poor and its fibre content is high, since they can process a higher throughput of bulk food than can ruminants. Elephants provide an extreme example of bulk processing: they produce 130 kg of droppings a day. Also, since species with the rearward bacterial cauldron have conventional foreguts they can still effectively digest rich foods like fruit, which are spoiled by the fermentation process.

These differences in gut structure also have implications for the body sizes and niches of their bearers (see p. 66). Gut structure also has implications for defence against predators – ruminants can swiftly graze, filling their forestomach like a shopping basket before retreating to a securer location to chew the cud at leisure and in safety. In contrast, all the chewing that a non-ruminant's food is ever going to get must be completed where it is eaten.

Ruminants do have one other ace up their intestines: they can recycle urea, the nitrogen-rich waste product conventionally excreted by mammals in their urine. Urea from the ruminant's bloodstream actually seeps into the saliva, whence it passes back through the gut into the rumen. In the rumen an enzyme with the predictable name of urease is secreted. This enzyme breaks the urea down into ammonia and carbon dioxide, which are fed upon by the foregut bacteria. Thus herbivores such as Fallow Deer benefit from this recycling twice: first, their bacteria are kept fit, second, they will eventually digest some of the bacteria. This recycling of urea has the additional effect of diminishing the concentration of their urine and therefore reducing the frequency with which ruminants need to drink. For this reason desert asses (hindgut fermenters) must drink daily whereas the Arabian Oryx (a ruminant) drinks rarely. This system also helps liberate ruminants from a pressing need to eat protein as a source of nitrogen, allowing each species to specialise on a narrower range of food plants than is characteristic of hindgut fermenters. This option to finely divide niches is sometimes said to explain why there are more species of ruminant than of perissodactyl today. However, this idea begs the question of how perisso-dactyls could be so abundant and diverse as they were during the Miocene (see p. 21); perhaps the weather then was wetter, and thus the perissodactyl's need to drink frequently was less disadvantageous.

The relative abundance of ruminants and non-ruminants in different niches ties up, as does almost everything, with body size. It turns out that larger mammals have relatively larger gut capacities than have smaller ones, and as a matter of fact food particles are held for longer in larger guts than smaller guts. Taken together, these two facts mean that larger mammals can digest food more efficiently than smaller mammals. Of course, larger ani-mals need to eat more food than do smaller animals, but their demands for food increase more slowly with increasing body size than does their gut capacity and hence their digestive efficiency (see p. 60). This state of affairs explains why, in a community of herbivores, the general rule is that medium-sized herbivores are ruminants, while small and large ones are non-ruminants. Small herbivores have a high demand-to-capacity ratio, i.e. their metabolic rate is high whereas their guts are small, which is loosely equivalent to the saying that their appetites are bigger than their stomachs. They are forced to feed selectively upon high-value foods which do not require long retention times. That is, they are forced to be hindgut fermenters, and so face nutrient loss (unless they are coprophagous). A high-fibre diet demands slower passage times and, therefore, larger body size. The ruminant system re-quires slow passage times, and it is efficient at dealing with fibrous diets. The relatively larger gut capacity (fermentation tanks) of larger ruminants increases their efficiency as they get bigger, putting them at an advantage over non-ruminants (e.g. cows are more efficient than horses). Medium to large herbivores are thus likely to be ruminants. However, there comes a point when diet is so high in fibre that it simply cannot be eaten fast enough to provide the amount of food necessary for an animal large enough to have a big enough gut to digest a sufficient quantity of it. At this point ruminants have no advantage over non-ruminants so the largest members of the group are likely to be non-ruminants (such as elephants).

Digestion in carnivores

The task of converting prey flesh and bone into predator flesh and bone is simpler than the alchemy of turning greenery to flesh. Therefore, although their dentition is highly specialised, the digestive systems of carnivores are simpler than those of herbivores. The inherent biochemical difficulty of converting plants into animals is exacerbated because, since they cannot run away, plants tend to focus their defences on being indigestible. Animal prey,

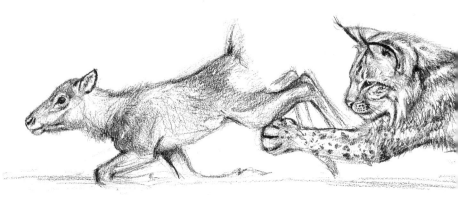

once caught, are easily digestible (although bats have had to evolve a special enzyme to digest the chitinous shells of insects). However, carnivorous diets bring their own problems including the initial one of catching the prey. The way animals are engineered means that the force (when a lynx swipes at a reindeer calf, for example) at the end of a limb is not merely doubled, but increases with the second power of length (i.e. length^2). That means that doubling the size of a predator, for example wildcat to lynx, or lynx to small sabre-tooth, increases the power of its forelimb swipe not twice, but 4-fold. Similar physical principles also have huge implications for mammalian agility: an animal twice the weight of another will hit the ground with an impulse twice as great if it jumps from the same height. A wildcat might jump down from a branch or crag to grasp prey. If the sabre-toothed cat that once prowled the same range had tried the same jump, it would probably have broken its legs.

Once the prey is caught and killed, its bone is difficult to chew and digest. Scavengers (such as hyaenas) tend to have digestive juices rich in hydrochloric acid capable of dissolving them (along with any potentially collywobbling pathogens picked up from foetid meat). Bone splinters are dangerous, but carnivores can vomit voluntarily to rid themselves of piercing stomach aches. Among the true carnivores, the length of the gut varies with diet. Flesh specialists like the wildcat and lynx have guts only four times their body length. For foxes and wolves, facing the problems of omnivory, the gut is five times their body length. For the Sea Otter, whose digestion has to battle with whole clams, the factor is ten. As bacterial fermentation is not relevant to pure carnivores such as cats and mongooses, the caecum (the pouch marking the beginning of the large intestine) is absent or small in these species. The more omnivorous fox does have a large caecum, but members of the weasel family (the mustelids) have none. For the flesh-eating weasel or wolverine this may be no problem, but the omnivorous Eurasian Badger may be disadvantaged by its ancestors' eschewing of a caecum. The Giant Panda, an herbivorous carnivore, has a short gut despite its depend-

The power of a cat's swipe increases substantially with limb length. If this lynx doubled its size, the forelimb would be four times more powerful, enabling it to bring down much larger prey than this reindeer calf.

ence on a 'difficult' diet of plant food. This paradox arises because the panda has no intricate adaptation or microbial allies to aid its digestion of bamboo. Rather, it simply eats masses of it (almost 8 kg, or 6% of its body weight in dry matter, daily), and processes it fast (in around eight hours) and inefficiently (20%). The panda's short and simple gut shows that its solution to the problems of herbivory rests solely on the quantity of accessible cell contents it can digest, ignoring the technically difficult task of digesting cell walls, which are expelled in a prodigious production of massive droppings.

Foraging

Life is full of decisions, and wrong ones are often costly and sometimes fatal. For example, even in the mundane business of finding food, mammals face a host of choices of when, where, how much and how often to eat. Considering the penalties, both personal and evolutionary, of losing in the competition for resources such as food (see chapter 7), we might expect animals to have finely honed abilities to make the right choices. A few moments' observation of Grey Squirrels in an urban park will reveal just how precisely they weigh up the pros and cons of their actions. I do not mean that they think out rational solutions to their daily problems; actually it is impossible for us to know what they think, or even if they think at all in the sense that humans do. Rather, to say they 'weigh up' something is a short-hand metaphor for the precise but unwieldy statement that natural selection has fashioned them to behave according to rules which can adapt behaviour to fit circumstances.

Grey Squirrels often scamper down from the safety of overhead branches in order to pilfer crumbs left by picnickers. There is, however, no such thing as a free lunch, and the squirrel's sortie into the open brings a heightened risk of predation. The result is a rather unhappy compromise as the squirrel dashes nervously between feast and foliage. But if you watch squirrels in this predicament you will see that the details of the compromise vary with the costs and benefits involved. For example, if the squirrel finds a large lump of cake it will carry it back to cover, but if it finds only crumbs it will eat them on the spot, trading off the increased danger of eating in the open, against the prohibitive waste of time and energy in racing back to cover with each crumb. Similarly, the squirrels are more likely to retreat to eat in safety if the picnicker's table is close to cover, because under these circumstances the time lost in travelling back and forth does not require such a sacrifice in feeding rate. These stresses also affect the squirrels' table manners: squirrels foraging for sunflower seeds actually eat the same amount in total whether the seeds are near to, or far from, cover. They achieve this by reducing what biologists call 'handling time' when they are further from safety; in other words, the greater the distance to shelter the more they gulp their food. Their fear of eating in the open is such that, given the choice, Grey Squirrels prefer larger items that can be carried to safety over smaller ones that cannot, even when the large food is protected inside fiddly husks and shells that slow down the total rate of food intake.

Similarly taxing compromises face all mammals as they decide between, for example, searching for abundant small food items as opposed to rare but large ones. The decision involves taking a gamble, but thinking about the payoff prompts the question: what are the gamblers trying to win? In the case of a mammal faced with gambling its life on its foraging behaviour, winning might mean minimising the risk of starvation, or perhaps maximising the rate of feeding. These two objectives may require different behaviour. Imagine, for example, a Common Shrew setting out to forage. Its tiny size fits it into a niche whereby it can race through the grassy corridors of a microcosmic world in pursuit of insects which, from the shrew's perspective, must seem far from trifling adversaries. Yet the same diminutive body size that opened the door to this lifestyle also lets out body heat at a fearful rate and imposes a racing metabolism on the shrew (see p. 60). If it should fail in the quest for prey then it will starve in only three hours. The ground is crawling with different types of prey – beetles, spiders, worms – how and where is the shrew to conduct the hunt?

Experiments in captivity have shown that when shrews have the option to hunt in two places, all else being equal, they concentrate on the site where they can, on average, capture most prey per unit of time. This is a very unsurprising decision on the shrew's behalf, but it is worth reflecting that all else may not remain equal for long in an uncertain world. For example, if the shrew foraged exclusively at the place (or for the particular prey) that yielded the richest pickings, it would never know if things were changing elsewhere – it might miss the development of an even better place. This is probably why most animals continue to check up on other hunting grounds even if they seem to have hit a winning streak. They may also seek out rare foods amidst common ones because the rare ones contain a particular nutrient – rats for example can select from a menu of junk food a diet which ensures they have the right balance of vitamins and food value (see p. 100).

The foraging shrew would face a brutal paradox if it based its choice between hunting grounds solely on the average rate at which it captured food there. For example, two different parts of a shrew's territory would, on average, be equally bountiful if one yielded two to four prey at each visit and the other either none or six prey. Both would average three, but when the chips are down the latter is a much more risky proposition. It turns out that Common Shrews are very alert to this problem, and since the stakes (their lives) are so high, they generally avoid unnecessary gambling. That is, given the choice, they prefer a reliable payoff, even if it is slightly smaller, over a highly variable but potentially larger payoff. When they are reasonably well fed, then they opt for the safer bet, because the risk of a run of bad luck outweighs the attractions of potentially greater winnings at less predictable sites. However, when hunting goes badly, and there is a greater danger of imminent starvation, shrews abandon their conservatism and turn increasingly to more risky sites where, although the risk of losing is higher, there is also a chance of hitting the jackpot. Under these circumstances the average payoff may no longer be sufficient to keep the shrew alive, whereas a

Tiny mammals, like Pygmy Shrews (above), have such expensive metabolisms that they face life-and-death decisions every hour of their lives as they hunt.

high payoff combined with high variability offers at least a chance of survival.

Shrews, as insectivores, tend to be thought of as rather simple mammals, but the task of designing a shrew, or more specifically its foraging behaviour, becomes mind-boggling when one thinks of all the choices to be taken into account. In many ways it seems that evolution has wrought astonishing precision of design. For example, shrews alter their hunting behaviour to forage harder and cache more when they sense another shrew in their territory (that is, they anticipate the consequences of competition), and they become less selective when time is short, thereby making the best of a bad job. In other respects, however, the design seems flawed: shrews will take larger prey in preference to small ones even when the difficulties of handling the big prey mean that in the long run the shrew would have eaten more by concentrating on the smaller prey. Of course, there are various species of shrew and the differences in their size affects their bodily energy reserves. When food is short, small shrews such as Pygmy Shrews and the Masked Shrew will increase the amount of time spent foraging to get through the crises, but bigger shrews such as Common Shrews (with larger fat reserves) will decrease their foraging time until food abundance increases.

A balanced diet

To the non-herbivore eye, one piece of greenery may look as gastronomically boring as the next, but foraging choices press hard upon herbivores too. Elk, for example, face a tricky problem when browsing in some deciduous woodlands because although the leaves are high in energy they are deficient in sodium. Happily, however, the leaves of aquatic plants are rich in sodium although poor in energy. In choosing how to apportion its browsing between these two, the elk's dilemma is worsened by the fact that its rumen (see p. 89) can only hold a certain bulk of foliage, and the aquatic leaves are so bulky relative to their energy content that the elk simply could not squeeze in enough of them to live on. Obviously, the elk has to find a balanced diet that provides sufficient sodium and sufficient energy, and fits into its stomach. Even within these restrictions the elk could get by on quite a few different combinations of woodland and water leaves, but what they actually do is apportion their time to get just enough sodium while otherwise eating as much woodland browse as possible. So, in these instances, it seems that the elk manage their affairs in order to maximise their daily intake of energy, while the shrews are intent upon minimising their risk of starvation.

As an Elk browses it faces decisions on whether to concentrate upon scarce but succulent buds or plentiful but coarse twigs.

The wintering grounds of elk differ in the quality and quantity of food they offer. Where only relatively indigestible birch twigs are available, the elk have no choice but to eat large amounts (over 4 kg per day) of low-quality food. This forces them to spend three-quarters of each day inactive as they sit out digestive pauses in the protracted (over 60 hours) struggle for their digestive system to draw nourishment from the stringy birch fibres. However, in areas where more diverse and nutritious plants are available, the elk nibble only the most select birch twigs along with those of Rowan, Aspen and Bird Cherry. These less bulky, more nutritious foods can be more swiftly digested, so launching the elk on a spiral of success; the log-jam in their guts is freed and they have more time to search greater areas for yet more nutritious shoots. The winter feeding of elk is then a network of options in which the choice of one limits the choice of others. The choice of a large mouthful of fibrous birch rather than a succulent snippet will, through its gut-blocking bulk, determine the elk's activity and ranging behaviour, and these in turn are limited by such external factors as snow depth which determine the difficulty of travelling from one patch of browse to the next. Therefore, each time an elk encounters a twig it must decide on which part to bite off in order to maximise its net gain in energy during the bleak Scandinavian winter. A lot hangs on that decision: a large bite of stocky twig leads to a different lifestyle than that resulting from a small bite of spindly twig. How does the elk make up its mind what to do? It is possible to answer this question because, happily, the elk leaves in the snow a complete account of its activities for the biologist to read. Tracks reveal its route, and the diameter of clipped-off birch twigs allows the sleuth to deduce whether the browsing elk opted for rapid intake of fibrous lumps or painstaking selection of nutritious soupçons. Not surprisingly, it turns out that where birch saplings grow in dense stands, the elk can afford to be choosy and takes small bites from only the topmost juicy twigs, selecting those only 2–3 mm in diameter. One consequence of this is that the saplings are less injured by the more selective browsing which takes less of the tree's flesh. This may mean that the response of birch trees to being browsed, which is to sprout numerous shoots in place of a few large succulent ones, is actually an attempt to alter the elk's behaviour in a way that minimises subsequent wounds to the tree.

The problem of deciding what to eat is worst for species with omnivorous or generalist tastes, because the more varied their menu, the more choices they face. Confronted with a smorgasbord of possible foods, the omnivore must not only eat enough quantity to provide energy, but also select the right quality to provide a balanced diet. Rats are proven connoisseurs in this regard: with tongues equipped with special taste buds to seek out such vital nutrients as sodium, they have an innate capacity to select a balanced diet from a wide menu. Mice have shown even greater gastronomic flair when faced with the gripe-causing defensive chemicals produced by plants to put off herbivores. Tannic acid and saponin are two such plant toxins, and young mice eating either of them for long get such indigestion that it stunts their growth. If mice in a laboratory are offered a cafeteria choice of foods, some containing and others free from these toxins, they actually select some of each, and grow normally. It turns out that the growth retarding effects of the two chemicals cancel each other out if they are eaten together in certain proportions and, remarkably, the mouse somehow knows how to balance its diet to best effect. Assuming that wild mice are as discerning as their laboratory cousins, this is bad news for plants relying on either chemical. However, such defences are still a nuisance to the mouse which is presumably forced to scuttle from plant to plant spending time finding the right combination of foods to keep collywobbles at bay.

A Red Fox foraging for earthworms alters the threshold capture success at which it gives up the hunt in a given patch of grass depending on the weather. When the weather is moist and mild, and worms therefore abundant, foxes will leave a patch and move to a fresh one as soon as they have creamed off a few worms, whereas when the weather is cold or dry and windy, worms are few and foxes will persevere in an area for much longer.

Deciding where to forage is a form of gambling, and all gamblers face the problem of when to quit. In the case of Eurasian Badgers and Red Foxes at least, the evidence suggests that they are often sufficiently prudent to quit when they are winning (but see p. 103). Both species hunt for earthworms, which they catch when the worms surface to gather leaves and to mate. Foxes, for example, pace methodically back and forth, cocking their head from side to side as they listen for the rustling noise of the earthworms' bristles on the grass. Having found a worm, the fox plunges its nose into the grass and, if the worm's tail is still anchored, pulls it from the burrow as might a blackbird on a lawn. Badgers probably rely more heavily on scent to find their worms, but both predators may eat upwards of 200 worms in a night. Both also face the problem that the numbers of worms surfacing varies with weather conditions from night to night, as do the places where they surface. It turns out that Red Foxes are very sensitive to variations in the availability of worms: they will concentrate the bulk of their worm-hunting in pastures harbouring the highest worm populations, and use clues, such as wind direction, to locate a patch of worms on the surface (worms tend to surface in the lee of shelters from the wind). Having once located a patch of worms, perhaps 20 m across, the fox may catch up to ten worms a minute, although two or three is more usual, and eventually it begins to deplete the supply. When should the fox or badger give up and move to another patch? The answer actually varies from night to night, depending on the prevailing conditions. Foxes give up and leave a patch of worms when their success rate there has fallen below the average for that night. So, on a bad night (which, in the case of worms, means cold and windy), because there is no option, foxes will persevere when capturing worms at a rate well below that at which they would move on to a fresh patch on a good night. In that sense, foxes quit when they are winning, but winnings vary widely from night to night.

Common Pipistrelles, which make hunting forays of up to 2.5 km from their roosts, may visit the same 'beat' at the same time night after night. They generally forage in groups of two to six, but up to 40 may congregate where insects abound. They locate their prey using echoes of high-intensity ultrasound. This takes great energy to produce: 0.067 joules per pulse (about the energy it would take you to flick a ping-pong ball half a metre into the air). Incidentally, bats can only produce this high-intensity ultrasound (other mammals can produce only low-intensity ultrasound, see p. 170) because they use their flight and respiratory muscles to produce it in synchrony with wing beats. Insect abundance varies from night to night and when it falls too low (less than 300 insects per 1,000 m^3 of air) the bats abandon a foraging beat. Under perfect conditions, pipistrelles swoop on prey at a rate of ten feeding 'buzzes' per minute, detecting, closing upon, catching and eating a new victim every six seconds.

A notorious and intriguing predatory behaviour is the habit of stoats and weasels to throw themselves into gymnastic convulsions that are believed to so mesmerise simple-minded rabbits that they allow the predator within reach. Remarkably it seems that the victims often die from fright, rather than the *coup de grâce* delivered as the finale to the stoat's performance. The odd thing is that stoats are quite often seen to dance with no audience in sight. This prompts the question of whether the dancing stoat really has rabbits in mind at all. An alternative suggestion is that these stoats are victims of skrjabingylosis – a condition brought about by parasitic nematode worms burrowing into the skull. Skrjabingylosis is even more painful to endure than it is to pronounce, so the convulsing stoat may be demented by pain, rather than playing to the crowd. This unromantic proposal remains to be tested, but it is certain that skrjabingylosis infects many stoats and weasels, because the damage can be seen as blisters in the bone of their skulls. The larval worm lives in slugs and snails, and is often eaten by shrews and sometimes by Wood Mice. It then lurks in these prey in the hope that they will in turn be eaten by a stoat. The parasite's dilemma is that while shrews often eat snails, Wood Mice only occasionally do so, whereas stoats

often eat Wood Mice and rarely eat shrews. On the Dutch island of Terschelling, 90% of stoats have skrjabingylosis, compared to about 20% on
the mainland. This is because there are no voles or mice on the island and
so the stoats are forced to eat lots of shrews. The same principle may explain
why the incidence of the disease increases as stoat numbers fall in
Switzerland, following a decline in water vole numbers. The water voles
never eat snails, and so while there is a glut of them, the stoats are not
exposed to the worm. However, when water voles decline, stoats eat more
Wood Mice and shrews and thereby contract more disease. Either way, the
worm does its best to ambush the stoats: it lodges in the heads of Wood Mice,
and this is the part that stoats and weasels like to eat the most.

*Dancing with pain? Stoats on the island of Terschelling (shaded on map) feed
mainly on shrews and have a high prevalence of the parasite skrjabingylosis.*

Surplus killing

In general the co-evolution of adaptations of predators and prey in the
evolutionary arms race for lunch versus life remains in an intricate balance.
Occasionally, however, a predator appears to go berserk, killing far more
prey than necessary for its immediate needs. The fox in the chicken run is
the most notorious example, but stoats, mink, badgers, otters, wildcats and
indeed all members of the Carnivora, will engage in this 'surplus killing' if
given the chance. For example, in Scandinavia human hunters provide food
at which Roe Deer congregate in winter. When particular snow conditions
compromise the deer's escape, Lynx may slaughter them *en masse*. This
may be a case of an adaptation going haywire when out of context (see p. 35),

rather like people doing things which are conspicuously bad for them, like eating too much sugar or smoking. One suggestion, applied to weasels, is that having evolved in the frozen north, surplus killing was adaptive because all the prey could be refrigerated. The implication is that weasels surplus killing in the south are doing so out of context. This idea ignores the fact that the same habit is widespread in species which did not evolve in cold climates. Another explanation is that these carnivores have evolved with hair-trigger killing behaviour, because an instant's indecision means a missed opportunity to catch prey that put a lot of effort into avoiding being caught. Usually, a Red Fox dashing at a group of rabbits will have the opportunity to kill only one or two at most; the question of killing too many does not arise because the prey take evasive action. If the predator happens to hit the jackpot, then a brace of extra rabbits can always be cached for future use (see p. 309). Under natural circumstances such opportunities for surplus killing are very rare indeed. However, in a chicken coop the prey behave unnaturally – they flutter about, flicking all the predatory switches in the fox's brain, but they refuse to run away. The fox has no mechanism, indeed it has never needed one, to resist this stimulus to kill. The inference is that although surplus killing seems wasteful, it has not disadvantaged predators sufficiently for natural selection to favour the invention of a safety catch on the hair trigger of killing behaviour. The surplus kill arises because the prey, not the predator, behaves abnormally. This explanation does not, of course, make the phenomenon any the less annoying to a poulterer.

Surplus killing by carnivores leads to some dreadful abuses of human language. People dub carnivores as vindictive and malicious. These are value judgements which may occasionally be applicable to humans, but cannot logically be applied to other species. Our mores are wholly inappropriate to them. In a related vein, people often ask whether predators enjoy killing. It is impossible to know for sure, because we cannot know what it is like to be one of another species, but in so far as natural selection has made people 'enjoy' things that promote their survival and fitness (see p. 36), such as food and sex, then if 'enjoyment' is a sensation felt by other mammals we might expect them to experience it as a reinforcement to behaving adaptively. To that extent, it would seem plausible that mammals that survive by killing would enjoy it; a mutation for compassion or squeamishness would be unlikely to spread in a population of predators.

For the most part, the selection of prey by predators is far from random, and there is abundant evidence that predators have a keen eye for a soft option, weeding out the young, the aged and infirm. For example, not only do wolves kill White-tailed Deer in the poorest condition, but they are also more likely to kill fawns (up to ten months old) whose mothers' nutritional condition had been poor during the previous winter when she was pregnant with them. Much more surprising is the 'grandmother effect': male fawns of young mothers are born as lightweights if their grandmothers suffered malnutrition due to deep snow preventing her from feeding during the winter when she was pregnant with their mother. Furthermore, and also irrespective of the mothers' condition (and, in this case, her age), the fawns descended from these hungry grandmothers suffered heavier than average wolf predation. Exactly what mechanism leads a White-tailed Deer to be so disadvantaged and vulnerable to wolves three years or more after its grand-mother endured a harsh winter while pregnant is uncertain. However, laboratory studies of malnourished grandmother rats have shown similar second-generation effects leading to stunted grand-offspring with impaired learning abilities and other indicators of poor brainpower. The insidious power of the past could hardly be more brutally illustrated: to be fated to fall prey to wolves because it happened to snow heavily after your mother was conceived reveals nature as a tangled web indeed.

Chapter seven

Competition
and coexistence

Predators and prey

The struggle of predator and prey is a matter of life and death for the individuals concerned, but how does the outcome affect their populations? It is fairly obvious that, ultimately, the numbers of predators are limited by the numbers of their prey – without clams there could be no Walrus, without moths no Long-eared Bats, without Ringed Seals no Polar Bears. But is it a vicious circle? Do predators limit the numbers of their prey? This question is more taxing. Of course, it is true that when a Eurasian Badger kills an earthworm or a Red Fox kills a partridge, there is one less of each prey. But, in terms of how populations tick, this truth may be a trivial one. What really matters is whether a predator's involvement reduces the breeding population of prey to a lower level than could be supported by other factors, such as its food supply. Alternatively, do predators merely deliver the *coup de grâce* to individuals destined to perish through starvation, disease or more immediately, being the 'have-nots' in an exclusive territorial system (see p. 160). Whether predators limit the populations of their prey depends on the question of whether by killing one individual, predators allow another to survive in its place which would otherwise have died.

American Mink, in some areas, prey extensively upon muskrats. This prompted the superficially reasonable proposition that without mink there would be more muskrats. However, more than two decades of study led to the conclusion that the number of muskrats in the breeding population each year was determined by food and weather, and that these restrictions meant that much of the autumn population, swollen by the season's young, was doomed to perish anyway. Because the number killed by the predators was within the total of the doomed surplus, predation, although crucial to the mink, was irrelevant to the population of muskrats (although, clearly, individual mink and muskrats were vitally relevant to each other's fitness). The notion that predators are the ecological equivalent of refuse collectors might be termed the Erringtonian view of predation, after the researcher who studied these muskrats and mink, and it has been very influential. Nowadays, however, biologists point to the inconsistency that even Errington himself proposed: while mink predation was irrelevant to muskrat numbers in prime habitat, it did limit their numbers in marginal habitats (perhaps because, by definition, the mink were performing poorly there and were less resilient to predation). Furthermore, even Carnivores that confine themselves to doomed prey may affect the size of the prey population. For example if Grey Wolves kill elk condemned by starvation and inclement weather, these deaths will affect surviving elk positively. In the absence of wolves the predated elk would have survived longer and continued to compete for food with healthier individuals, which might have led to mass famine. So paradoxically there are times when wolf predation increases the number of elk by preventing doomed animals stealing food from companions that might otherwise survive. Nevertheless, there are many cases where mammalian predators appear to be incidental to the population dynamics of prey, and this generalisation applies whether either or both parties are mammals. For example, it is hard to believe that Eurasian Badgers, although in some regions heavily dependent upon earthworms, can seriously affect worm populations (in fact, badgers consume about 5% of the worms produced annually). Of course, it remains possible that the combined effect of badgers and all the other predators that feed on worms does limit their numbers, so it is slightly unfair to consider the impact of one predator in isolation from all others. Nonetheless, an important point is that badgers have a small impact on worm populations at least partly because the worms have a refuge underground, and badgers cannot influence their availability, i.e. badgers cannot affect the total numbers underground or the numbers that decide to come up. Similarly, Musk Ox have a partial refuge in adulthood, when their power renders them almost unavailable to wolves. Wolves can keep low Musk Ox populations low by catching calves before they enter the refuge of adulthood.

In contrast to the Eurasian Badger and the worm, the Red Fox may actually be limiting the breeding stock of partridge, because modern farming forces these ground birds to nest in a neat line around field edges, where foxes can hardly fail to stumble upon them. Since the prey are only a small component of the predator's varied diet, by causing partridges to decline the fox is not sealing its own fate (at least not directly by depleting its prey, although it may do so by inspiring the wrath of a gamekeeper). The crucial point is that because foxes are generalists, their numbers can remain steady or even increase in the face of declining supplies of partridge, and so can continue to pressurise the prey. In other cases, where the predator is heavily reliant on one species of prey, its own numbers decline as availability of the prey declines, so it is unlikely fully to eliminate the prey. However, a predator with access to only one prey is in the precarious position of having all its eggs in one basket. The instability of this situation was illustrated by Charles Elton, father of ecology, when in 1929 he published the story of Berlinger Island, off Portugal. There, the lighthouse keeper, overrun with rabbits, imported a colony of cats. These cats, having killed off the rabbits,

Many early influential ideas on the relationship between populations of predators and their prey were developed from observations on American Mink and muskrats.

subsequently starved. If they had had access to an alternative prey, the cats would doubtless have switched to them before exterminating the rabbits.

Ironically, the American Mink that inspired the concept of the doomed surplus has more recently furnished an example of the anti-Errington view. American Mink hunting along the streams of the Yorkshire Moors in England feed on Northern Water Voles which tend to occur in pockets of suitable habitat. Where these refuges are isolated and small, intense mink predation and an inadequate influx of immigrants can lead to local extinctions of the water voles. However, rather few conclusive studies of mammalian predators prove that they maintain their prey at stable numbers below the level set by the prey's food supply. The case of the American Mink in England is complicated because it is an introduced predator. One example may be a study of wolves preying upon elk. In a national park in Canada about 30 wolves lived in packs at a density of one wolf per 70 km², feeding in winter largely on a population of about 500 elk. Elk numbers were at best stable, and probably declining, whereas their breeding potential, food supply and rather low tendency to disperse all suggested that they had the potential to increase. The wolves were the most frequent cause of elk deaths, but this does not mean that wolves were necessarily limiting elk numbers, as they might simply have been executioners of the doomed surplus. However, and more importantly, fewer elk calves were surviving than were killed by the wolves annually. In this park there were less than 20 elk per wolf (a very low ratio), with about one elk per 4 km². In contrast, in nearly similar habitat on Isle Royale (a place famed for studies of wolves as fascinating as they are difficult to interpret), there was six times the density of elk, but only one wolf per 30–80 elk. Both on the island and in the park, it seems likely that wolves were limiting elk numbers. The paradox is that the balance between predator and prey reached a stable point at different population densities in the two places, despite the actors in the plot being the same, and the habitats being boreal forest in both places. The reason may be that the mainland habitat offered less opportunity for elk and their calves to escape the wolves (in comparison to the many coves and offshore islands around the island population), and this may have forced each elk to stay well away from others to decrease the predator's efficiency. In both the mainland and island cases, however, it seems that the wolves not only limit elk numbers (albeit at different levels) below what could be sustained by the available forage, but also bring stability to their numbers. One suggestion is that if the wolves were absent the elk populations would rocket, to say five per km², before devastating the supply of browse and thereby precipitating mass starvation – a predator-free system which would be wildly unstable. A good example of such a catastrophe is provided by the reindeer of St Matthew Island, which increased to such large numbers that they exceeded their food supply and succumbed to mass starvation. In some prey species, such catastrophic increases are prevented by social behaviour (such as territoriality – see p. 160), but some deer such as elk and reindeer appear to lack these behavioural safety valves, perhaps because they have evolved under circumstances where predators prevented the problem from arising or where resources were too costly to defend.

One neat explanation of the effects of predators upon their prey concerns the relationship between the Red Fox and Rock Wallabies – a regrettable encounter between species thrown together in Australia by mankind's meddling. A count of wallabies on five rock outcrops revealed that all five populations were declining or, at best, stable. However, when foxes were killed off on two outcrops the wallabies increased by 138% and 223% respectively. Meanwhile, on two of the three fox-besieged outcrops wallaby numbers fell by 14% and 85%, but increased by 29% on the third. Furthermore, fox control coincided with a decline in the average weight of wallabies, and the vegetation showed signs of heavy grazing, symptoms of over population not seen on those three outcrops where foxes persisted. This is strong circumstantial evidence that the foxes were limiting wallaby numbers below the level at which they would otherwise be limited by food.

There is really only one way to disentangle the impact of predator upon prey, and that is to do an experiment in which predators are removed from one location, but not another. It is then possible to compare what happens in the two places for several years, before reversing the conditions (i.e. letting predators return to the first area and removing them from the second) to see whether the results are also reversed. This is exactly what has been done with Pine Martens and Red Foxes on two large islands in the Bothnian Gulf. The results were a 40% increase in game birds, and a 234% increase in Mountain Hares under predator-free conditions. Were the martens and foxes merely picking off surplus prey or biting into the breeding stock? In this case there was evidence that they limited spring breeding populations, at least in the short-term. Either way, the results have implications for wildlife management because, in the case of game species, predators and sportsmen are in competition, each striving to doom the same surplus and more (see p. 311).

Two field experiments have revealed the impact of European predators on their prey, one in the short-term, the other in the long-term. In the first case, the predators and prey, although both European in origin, happened to be in Australia. Red Foxes and rabbits were both introduced by the early colonists and now both are considered pests, the foxes because they eat native marsupials and the rabbits because they eat grass destined for sheep. In 1979, in New South Wales, rabbit numbers irrupted and a staggering 5,580 rabbits were counted in one spotlight survey along 18 km. Four months later, as the summer drought withered their food supply, their numbers had crashed, and a spotlight survey along the same route revealed only 50 rabbits. Rabbits must drink if the moisture content of their food falls below 55%, and as the drought worsened the grass withered and surface water disappeared, leaving the rabbits parched. At this point the experiment began and in one large plot (70 km^2), a sustained effort was made to shoot foxes and feral cats, whereas in two other plots predators were unmolested. Fourteen months (two rabbit peak breeding seasons) later, the number of rabbits in the plot where predators were shot had almost reached its former peak, and was four times higher than on the plots where predators abounded. This imbalance between the plots prevailed for a total of two-and-a-half years, until the next drought intervened, causing the rabbit populations in all plots to crash.

The foxes, therefore, could neither cause the rabbits to decline, nor prevent them from increasing in the long-term, but once rabbit numbers had been reduced by drought, the impact of predation was sufficient to slow down their recovery in the short-term. This means that, at least in the semi-arid lands of Australia, the answer to the question of whether or not foxes regulate rabbit populations depends on the weather. If a succession of droughts keeps rabbit numbers low, as a consequence of destroying their food supply, then foxes can slow down their recovery. In contrast, a prolonged period of rainfall and grass growth allows the rabbit population to increase so fast that it escapes from the impact of predation. The result is an irruption which only ends when either the next drought strikes or the rabbits eat themselves out of food. When rabbits are very scarce, foxes turn to other prey, and when rabbits are very populous they breed so fast as to make fox predation irrelevant. The ultimate cause of the weather's impact in bringing rabbit numbers into the zone where fox predation has a limiting effect is that while the foxes breed only once annually, the rabbits can breed at least to some extent throughout the year if rainfall is sufficient to sustain the quality of the grass. Just as poor rainfall brings rabbit numbers within reach of regulation by foxes in New South Wales, so myxomatosis may have done so in Spain and Great Britain. The results of this work illustrate the complexity of designing pest control programmes: both rabbits and foxes are considered pests in New South Wales, but the presence of foxes may make rabbit plagues less frequent than the pasture conditions would allow, making it injudicious to control foxes without first controlling rabbits.

The long-term effect of predators on prey numbers is illustrated by the case of badgers and hedgehogs in Great Britain. A comparison of two seemingly similar rural sites in Oxfordshire revealed that hedgehogs abounded at one (where there were no more than two badgers per km^2), but were absent from the other (where there were tenfold more badgers). The absence of the hedgehogs might have arisen at the second site either because the nearby river and motorway prevented their access, or because the habitat was subtly unsuitable, or because the high density of badgers was inimical to hedgehogs. The latter might apply if the badgers preyed on the hogs, or if they drove them away as competitors (both badgers and hedgehogs are members of the same professional guild, in terms of their penchant for feeding on earthworms). To find out whether the site devoid of hogs could support them, the inhabitants of the hog-rich site were captured and transplanted there. Meanwhile, hedgehogs from a third site were moved in to fill the places of the transplanted individuals. Two months later only 10% of

The Western Hedgehog's spines are no protection against the Eurasian Badger, with the result that where the badgers are numerous, hedgehogs are absent. Not surprisingly, hedgehogs react strongly to the scent of badgers and try to leave the vicinity.

the hedgehogs moved into the badger zone were alive, whereas 65% of those transplanted into the second site were thriving. Furthermore, by tracking their nightly movements, it emerged that in their effort to seek out what, in the jargon, is called enemy-free space, hogs in the badger zone dispersed twice as far from their release point as did those released in the area where few badgers lived. The fate of the disappearing hogs was all too clear: their coats of spines were found, neatly eaten out and tangled with tell-tale badger fur. Badgers can simply prize open a rolled-up hog. Subsequently it emerged that when presented with the odour of badger, the first thing a hedgehog does is, not surprisingly, to run away as fast as possible. In this case, the predator's effect on the prey is complete, albeit local, annihilation. The effect was only a local one because, despite their superficial similarity, the two sites were clearly different in that one supported many badgers and the other did not.

In practice, the fates of so many different predators and prey are wound together in the same habitat that it is horrendously difficult to disentangle their influence on each other. For example, after the disease myxomatosis more than decimated rabbit populations in Britain in 1953, a decline in the number of stoats coincided with an increase in weasel numbers. The estimated stoat:weasel ratio fell from 2:1 before myxomatosis, to 1:2 afterwards. The increase in weasels may have been partly due to reduced competition from fewer stoats (although those that survived in the absence of rabbits were presumably forced into closer competition with weasels for voles), but was mainly due to the greater grass growth possible without rabbits, which in turn supported many more Field Voles as prey for the weasels. Stoat numbers began to pick up as rabbits increased after the epidemic, and in the early 1970s weasel numbers began to fall as the rabbits once again grazed grassy banks bare and thereby diminished the abundance of voles by eating their food and cover. This not only reduced the weasels' food but also, to make matters worse, the revival of stoats may have led to weasels losing in direct competition with their larger cousins.

So predators kill their prey, but do they invariably limit the populations of prey? At first it seemed obvious that the answer must be yes – one prey killed is one prey less. Indeed, at least for a short while, there must be fewer prey after predators have killed some, but this is a trivial truth if some other force will inevitably limit the prey's numbers at even lower numbers. Anyway, predation cannot be the factor that limits all populations – what limits the predators, especially those at the top of the food chain which tend to be rare? In fact, it seems that the answer to the question of whether predators limit the numbers of their prey is, in some cases, yes. In other cases, the numbers of a predator has no lasting effect on the numbers of its

The impact of predators, such as Barn Owls, on numbers of Wood Mice is affected by the structure of their habitat. In arable fields harvest removes the crop, leaving the mice without cover. In the following nights owls swoop over the field with the result that many mice are killed and others vacate their home ranges and take refuge in hedgerows.

prey, because the latter have an even more punishing gauntlet to run. One major study of Tawny Owls in Britain indicated that they do not determine the numbers of Wood Mice and Bank Voles, although they can exaggerate the fluctuations in their numbers. Conversely, the abundance of these rodents in June does determine the owl's breeding success. In cases where predation is not the critical factor, what other factors might limit populations? One answer is shortage of resources, such as food.

Competition and numbers

From one summer to the next, the numbers of Wood Mice living in a deciduous woodland may be dramatically different. In May of one year there might be 50 Wood Mice per hectare, in another year, only two per hectare. Their numbers in November can be less variable, perhaps averaging 25 per hectare. These members of the early winter population represent the survivors of the breeding season that ended in late autumn. An important question is: how many of those youngsters, recruited into the adult population at the end of the breeding season, will survive the winter? The answer appears to depend on the reproductive efforts not of the mice themselves but of other species, such as oak and beech trees. At the same time as the Wood Mice are producing their autumn crop of young, the oaks and beeches are shedding their acorns and mast. In some years seeds will carpet the ground, in others the crop may fail. These seeds will be stored in the larders of countless Wood Mouse homes, and their abundance in autumn will largely determine the number of Wood Mice that will survive the ensuing winter. Those survivors will constitute the next spring's breeding population. So, the number of Wood Mice in spring varies widely because the crop of acorns on which they depend may succeed or fail during the previous autumn. However, irrespective of how many Wood Mice squeeze through the 'bottleneck' of winter shortage, their ability to churn out offspring is so great that they are likely to produce sufficient recruits for a reasonably similar population to run the winter gauntlet each year. The size of that autumn population will depend greatly on the capacity of the particular woodland to feed them (i.e. its carrying capacity). This is rather a glib summary of the Wood Mouse's story – different studies have revealed all sorts of subtle variations.

A further twist to the Wood Mouse's tale is that the number of adults in a woodland population may remain rather stable as summer wears on, despite the maturation of litters of two to seven young born to each female.

Red Deer live partly segregated lives. The larger males spend part of the year on the hard hill eating rough grazing; the smaller hinds graze at lower altitudes on the more nutritious green flushes.

Then, suddenly, their numbers increase, doubling every month. Where more Wood Mice have survived the previous winter the increase in numbers begins later. This paradox arises because of competition, as the young born early in the breeding season often have to emigrate (and many probably die). The breeding females compete for food resources, and are spaced out in largely exclusive territories. The breeding males occupy larger ranges than those of females, and their ranges overlap those of several females and those of other males too. The breeding males compete for access to females. The result is that few opportunities arise at home for early born young in woodland, except in springs following winters when survival was especially poor. However, towards the end of the summer many of the breeding adults will have died, the fervour of competitiveness may be draining out of the breeding season, and the beginning of the beech mast season may increase the carrying capacity of the wood. The later-born young may then be able to settle within the population where they were born. The influence of aggression on this whole process has been highlighted by an experiment in which adult male Wood Mice were removed from a spring population, with the consequence that young males settled in the area immediately.

The proposition that competition for food limits many populations may seem silly when one often sees mammals amidst apparent plenty. However, three points, illustrated by the Wood Mouse's story, are worth emphasising.

First, the limiting effect of shortages may apply only at particular times of the year, or even only in particular years. Lemmings are often surrounded by lush lawns of vegetation in summer. In winter they continue to feed on

the greenery hidden under the snow. But now and again, when lemming numbers are high, the snow blanket may melt in spring to reveal that they have consumed every last one of the grassy stems below. Then a late spring can spell disaster as the food is exhausted before the flush of spring growth begins.

Second, the link between resources and population density may be obscured because the effect is delayed. Arctic Foxes can gorge themselves on rodents from June to October, but during winter the prey scuttle about inaccessibly below a hard blanket of snow, leaving the foxes to subsist on caches. Scarce prey in autumn means inadequate stores of cached food. Thus the tourniquet of starvation does not tighten on the foxes till late winter when their larders are emptied.

Third, where competition is decided by contest rather than by a scramble (see p. 162) the fact that the winner takes the bread from the loser's mouth is less cruelly immediate. Among Roe Deer, territorial bucks expel younger, subordinate males. The competition is, superficially, over real estate, rather than a sprint for a succulent bud or perfumed doe. However, the result is the same in that the losers thereby suffer higher mortality and negligible reproductive success. The intervention of behavioural mechanisms in the competition for resources determines the number of slices into which the cake will be cut. It is often the case that the ultimate limit to mammalian populations is food, but that is translated into immediate (or 'proximate') behavioural mechanisms which limit their numbers. Such mechanisms for population limitation include dispersal (see p. 264), and the reproductive suppression of subordinates (see p. 154).

Competition is not necessarily over access to food. Rabbits living on chalk grasslands, for example, must have burrows if they are to survive the attentions of Red Foxes and Eurasian Badgers. But while chalk supports good grass, it also offers hard digging, so burrows can be a limiting resource. Under such circumstances small groups of buck and doe rabbits share a territory centred on their warren. If the population of chalkland rabbits expands, the number of warrens remains unchanged, because all the diggable ground has been dug. This puts a premium on defending the burrow and territory, and both sexes do this: males make horseshoe-shaped scratch marks with their forepaws, sometimes at the territory border, which may be relevant to the eviction of male intruders. Females concentrate their attacks on intruding members of their own sex. Under these conditions, contests for burrows and associated territory intervene to cause the dispersal, and probably death, of losers before competition for food begins to bite.

In this account of competition it is worth interjecting that an alternative argument can explain juvenile dispersal without reference to competition at all. Take the case of the wood mice described above, where dispersal of early-born young was explained in terms of shortage of space in which to settle at home. However, another explanation is that early spring litters disperse so that they can breed in their first year with non-relatives. Young born later in the summer will not mature until the following spring, therefore they remain in residence and overwinter with their family. If elderly parents are alive in the following spring, individuals will again need to disperse to avoid inbreeding. However, often many of the previous adults will have died over winter and consequently juveniles can breed in the area where they were born. There is thus a convincing argument that juvenile dispersal (see p. 265) is more to do with getting away from an opposite-sex parent than it is to do with escaping competition for food.

The same species may be limited by different things in different places. For example, on sand dunes rabbits have no difficulty in digging as many burrows as they wish. There, they do not form warrens, but spread out, each individual occupying an undefended range which overlaps somewhat with those of several others of each sex. In these circumstances, as the population increases the rabbits simply dig more burrows, but as the population increases and food grows thinner on the ground, they are directly exposed

In chalk grassland, where digging is hard, rabbit numbers may be limited by the availability of burrow sites.

to the tourniquet of competition and the growth rate of rabbit kittens slows. With this more intimate link between food supply and numbers, the only way to compete is to eat faster, which means risking spending more time above ground and thereby increasing the danger of being eaten by a predator. Such a system is inherently less stable than that under which resources are monopolised by the few. Where all the rabbits scramble to eat their way to victory, there is a great risk that they will eat themselves out of house and home, and cause a catastrophic crash in their own numbers. In this case competitors in a scramble share the burden of failing resources, while the essential consequence of contest competition is that the burden of shortage is borne largely by the have-nots of those societies.

Circumstances often combine to narrow the survival gap through which mammals must squeeze. As the numbers of Mountain Hares increase and their food supply therefore declines, they are forced to be less choosy and to eat lower quality food. Worse still, due to the influx of maturing youngsters, maximum numbers generally build up in winter, when the hare's easy life feasting on a rich summer diet of herbs is replaced by a more ascetic dependence upon woody stems. Furthermore, the plants respond to intensive browsing by producing more protective chemicals, such as phenols. These so-called plant secondary compounds act on the herbivore's digestive system to render it less efficient (phenols cut the hare's efficiency at digesting plant protein by 50%).

A bitter twist is dramatically illustrated by the fact that elk can starve to death gorging on the flush growth of their favoured food plants. The reason is that the buds are protected by resins making them indigestible. Further emphasis that all that glistens is not gold is provided by the Brush-tailed Possum. In Australia, where it cannot digest a diet of eucalyptus because the leaves are full of secondary compounds, it is forced to ground level (where risks of predation are high) in order to eat leaves of low shrubs. In New Zealand, whose native flora did not evolve secondary compounds, possums happily eat trees to death and reach huge numbers.

Limiting factors

This discussion of predation, food and shelter has shown that any or all of them may be among the limiting factors that determine the size of a mammalian population. Indeed, although it has been simpler to discuss these factors one at a time, the reality is that they all interact, so it seems most likely that several factors will contribute to limiting many populations. Asking what sets the limits on a population's size is not the same thing as asking what factors keep it at roughly the same size year after year, sometimes for hundreds of generations. This long-term constancy led biologist A.J. Nicholson to propose, in 1933, that populations were regulated by factors that acted severely when numbers were high, but were mollified when numbers were low. Such factors react like an elastic shackle to drag the population back towards a constant level.

To summarise, there are two possibilities. First a population might be limited by factors that operate with a severity independent of their numbers: cold winters or hungry lynx might kill 50% of Roe Deer come what may. If this is the case, and no regulatory factor is involved, sooner or later the Roe Deer or the lynx will have a run of bad luck and their numbers will be thrown off balance and ultimately towards extinction. Second, and in contrast, if the Roe Deer are limited by factors which cause a high percentage of them to die when they are abundant, and a low percentage to die when they are scarce, this regulatory pattern can allow them to persist at rather constant numbers indefinitely. This latter process of population regulation is called density dependence.

How might predators contrive to exert a disproportionately heavy death toll on an increasing prey population? There are two ways in which predators can react to changing prey populations. First, each predator may vary the number of a given prey that it eats. For example, when voles are abundant, weasels and stoats eat lots more of them per head. Such a disproportionate change in diet is termed a 'functional response' to an increase in the numbers of a particular prey species. The limit to this response is the time it takes to catch and handle prey and, ultimately, the sated appetite of bloated predators. For example, as numbers of Canadian Snowshoe Hares increase during a cycle (see p. 127), they increase disproportionately in the diet of each individual lynx. This relationship has not been demonstrated for Mountain Hares and European lynx, perhaps because in Scandinavia the lynx mainly eat Roe Deer and numbers of Mountain Hares never reach the high peaks that occur in Snowshoe Hare. A related phenomenon to the functional response is 'switching', which occurs when a predator turns its attentions away from a declining prey or towards an increasing one. For example, when voles are in short supply, weasels may switch their attention to small birds, while when rabbits are scarce, stoats turn to voles.

The second possible reaction is a change in the numbers of predators eating a prey species, the so-called 'numerical response'. In the short run this can involve an influx of predators to a bountiful area, like bees to a honey pot. In the longer run, an abundance of prey can sustain more successful predator breeding and recruitment the following spring. In this sense the numbers of predators is dependent on the density of the prey, but there is a delay in the dependence. In the case of the lynx and Snowshoe Hare, when hare numbers are low, lynx and other predators cause three-quarters of hare deaths during winter. When hare numbers are high (even though lynx numbers are also high and they are all stuffing themselves with hare), the predators cannot, so to speak, keep up with the prey, and cause less than a quarter of their deaths. Similarly, the impact of predators on voles in parts of Poland varies between 33% and 97% when the rodents are at peak and trough numbers respectively.

The consequences of predators eating into the breeding stock of prey may be complicated. At first sight, such over-harvesting would seem to be a recipe for disaster, leading to annihilation of the prey. But prey can compensate: if they are reduced below numbers that could otherwise be sustained in that environment, the survivors produce more offspring. More resources are available per head to the survivors and this provides extra nourishment, enabling them to produce more young. Reduced social suppression of breeding (see p. 154) and increased opportunities for dispersal are other forces that could lead to increased production of young per head in low populations.

The immediate effects of food shortage include reductions in litter size and number of litters, together with postponed maturity. For example, litter size in stoats (varying between 6 and 13) depends on the abundance of food, and weasels postpone sexual maturity when food is short. The number of female rabbits occupying a warren increases with the number of entrances (which mirrors the space available for breeding nests below), but their per capita production of young falls in larger groups. The same density-dependent fall in reproductive success typifies Eurasian Badger clans with greater numbers of females and larger herds of Red Deer hinds, and in each case the decline in reproductive success associated with membership of larger social groups would seem to be an added incentive for dispersal.

Common sense and our own family histories give us a fair idea of what determines how numbers will change from one generation to the next. When a pair launches into its reproductive career the overall outcome will depend on the birth rate, the death rate and luck. If young are born at a greater rate than that at which they die before breeding, then the pair will more than replace itself in the next generation; if deaths leave the pair fewer than two descendants, then the lineage looks set to dwindle. But how are the fates of individual families woven into those of whole populations? Knowing the number of mammals in a population this year, what determines how many there will be next year?

In horror stories, populations increase endlessly with the excess of births over deaths. Under ideal conditions female Brown Rats become sexually mature at two months old and thereafter churn out litters at intervals as short as one month, averaging about nine embryos per litter. These statistics might lead the unwary to calculate that an adult female produces 108 offspring and 450,000 descendants per year. However, although a disheartening number of people talk as if this Malthusian nightmare were a reality ('if we don't keep down these rats/foxes/badgers/stoats etc. we'll be overrun with them') the evidence is that most mammalian (and other) populations are either stable or fluctuate within clear bounds. Two schools of thought have claimed to know the secret of what regulates populations. The 'density-independent' lobby focused on erratic fluctuations in numbers and associated these with the random workings of external forces such as benign or inclement weather. In other words, things beyond the control of, and independent of the density of, the members of the population itself. The 'density-dependent' lobby perceived stable populations in which occasional increases or decreases were self-correcting as numbers were drawn back to an equilibrium about which there were fluctuations. Under density dependence, when numbers fall low a baby boom will compensate, but when they are high, counteracting forces (e.g. social pressures or starvation) will restrain population growth. In this case, regulation arose from forces internal to, and dependent upon the density of, the population itself. In short, one school was more impressed by departures from the average population, the other by the average itself.

A flair for mental arithmetic, or failing that a calculator, will quickly expose some intriguing consequences of this often acrimonious debate. Think of a number, call it NOW, add to it a net reproduction rate, say 10%, and call the result THEN. This is the Malthusian nightmare of population

Brown Rats mate promiscuously and have the potential to increase in numbers very rapidly. However, other factors generally prevent that potential being realised.

explosions, or the dream of perpetual compound interest on your bank account: if the population is 10 rats NOW it will be 11 rats THEN, and on *ad infinitum* until rats carpet the globe or, in the case of the bank account, you are rich. To regulate the population in a density-independent way, simply throw dice to determine whether to kill off more or less of the current crop of youngsters (or spend your savings with profligate and erratic disregard to your bank balance). On the other hand, imagine that the population can only increase up to a certain limit before exhausting its environment. When it is far from that limit allow prolific breeding, when it approaches the limit, allow minimal breeding (spend when you are rich, save when you are broke!). The result is that the numbers will increase up to an equilibrium point, that point being determined by the initial level of the reproduction rate. To make this game easy on the calculator, say that the population can vary on a scale between 0 and 1. In that case a simple density-dependent state of affairs would be: $THEN = rNOW(1-NOW)$, where r is the reproduction rate (e.g. $r = 1.1$ in our 10% example). This relationship between NOW and THEN is known as the logistic difference equation. This intimidating name should not blind you to its beguiling attribute, namely that $(1-NOW)$ will be small when NOW is big, but will be big when NOW is small: the result is that THEN is determined by NOW, and that is what density dependence is!

Try this on a calculator – it is not only fun, it may change your view of the world. That is what happened to Robert May, a biologist who fiddled around with this simple equation until he stumbled upon a result that not only shatters the density independent versus dependent controversy, but resounds to the roots of our thinking about animal numbers. He found that if you allow r, the reproduction rate (i.e. births divided by deaths), any value between 1 and 3, the population will increase up to a stable point of equilibrium at which births and death are balanced. However, as reproduction rate is slowly tweaked up over 3, the pattern suddenly changes, first to an oscillation between two stable levels, then between four stable levels, and so on until suddenly there are no equilibria at all, but chaos (by the way, the mathematics behind this particular game mean that it won't work if you try reproduction rates higher than 4).

A number of conclusions, as far-reaching as they are bewildering, emerge from this. The first is a new mathematical fact of life: even this very simplest of population models yields results which are wildly different in both quantity and quality depending upon the reproduction rate. (The very same principle applies to *everything* that 'reproduces' or spreads: it applies to predicting how everything from flu to rumours may spread through a society.) We can expect reality to be much more complicated than the outcome of the simplistic equation. In particular, at the chaotic end of the spectrum, outcomes that appear to have absolutely no pattern are not at all random, but can demonstrably result from this very simple equation relating NOW to THEN. The part of the equation causing the chaotic outcome is called, in the quaint language of mathematicians, a 'strange attractor'. How can a strange attractor be diagnosed as it lurks in the data? How is the biologist ever to know whether what appear to be random changes in the numbers of a population are really random (i.e. density independent), or just the unimaginably complicated outcome of a strictly non-random process? The answer may well be that it is often impossible to tell! This realisation may dampen the pragmatic biologist's exhilaration at the discovery that what looks like a numerical mess is actually an infinitely exquisite pattern.

Ironically, this state of affairs dissolves the warring camps in the density independent versus dependent debate: both are smitten. The density-independent school must face the fact that apparently random fluctuations in populations can be caused by a strictly density-dependent process. The density-dependent school, on the other hand, blanches at the realisation that even the most simplistic density-dependent process can produce fluctuations which are not mere noise about an equilibrium, because there is no equilibrium, just chaos.

The fact is that the simplest of non-linear relationships can produce wildly complicated results, and very different results can arise due to the tiniest differences in initial conditions. The mathematicians who discovered this called it the Butterfly Effect, having in mind that a butterfly's flight fanning the air in Beijing might, in principle, tip the balance in air turbulence to effect storms in New York a month later. More to the point, a female lynx catching a cold and losing her litter may just jolt the population's reproduction rate over the critical difference between cycles and chaos.

With this extraordinary view of fate and consequence in mind, biologists looked more closely at some 200 years of trapping returns for lynx fur in Canada. There was a rather stable periodicity of nine or ten years, but the amplitude of the peaks and troughs varied widely: peaks ranged from 32,000 lynx skins in 1857 to 78,000 in 1878. There were periods of low peaks (around 5,000 per year between 1735 and 1820) and high peaks (around 40,000 per year between 1821 and 1913). The extraordinary behaviour of the logistic equation raises the possibility that these variations are not the chance fluctuations they were previously thought to be but are, instead, the highly deterministic result of some 'strange attractor' working density-dependent devilry in the population process. Of course, the cycles in lynx numbers are

The relationship between populations of a predator and one prey species may be affected by its relationship with other prey. For example, the numbers of Field Voles available as prey may affect the Red Fox's tendency to feed on leverets.

beset by complicating 'noise', such as fluctuation in the weather and in the value of fur. Despite this, mathematicians expert in chaos now think that what once seemed a 'noisy' ten-year cycle is actually a twenty-year cycle teetering on the edge of chaos, and driven by three factors. Nobody can yet prove what they are, but strong candidates are the numbers of lynx, the numbers of hares for them to eat and the quality of the grass for the hares to eat.

But what, then, of the 450,000 Brown Rats spawned by our Malthusian pair on p. 123? As the first born offspring begin to bite into the food supply, the ideal of maturity at two months probably slips to three months. Similarly, the interval between litters probably increases as the mothers' plane of nutrition falls, and infant mortality may rise through competition and disease. Each female may end up producing only 20 or 30 young annually. On the other hand, as competition between males may lead to emigration (as may the need to avoid inbreeding with their mother and sisters), females may come to predominate in the population, so elevating the per capita production of descendants. However, crowding causes a sharp decline in female breeding, so more and more females may each produce fewer and fewer young (and these crowds may be attracting more predators and fostering contagious disease). It is indeed a density-dependent world, and when all these factors are taken into account an informal guess is that our initial pair may produce fewer than 200 descendants annually (of which only a fraction will survive to reproduce). This is a far cry from the 450,000 that were 'possible', but quite enough to make them one of the most serious pests in the world (see p. 315).

Mammalian populations may sometimes be limited by predators and are often limited by food or some other resource. Many also persist at roughly the same abundance for years or even centuries. This long-term persistence implies that they are regulated, that is that some process chivvies a population's numbers back towards its long-term equilibrium whenever other forces jolt it towards increase or decline. Such density-dependent, regulatory forces include social effects on reproduction and predation. But what of the case where no one equilibrium exists in population size, and where numbers persistently cycle?

Cycles

In the Fennoscandian tundra and taiga there are dramatic variations, from year to year, in the numbers of some small mammals. The autumn populations of voles and lemmings may soar to 300 per hectare, or plummet to almost none. In Europe, numbers of Mountain Hares fluctuate many-fold from year to year. In northern North America, fluctuations in Snowshoe Hares are even more dramatic: they may abound (5,000 per 10 km^2) or virtually disappear (5 per 10 km^2). These fluctuating populations have several truly remarkable features. First, the changes in numbers are synchronised across vast areas. Second, the numbers of very different prey species may vary together (e.g. lemmings and ptarmigan or voles and shrews), and changes in the numbers of prey are mirrored, after a short delay, in similar changes in the numbers of predators (e.g. weasels, foxes and lynx). Third, and crucially, the peaks and troughs in population size follow a pattern: they are arranged as cycles which recur every three or four years (or in the case of North American lynx, hare and many others, nine or ten years). What is more, this extraordinary state of affairs contrasts with conditions further south, where populations of the same species are much more stable and do not cycle.

One early explanation was that these population cycles are the almost inevitable result of inbuilt, universal features in the relationship between predator and prey. This idea was very appealing in that it supported an old (some would say ailing) theory concerning how the numbers of predators and their prey might vary. Starting from a moment at which both predators and prey were rare, one might expect prey numbers to increase rapidly at first (there would be few predators to eat them and plenty of food to go around), but to slow down as they approached the carrying capacity of the environment and began to compete among themselves. As numbers of prey increase, so too the food available to their predators increases and thus, perhaps one breeding season later, their numbers build up too. Once predator numbers reach high levels they begin to produce more young than the peak prey population can sustain, and so they over harvest the prey and start a downward tumble in numbers. This predation reduces the food for the predators, causing them, in turn, to starve and decline until both predators and prey are once again rare. This simple model is highly plausible and suggests that synchronised cycles are in the very nature of predator–prey relationships. Indeed, just such cycles can be observed in the laboratory when simple predators, such as single-celled animals, are kept in bottles with their prey. The difficulty is that conditions in the wild are so much more complicated than in a bottle that other factors, such as the effects of variations in the weather, seem likely to cloud any relationship that exists between predator and prey numbers. Thus even if neat, laboratory-type relationships between predator and prey are the driving force behind cycles in the wild, it might be impossible to prove this due to distortions in the patterns caused by all sorts of chance factors. Furthermore, predator–prey relationships cannot be the universal explanation for cycles because they occur among some prey, such as voles and hares, on islands without any predators. For example, on the predator-free Danish Island of Illyn, the variable survival of Brown Hares appears to follow an eight-year cycle.

Another possible explanation of cycles is that small mammals increase in numbers to a point at which they literally eat themselves out of house and home; the effect of food shortage might be worsened if loss of cover and malnutrition both increased predation. The lemming is indeed a voracious lawnmower: a 32 g adult eats 12 g dry weight of grass daily. During lemming peaks food may be limited or, if not, the vital nutrients essential for growth and reproduction may be tied up in the animals' bodies or undecayed vegetation and animal droppings. Perhaps, as the lemmings increase in number they use up more and more of the vital elements from the environment (such as calcium and phosphorus in their bones and milk), thereby withholding, so to speak, these elements from the plants and so cutting back plant growth. Furthermore, the nutrients locked up in the rodents' droppings can take two to three years to decay in the cold tundra (in contrast, nutrients are released back to the soil almost immediately in more southerly latitudes). This rodent-imposed limit on plant growth would lead to their own starvation and thus an eventual return of the nutrients from their bodies to the soil leading, in turn, to recovery of the vegetation. Actually, there is no evidence that this sequence of events happens, but it is an intriguing possibility and emphasises the interdependence of plant and herbivore communities.

Indeed, in the case of the ten-year cycle synchronised between lynx and Snowshoe Hare in America, both the prey and the predators which depend upon them may be victims of chemical warfare in the plant–herbivore arms race. Once the hare numbers have peaked they face a shortage of winter food. This shortage is exacerbated because the very act of their browsing prompts the plants to secrete toxic substances (terpenes and phenolic resins) which hinder digestion. The concentrations of these indigestible chemicals remain high for two years after the peak in hare numbers. Fewer hares survive to feed the ever more hungry predators, and so the downward spiral is initiated.

The consequences of the peculiar phenomenon of chaos, namely that simple numerical relationships can produce unpredictable outcomes (see p. 124), may explain why it has proved so difficult to identify the cause of cycles. In one study in Alajoki, western Finland, biologists recorded the numbers of Least Weasels and those of their rodent prey, particularly Field Voles, for five years. They then produced a series of simple equations to

Norway Lemmings are notorious for their eruptive population increases. These eruptions have a major impact on the vegetation on which the lemmings feed.

describe how the numbers of weasel and vole might vary, and used the various measurements they had made in the field to test the behaviour of these equations. For example, in Alajoki they found that the maximum number of Least Weasels was 5 per km^2 in autumn, and the maximum number of voles was about 10,000 per km^2. These figures gave them an idea of the maximum carrying capacity of the area for each species. They knew how much food each weasel eats daily (31 g for an average female weighing 35 g, and 29 g for an average male weighing 48 g) and so they could translate this food consumption into numbers of voles each weighing about 25 g. They also knew that lactating female Least Weasels consume about three times the amount of food eaten by non-breeding females, and furthermore, weasels can only breed when vole numbers exceed a critical threshold of about 10–14 per hectare. The result of incorporating this threshold into the equations was that the simulated weasels reproduced at a rate determined by numbers of voles when voles were abundant, but merely died off at a rate determined by shortage of voles when voles were scarce.

All of these facts and figures about voles and weasels could be fitted into the equations, so that a computer simulation of the populations of predator and prey could be based on real numbers. The equations assumed density dependence (see p. 124, the logistic equation), so that the rate of change in the numbers of each species depended on the numbers of the other species (because more voles support more weasels, but more weasels eat more voles). However, this dependence was such that both species increased more rapidly the further their numbers fell below carrying capacity. The biologists knew the maximum possible rates of increase from their field studies (for weasels the fastest observed increase was from 1.3 individuals per km^2

In Finland populations of Least Weasels and voles cycle in synchrony.

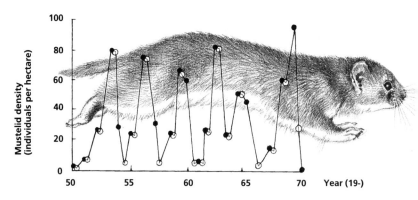

in one spring to 5.0 individuals in the same area the following autumn), and so they could program the computer to work within realistic limits. The clever idea that distinguished this computer model from its predecessors was that it also incorporated differences between the breeding season, in summer, and the remaining six months of the year. Thus, because vole food is scarce in winter, the numbers they used in the equation to simulate winter and summer conditions were different: they substituted lower numbers for vole carrying capacity and potential rates of increase in winter. This had the realistic consequence that the simulated voles bred during winter if, and only if, their numbers had been low in the previous autumn.

Looking at the raw data on numbers of voles and weasels at Alajoki, there were three- to five-year cycles in both, with the weasels lagging behind the voles. However the cycles were far from tidy. Indeed, there were so many blips in the pattern that it was impossible to be confident that the numbers of voles and weasels were directly linked – perhaps both were driven by some other factor, or perhaps chance factors were obscuring the true predator–prey relationship. Chaos theory played a crucial role in resolving these possibilities. By incorporating the differences between summer and winter, the equations acquired the mathematical potential to behave chaotically, and this is exactly what they did. When the computer simulated the predicted numbers of voles and weasels year after year, using the basic parameters measured at Alajoki, the simulated results were strikingly similar to the cycles that had been observed in the field. That is, predator and prey numbers varied according to cycles of between three and five years long, but with plenty of complicating blips. Because only information on predator and prey had been fed into the computer, it was clear that no complicating factor (e.g. weather) had caused all the erratic blips – they arose purely because of chaos – a simple interaction between predator and prey had

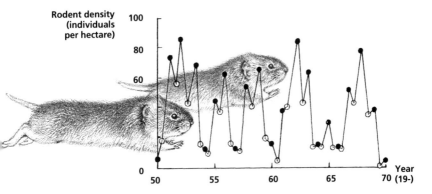

Rodent density
(individuals
per hectare)

100
80
60
0

50   55   60   65   70   Year (19-)

produced a very 'noisy' relationship between them. Thus the fundamental relationship between predator and prey is sufficient, without any further complications, to explain entirely the patterns of population cycles seen between the voles and weasels (and probably between Arctic Foxes and lemmings) in the far north.

Although predator–prey interactions can fully explain the Finnish data, it remains possible that some population cycles involve a combination of factors. Once the prey population has peaked, perhaps the slippery slope to the next trough is speeded by exhaustion of food supplies, increased predation and social pressures affecting breeding and promoting dispersal. But why are these cycles confined to the north? In the north, the most effective predators in winter are the specialist weasels which hunt under the snow. In the more fragmented, variable habitats further south, there are several winter-resident, generalist predators which have the option to switch from one prey to another. Such switching can prevent the population of any one prey species from exploding because lots of predators would focus attention on any burgeoning prey species before its numbers got out of control. Switching also diminishes the dependence of more southerly predators on any given prey, because if one prey becomes too rare the predator can turn its attentions to another before starving.

Even in the far north, predators switching from one prey to another can have remarkable effects. Dark-bellied Brent Geese nest in the Taimyr Peninsula of north-eastern Russia, having spent the winter in western Europe. Their breeding success varies radically from year to year, between 0.1% and 53%. This variation was originally thought to arise from random fluctuations in the time that snow melted on their Arctic nesting grounds. However, it is now clear that the breeding success of the geese follows a three-year cycle, in synchrony with similar cycles in such diverse species of wading bird as Turnstones, Curlew, Sandpipers and Sanderlings. Furthermore, the three-year cycle in all these birds mirrors, but lags one year behind, a similar cycle in lemmings. It seems that the whole process is driven by the behaviour of Arctic Foxes, which feed on the lemmings. When the lemming numbers crash, the hungry foxes turn their attention the following year to the eggs and nestlings of the birds. Another bird, the Long-tailed Skua, finds itself on both sides of this predator–prey fence, as it is both prey to foxes and predator on lemmings. When the lemmings crash, the skuas suffer a double whammy: not only do they lose more young to foxes, but they lay fewer eggs because they have less food themselves. In winter the brent geese fly south. On the eastern shores of England they feed on a wild plant called Zostera, but the more geese there are, the faster this food supply is exhausted, whereupon the geese move to fields of winter wheat. Thus, the extent, in a given year, to which the brent geese are a pest to wheat farmers in England is determined by the number of lemmings in the high Arctic.

The interactions between populations of predators and their prey have subtle implications at the level of individual behaviour. In Finland numbers of both predators and prey cycle in synchrony, with the numbers of Least Weasels lagging a year behind those of Bank Voles. The female Bank Vole (right) resists the sexual advances of male voles when confronted with the smell of weasels, but will mate willingly in the absence of this smell. A consequence of the cycling populations is that if weasels are abundant one year, and hence their smell permeates the environment, they are likely to be rarer the following year. A female vole breeding when weasels are abundant is likely to exhaust herself, and perhaps shorten her life, only to have all her offspring eaten. In contrast, by postponing breeding to the following spring, by which time weasels will be rarer, she may end up successfully rearing a larger total of young.

Competitive exclusion

From about 1828 a succession of enthusiasts strove to introduce the American Grey Squirrel to Britain. The introductions really took hold when ten Grey Squirrels were released at Woburn Abbey, Bedfordshire, in 1890. By 1920 their descendants occupied some 3,500 km². No less dramatic in their colonial zeal were the progeny of a single pair liberated in Scotland in 1892. Over the next 25 years they increased their range at an average of 31 km² per annum. Ever since the last Ice Age, the tree-top niche in both conifer and deciduous woods had had another occupant, the Red Squirrel – an indigenous (i.e. naturally local) species. As we move towards the close of the 20th century the situation is much changed: Grey Squirrels are found throughout much of England, and have replaced Red Squirrels in all save coniferous forests. Where once the Grey was a novelty and the Red abounded, the fortunes of the two species have been dramatically reversed. Why?

Although it is difficult to prove, it is tempting to believe that at least part of the answer is competition. After all, there is an incriminating hint of cause and effect in the coincidental arrival of the Grey Squirrel and the decline of Red Squirrel in Britain. Furthermore, this happened after British Red Squirrels had survived the shift in character of Britain's forests from the post-Ice Age Scots Pine (in which they had evolved) to a contemporary mixture in which oak and hazel predominate, with which the Red Squirrels' evolutionary credentials were nil. This transformation of their habitat was caused by a warming of the climate which may have been to the Red Squirrels' long-term cost. Worse still, human effort was soon to fragment vast forest-scapes to a patchwork of copses. How could the Greys oust the Reds that had weathered the might of climate and mankind? An obvious, but apparently wrong, thought is that the Greys bully the Reds, profiting from their larger size in direct combat (they are twice the weight). Although Greys are reputed occasionally to chase and even kill Red Squirrels (and kill, without eating, Red nestlings), most such reports are unsubstantiated and aggression is certainly rare. On the contrary, the general rule is that Red and Grey Squirrels coexist in superficial equanimity where they meet.

Another possibility is that Reds have a disease problem: a recently discovered virus appears to be confined to Red Squirrels in Britain and during the late 1970s this devastated some populations. Although this virus has not been found in Grey Squirrels it is conceivable that they brought it in originally. However, undiagnosed local epidemics caused Red numbers to plummet between 1900 and 1930, before the Greys were really a factor in

The Red Squirrel's inability to digest acorns may be a key factor in the competition with Greys.

the equation. Incidentally, other epidemic diseases also afflict Red Squirrels elsewhere in Europe, generally delivering a *coup de grâce* after failure in the pine-cone crop has precipitated famine among them. Famine may also trigger 'irruptive migration' (the phenomenon made famous by lemmings) whereupon vast numbers of doomed Red Squirrels emigrate, sometimes plunging in hoards across lakes and rivers in the generally vain search for richer territory.

Competition works subtly, and in this case it may pivot around the robustness of two traits: the squirrels' digestive systems and their physical agility. In an effort to avoid being eaten, acorns and the seeds of many other temperate trees have packed themselves with toxic chemicals designed to give their predators an upset tummy. Foremost among the acorn's chemical arsenal are tannins (the same stuff with which tea drinkers daily poison themselves). Neither an acorn nor tannin have ever been sighted in the diet of Red Squirrels in the boreal forests in which they evolved, but both are commonplace in the temperate forests of North America, whence the Grey hails. This difference in ancestral experience probably explains why Reds succumb when fed exclusively on acorns, whereas Greys flourish (although given the choice even they prefer species of acorn lower in tannin). It is noteworthy, considering the tendency to look for perfection in adaptations, that 10,000 years has not been sufficient for the Reds' digestion to catch up with the times.

The importance of the acorn factor was revealed by a clever study that compared the behaviour of Red Squirrels in an oak wood on the Isle of Wight with that of Grey Squirrels in a similar wood on the nearby mainland. The Reds foraged for hazel nuts or, when they ran out, on fungus living under the dead bark of oak trees. They eschewed acorns and their population was unrelated to variations in acorn crop. The Greys, meanwhile, concentrated on acorns, and peaks in their populations followed bumper acorn crops. To clinch the story, captive squirrels were offered a diet of acorns: the Reds ate 45 g per day and lost weight from 270 g to 175 g over three weeks, whereas the Greys ate 41 g per day and gained weight. This is because the Greys' digestion is capable of disarming some 60% of the acorn's gripe-inducing polyphenols, whereas the Reds can detoxify less than 10%. The fact that oaks amount to scarcely 2% of Scottish woodland may explain the slowness of the Grey's advance northward. Ironically, the planting of oak trees in conifer areas to break the visual monotony and to benefit insects and birds that feed on them, may turn out to be the last nail in the Red Squirrel's coffin.

The Grey Squirrel's robust build comes into play when the going gets tough up above. Both species can forage on the ground, but the Grey has a greater tendency to do so, and may be better at it. Reds have a lighter frame and are more arboreal, so they can move on the outer branches of conifers in search of cones, buds and flowers – a flair for the high wire that is beyond the Grey's agility. Greys are much bulkier than one might expect: a Grey's shin length is 10.6% greater than a Red's (78 mm versus 70.5 mm), which would predict a 35% weight difference, whereas Greys are actually between 80% and 138% heavier than Reds. Furthermore, Greys become positively podgy in winter while Reds remain sure-footed sylphs (winter fat reserves are 20% for Greys versus 8–12% for Reds). The difference in bulk and fat may arise because the more arboreal Red Squirrel needs to be more agile and therefore cannot afford to be plump in winter. Indeed, winter is the crucial time for plucking the seeds that develop in pine cones during autumn, and shed in spring whereupon the squirrels face free-for-all competition with ground-dwelling rodents. The cosy consequences of their greater fat layer may explain why Greys reputedly use dreys less than Reds do in winter. The roots of these differences lie in the deciduous forest of America. There the acorn crop falls earthward, leaving the branches bare in winter, forcing the Grey to the ground, and opening the door to a portliness that would be the downfall of its nimble Red cousin. In contrast, Red Squirrels have evolved principally to feed on cones, which are available on trees all year round. In terms of agility, extra winter fat might be more a hindrance than a help (Reds already don as thick a winter coat as they can get away with).

So the decline and fall of the British Red Squirrel may be due to two cards up the Grey Squirrel's competitive sleeve: a cast-iron gut able to cope with tannins, and possibly a greater facility on the ground – cards which can only be played in mixed or deciduous woods. Red Squirrels still survive in mixed woodland on islands where Greys are absent, such as Brownsea and the Isle of Wight, and in large tracts of Scottish and Irish conifer forest.

Ironically, this off-shore skirmish between the two species is of peripheral importance to Continental Red Squirrels as a whole. Britain always was at the edge of the Red Squirrel's range, and they still flourish in the coniferous forests of Scandinavia and Siberia (where they confusingly turn grey in winter!). In these forests the Red Squirrels' fate is linked to an unpredictable currency: the spruce seed crop fluctuates from year to year, and with it the numbers of squirrels. This raises a final thought: it may be important to Red Squirrels to have the option of travelling from an area where the crop fails to one where it has come to fruition, and the fragmentation of British conifer woods with the spread of agriculture must have reduced the opportunity to do so. On the other hand, because Greys cache and recover food on the ground, they are less vulnerable to temporary food shortage during severe winters.

The case of these two species of squirrel pivots on ideas at the very core of ecological thinking. The great similarities between them throw them into competition for limited resources. They occupy, in ecological parlance, very similar niches. A species' niche is its role in the community, its relations with food, predators and disease, and a host of other factors which together amount to its particular way of doing business. The fundamental principle at stake, known as the principle of competitive exclusion, is that if resources are limiting, members of two species cannot occupy identical niches at the same time and the same place. If two species are that similar then, sooner or later, one will oust the other. Remarkably tiny differences can tip the balance in such contests. The delicacy of the balance of power in contests has been much more clearly shown for flour beetles in laboratories than it has for mammals in the wild, but that is probably largely due to the infinitely greater ease of measuring things in simplified laboratory 'worlds'. For example, some of these flour-eating beetles are so similar that telling them apart taxes even specialists, yet if members of two species are housed together then eventually only one species will survive. However, which of the two species triumphs can depend on tiny changes; say of temperature by only 3 °C, or if a parasite is present or absent, or if the humidity is higher or lower. These differences can cause a reverse in the outcome, turning the winning species into the loser. This is because the requirements of the species are so similar that they cannot coexist, and their respective adaptations are such that one performs just slightly better in one set of circumstances, whereas the other has the edge under other conditions. In the case of the squirrels, both can flourish in all sorts of woodland when unencumbered by the other, but where they are thrown into competition each retreats into its so-called realised niche – the Red into coniferous woodland, the Grey prospering everywhere else.

The shifting balance of competition

The existence of other species is as much a part of each species' environment as rainfall or temperature, and constitutes equally strong selection pressure. Of course, circumstances can change, and thereby change the balance of competition. For example, following the downfall of rabbits due to myxomatosis, the number of Brown Hares increased. Among the factors which may explain this are that rabbits were no longer there to transmit a stomach worm they had previously passed on to hares, nor to compete directly for food, nor to prevent successional changes in vegetation. A further, albeit speculative, possibility is that more rabbits had supported more Red Foxes which in turn took sufficient young hares to suppress their numbers. Each idea has its flaws – the parasitic worm in this example is actually not very common in British rabbits. The consensus view is that it was the increased cover caused by reduced rabbit grazing that allowed higher leveret survival. Indeed, following myxomatosis, hares increased most in open heath, which is the sort of habitat where cover for leverets might be especially critical. To the onlooker in Britain it seemed like a cause-and-effect relationship. It may be mere coincidence, however. Hares have declined in Denmark, and rabbits are rare there. So the question now is whether the current decline in hare numbers is at all associated with the recovery of rabbit populations, and the answer appears to be 'no'.

Rabbits are relative newcomers to Britain; they were introduced by the Normans in the late 11th century. Although originally they were kept in warrens, rabbits escaped regularly throughout the Middle Ages, and were first recorded in the wild in the 14th century. Perhaps their spread was encouraged when efforts to foster game species led to increased control of the rabbits' predators. Similarly, rabbits may have benefited indirectly when farmers started to raise fodder crops on which to feed their stock during the winter. Brown Hares have been in Britain some 1,500 years longer than rabbits, and their decline is probably also linked to farming practice. A recent survey, ingeniously deploying a formidable army of volunteers, estimates that the British population of hares was only 900,000, ranging between concentrations of up to 50 per km^2 in parts of East Anglia and eastern Scotland, and almost none in southwest England (where they had been plentiful at the turn of the century). More hares survive where there are gamekeepers, perhaps because by killing foxes they reduce predation on leverets, or perhaps because by planting cover crops for game birds they enhance the habitat for hares. Indeed, hares require a diversity of habitats to provide food for each season of the year, so the monocultures typical of modern farming are to their disadvantage, especially where the crop is grass for silage. Silage is cut up to three times annually and the flailing blades of the mower are fatal for leverets.

The changing distributions of Red and Arctic Foxes provide a mammalian equivalent of the flour-beetle examples. The ranges of these two species are largely separate, the Arctic Fox's distribution forming a circumpolar ribbon to the north of the Red's range. The two overlap in the Eurasian tundra. However, during the early 20th century the geographical range of the Red Fox expanded, while that of the Arctic Fox contracted. Looking at the two species it seems obvious that their largely separate distributions are due to the Arctic Fox's superior adaptations to cold winters and severe snow. Certainly, it is true that 70% of the thickness of Arctic Fox pelage is underfur, in comparison to 20% for northern Red Foxes. Nonetheless, Red Foxes begin to shiver only at about $-13\,°C$, and Arctic Foxes at about $-40\,°C$, so the fact is that both species are impressively adapted to the cold. Indeed, Red Foxes are found in places that are equally as cold as those inhabited by Arctic Foxes (and Arctic Foxes are found in the relatively warm conditions of Iceland, where there are no Red Foxes). It seems that adaptations to cold are insufficient to explain either the distributions, or the fact that Red Foxes have been spreading.

Red and Arctic Foxes are remarkably similar in everything they do. The result is they are thrown into direct competition when they meet. All else being equal, Red Foxes seem to treat Arctic Foxes as smaller, and thus inferior, copies of themselves, and drive them away (Red Foxes have even been seen to kill an Arctic Fox when they met at carrion). How, then, do Arctic Foxes survive at all? The answer is that they eat less. Red Foxes are 60% heavier and so to feed themselves require a home range 90% larger than that of Arctic Foxes (because required home range size increases disproportionately with body size, see p. 160). The Red Fox has a longer stride, and therefore probably gains time in its race to cover its home range (indeed, Red Foxes generally trot, while Arctic Foxes often canter in order to cover sufficient ground), but the fact remains that Red Foxes need more space. The productivity of food diminishes towards the north, and there comes a point in their northward range when it simply runs out. The larger body that allows the Red Fox to bully the Arctic Fox further south shackles it to food demands that cause Red Foxes to reach, sooner than Arctic Foxes, a point at which prey are so scarce that they cannot maintain adequately large home ranges. So, the Red Fox's brute strength sets the southern limit to the Arctic Fox's range, while its hefty appetite sets its own northern limit. This means that there is a sense in which cold limits the Red Fox, but it is indirectly through an effect on productivity of the landscape, rather than directly.

But why have Red Foxes spread north? Over the last century the temperature of the Northern Hemisphere has been warming. Between 1880 and 1940 the mean annual temperature increased by 2.5 °C in Spitzbergen. In Scandinavia there is a 1 °C fall in temperature for every 5.2° of latitude to the north. Thus the 2.5 °C warming in Spitzbergen will give it the climate previously enjoyed 1,500 km to the south. Equally, the tree-line will be creeping upwards as well as northwards, as mountain tops become warmer. The rise in temperature will be accompanied by an increase in density of prey, so the result is probably that areas previously too unproductive to sustain Red Foxes can now support them, and the Red incomers then oust the Arctic Foxes. This suggestion gets indirect support from the changing colour of Scandinavian Arctic Foxes: blue Arctic Foxes are characteristic of coast land, white ones of the inland; previously, blue individuals made up a fair proportion of Arctic Foxes in northern Sweden, now they number less than 1% of the population. This may be because invading Red Foxes have pushed Arctic Foxes out of the warmer low-lying coastal land, and into higher altitude inland sanctuaries where the white phase predominates.

Can species coexist?

Two species need not look very similar, or even be close relatives, in order to compete, and even fierce competitors need not necessarily compete in all aspects of their lifestyle. For example, the winter diet of Elk and Mountain Hare can have much in common (both eat shrubs, especially birch), which is to say that the 'food dimension' of their niches overlap (although there are clearly a vast array of other respects in which their niches do not overlap at all). It is thus plausible that these unlikely combatants are thrown into food competition. The obvious question is: how different do two species have to be in order to coexist? For a while it was fashionable to answer 'by a factor of 1.3'! The mystical significance of this number arose from a study showing that the dimensions of the feeding apparatus (e.g. jaws, beaks etc.) of coexisting species generally differed by a factor of 1.3. This number was

The relationship between similar predators is often aggressive. Red Foxes may kill Pine Martens not only to eat them, but also to rid themselves of tiresome competitors.

adopted as the basic rule of limiting similarity. At first encounter such a general rule seems likely to be 'baloney', because the niches occupied by each species are so vastly complicated, and have so many facets, that no universal answer to the question can exist. However, inspired by the '1.3 scaling rule', two eminent biologists set about measuring various sets of objects such as recorders, skillets and bicycle wheels, and found that on average these too assembled into 'guilds' scaling by 1.3. An example is the progression from violin to viola to cello and bass. They concluded that this ratio was somehow mysteriously fundamental to assembling sets, and thus not to do with competition at all. However, the original question of how different two species have to be to coexist throws up a problem. Despite the enormous intuitive appeal of the idea of competitive exclusion, it is hard to prove logically because the very fact that two species are recognised as species means by definition that they are different, so there can be no surprise in finding differences between them when they occur side by side. Circumstances could *sometimes* allow almost identical species to coexist – in an unstable environment conditions might change so fast that no sooner had one species gained the upper hand than conditions change to allow the other to steal the advantage.

Where both of two competitors are kept, numerically, firmly under the thumb of a predator, competition may be the last thing they have to worry about. In the North Pacific, Sea Otters effectively control the abundance of sea urchins, which in turn control the algal seaweed community on which they graze. The algal floras of islands with and without Sea Otters are

In theory, competition prevents very similar species from coexisting, and species that do coexist are sufficiently different to defuse strife. However, such neat integration has been upset by human meddling. People have introduced both Raccoons (left) from North America, and Raccoon Dogs (right) from South-east Asia, to Europe. Both were imported for fur farming and have escaped. It remains to be seen how these two alien members of the Carnivora will get on in the European arena. Will there be room for both, or indeed either, of them?

considerably different. In communities without Sea Otters, urchins are abundant and reduce the number of algal species which in turn reduces competition among similar algal species. Where otters are present and urchins are reduced in number, algae flourish and compete so severely that some species are eventually excluded. Thus the presence of otters has an indirect effect on competitive interactions between species lower in the food chain – in this case, on the diversity of algal species. Where urchins abound, the competitive balance between the seaweeds is shifted. For example, a species of seaweed which might overwhelm another if competition were unfettered can never gain the upper hand if it is kept in check by urchins. The otters, in turn, limit the populations of urchins. Thus, taking islands without otters and either introducing otters or removing urchins has the same effect: in both cases after only a year a diverse kelp flora with a high biomass develops, and after two years one seaweed, *Laminaria groenlandica*, comes to dominate the flora.

Character displacement

One consequence of competition forcing two species to evolve in ways that permit their coexistence is called character displacement. For example, weasels, stoats, polecats and martens are all very similar in design, so one might expect them to be pitched into fierce competition. Indeed, weasels avoid stoat odour, but not vice versa and when the two meet, stoats dominate (their individual territories do not overlap where the two species live in the same area, doubtless because the stoats oust the weasels). However, competition between the various members of the weasel family may at least be minimised by the fact that their sizes can be arranged on a continuum, each neatly spaced out in order of size and accommodating the fact that males are much bigger than females in each species. From the smallest to the largest, the order is female weasels, male weasels, female stoats, male stoats, female polecats, male polecats, female pine martens, male pine martens. The idea is that the niche of each species (and of each sex) is defined by its larger and smaller competitors.

This separation allows partitioning of resources between the species, and perhaps even between the sexes – although there are other good reasons for a size difference between the sexes (see p. 256). One largely discredited proposal is that their burrow-hunting habits threw ancestral weasels into fierce competition, making it advantageous for males and females of each species to evolve different sizes to defuse marital strife by hunting different types of prey. However, there is no good evidence for this battle-of-the-sexes proposal, which is logically weakened to the extent that male weasels still hunt in rodent burrows; of course, female weasels can still hunt easily in any burrow a male can fit into.

An alternative idea is that the need for the female to feed the young without help keeps her small in size so as to maximise efficiency in hunting in burrows. The females have to enter prey burrows during pregnancy, and so must be 'scaled down' throughout the rest of the year. When not pregnant, females are 'scale models' of the larger males, and the body diameter of a pregnant female weasel is similar to that of a male. A similar suggestion is that the female's task of rearing young confines her close to the den, limiting her home range and thus her body size. Unaided by her mate, a female stoat has to catch up to four times more prey daily when nursing. If she was the size of a male, she would need yet another extra vole a day. Hunting for that extra vole would keep her away longer from her young, which need her protection and her body heat for their first five to seven weeks. The costs that would be incurred by a larger female have been worked out in detail for

one North American member of the weasel family, called the Fisher. A mother Fisher, which looks rather like a Pine Marten, needs to eat one hare every 4 days, one porcupine every 22 days or 1 kg of carrion every 5 days when her kits are young. By the time her babies are eight weeks old she needs to double this. She is caught in a vicious circle: producing milk requires her to hunt more, which causes her to burn up more energy so she must consume still more. The Fisher may travel 10 km to make a kill and nursing pups can force her to hunt 21 hours a day, leaving her exhausted. If the female was twice as big, like the male, her bigger appetite would force her to hunt round the clock, leaving cubs untended, and she would still probably fail to make ends meet.

Mink and otter also occupy similar habitats and eat similar foods. As otters have declined over much of Europe since the introduction of American Mink, this prompted speculation that competition between the two had led to the demise of the otter. In retrospect, it seems more likely that this was no more than coincidence, as the otters were already suffering from pollution, disturbance and over-hunting when the mink arrived. In Scandinavia it seems that the two species have rather different diets during summer: the otter specialises on large fish and the mink on small mammals.

Character displacement may explain the gradations in size between species (but perhaps not between sexes within species) of European members of the family Mustelidae. From left to right (a female and male of each) are Common Weasel, Stoat, Western Polecat and Pine Marten.

In winter they are thrown into stiffer competition as the lakes freeze over and both are forced into open water. Under these circumstances the mink are scarce in any unfrozen lakes where otters abound, but mink predominate in overgrown waterways, where ice inhibits the fishing skills that are the otter's forte. In head-on competition in open water it seems highly likely that the otter could use its much larger size to overwhelm and expel the mink. Certainly, there is overlap in the niches of the two. Indeed, with its penchant for fish, crayfish and frogs, the otter's specialities fall almost entirely within the scope of the mink's more generalist traits. They illustrate the coexistence of a jack of all trades and a specialist.

Chapter eight

Social behaviour

Why are animals sociable? Possibly it is the fascination of poking one's nose into the business of others that makes this question one of the most exciting in biology. In seeking the answer, and with an eye on the process of natural selection (see p. 36), we should seek factors that put members of a society at an advantage (ultimately, in terms of their lifetime reproductive success) over outsiders. In other words, what is the survival value of socialising? Because of their powers of long-range communication (p. 175), especially through scent (p. 185), members of some mammalian societies can keep themselves abreast of social affairs without spending much time in direct contact with others. Eurasian Badgers, Red Foxes, Brown Rats and House Mice for example, conduct most of their affairs single-handedly, but none-theless are part of social groups as closed to outsiders as any exclusive club. On the other hand, sociality in herds of Fallow Deer, packs of wolves, and flocks of ibex is much more overt. Turning first to this latter arrangement, in which individuals operate as a cohesive group who spend time in each other's company, two advantages of a social life emerge. Grouping improves the member's chances of securing food and of avoiding becoming food.

Securing food

Both carnivores and herbivores form groups in order to secure food more effectively. A striking example of many hands making light work is the ability of a wolf pack to kill prey as large as Elk and Musk Ox. The rib-crushing hooves and disembowelling horns of such prey generally put them far beyond the predatory aspirations of solitary wolves or like-sized carnivores such as lynx. By combining forces, the pack can overcome such quarry. Strength of numbers may also help the pack defend its spoils, whether killed or scavenged from neighbours, and to pilfer from smaller packs. Pack sizes vary regionally in a way that broadly ties up with local prey size. For example, foraging packs involve up to 30 wolves where Elk are an important prey and less than ten where smaller deer prevail. Where wolves live mainly by scavenging, in Italy for example, they travel alone.

There is evidence that there is more to wolf sociality than cooperative hunting, however. First, packs often exceed the membership that would be optimum if hunting were the only consideration. This means that pack size may depend more on how many wolves can feed from a typical prey than on how many are needed to kill it. Second, wolves continue to live in closed packs, even if they travel and hunt alone. Third, pack members cooperate in other ways too, for example tending pups and defending the territory.

It is worth pointing out that single wolves can kill prey as large as Elk, even if it seems reasonable that a pack can do it more easily and with less risk. In the mid-1980s several wolves invaded Sweden (see p. 279) and proved proficient at killing Elk single-handedly; perhaps the Elk were disadvantaged by previous years without experience of wolves. Elsewhere, there are reports of lone wolves killing Elk by first injuring them, and then waiting for the victim to weaken. Such observations prompt the intriguing question of whether cooperative hunting is as great an advantage as has been supposed. To answer this we need to know more of the costs to these wolves of hunting alone.

It is not simply the might of prey that can thwart solitary predators; it is also the fact that a single attacker cannot be in

Killer Whales fling themselves onto a beach in order to grab infant sealions. This is a high-risk tactic, because the whales may get stranded on the beach.

more than one place at a time. A Golden Jackal can easily kill a young gazelle, but only if it has a partner to distract the mother. Similarly, some Killer Whales hunt in packs (pods) in the three-dimensional underwater world where it requires team-effort to cut off a porpoise's escape routes. Killer Whales hunt cooperatively, but individuals within a pod may specialise in particular roles. This was especially clear in the behaviour of one pod that formed an unusual alliance with a whaling boat. When the whalers harpooned a whale, four Killer Whales would swim beneath its head to stop it diving, while two others would throw themselves on top of its blow-hole. Other pods have been seen to develop hunting specialisations: some herd herring, others create a bow wave to wash unwary seals off ice-floes. One seemingly perilous hunting technique (although not a cooperative one) is voluntary beaching: the Killer Whale accelerates towards the beach with such vigour that it slithers well on to dry land to grab an infant seal, with which it then writhes back into the water. Females probably do this more than males whose greater bulk prevents them getting so far inshore. Young Killer Whales play at beaching, perhaps being tutored by experienced females, although not necessarily by their mothers. The stable family lives of Killer Whales doubtless facilitate the development of cooperative relationships. In one 17-year study of these matriarchal pods there was not one instance of dispersal; mating occurred when two pods associated, but males always returned to their own pod afterwards. Pods may use the same hunting grounds for generations – in one case for at least a century, and reportedly involving the same recognisable individual for 50 years.

Killer Whales hunt in different ways for different prey. A pod might sweep in line up a river mouth to intercept migrating salmon, but in the northwest of Norway they operate quite differently when faced with massive autumnal migrations of herring. The herring move in from the North Atlantic to find coastal waters in which to winter. Large groups of Killer Whales, presumably comprised of several pods working as a team, round up the herring by circling them. If the fish try to break away, the circling

Chamois graze on the grasses of alpine meadows and live in herds. By feeding together, Chamois ensure better quality grazing, while the muntjac (below) browses alone in a defended territory.

whales flash their striking white undersides at them until the herring are bunched into a seething sphere in shallow water. As some whales continue to shepherd the mass of herring, others dart amongst them, thrashing with their tails to stun the fish. The slaughter over, the whole team shares the pickings.

A very different principle may affect the foraging behaviour of some herding herbivores. Arriving at a shop to find the previous customer has bought the last item of the commodity you require is a waste of your time, and no less so for the herbivore who finds that the bud has been nipped by a previous browser. One solution is to defend a territory from which other foragers are barred, as muntjac and Roe Deer do. Alternatively, if the food

resource is not easily monopolised it may be better to harvest it collectively. This probably explains the flocking of seed-eating birds, and it might also be relevant to herds of grazing ungulates. Mammals such as Chamois and ibex crop grass regularly. By moving as a herd, each individual may be able to ensure its return visit to an area is timed to coincide with the grass there reaching its most appetising height. Furthermore, as mowing the lawn stimulates grass to grow, so the whole herd's grazing may keep the sward maximally productive. The act of grazing disadvantages palatable plants which cannot tolerate being grazed, and selects for those (such as grasses) which form a good sward. The result is that each member of the herd does better in company than it would alone. The key point is that the meristem (growing point) of the grass is the most nutritious part; cropping the grass frequently ensures the availability of younger, i.e. nutritious, growth.

Brown Rats provide evidence of a quite different foraging benefit of sociality. Each individual forages alone, but meets its group-mates in communal burrows or when they pass on trails. When a rat smells the scent of a particular food on a companion it will then visit the site where that food is found, presumably basing its itinerary on the assumption that if the first rat found food there, then the place is worth a visit. Of course, this sequence of events may be of immediate disadvantage to the individual that finds its private larder ransacked by a mob of plagiarists, but presumably this is balanced by the opportunity to benefit on other occasions by cashing in on the good fortune of others. We do not know whether rats try to disguise the tell-tale odours of a particularly valuable source of food, as one might keep quiet the whereabouts of a particularly unspoilt restaurant, but House Sparrows are known not to give away more information than suits them. On spying a few crumbs of bread a sparrow will give a chirp before flying down to eat, and that chirp summons its flock-mates to join it, thereby providing the protection of many pairs of eyes to keep a lookout for danger. However, if a large lump of bread, not readily divisible between companions, is visible to one sparrow, the individual which first spots it does not announce its discovery with a chirp, but keeps quiet while it dashes for the food, preferring to forsake the protection of the flock in exchange for first access to the feast.

Another food-oriented benefit of sociality for Brown Rats is the inference they draw from each other's behaviour about the safety of unfamiliar foods. Generally, and with good reason, rats are exceptionally wary of unfamiliar food. This so called neophobia (neo = new, phobia = fear) has doubtless been enhanced by at least four centuries of concerted attempts by people to poison them. The result is that wild Brown Rats may avoid a pile of wheat in an unexpected place and continue to treat it with great caution for more than a month. Although adopting the attitude that it is better to be safe (or in this case hungry) than sorry (dead), has saved many a rat, it is also a great restriction upon their opportunism. The rats have evolved a characteristically ingenious compromise: when the smell of a new food is on the lips of a rat then its companions will more readily overcome their neophobia. Thus, on the principle whereby medieval European royalty ate after food-tasters had tested for poison, rats will infer that if one of their number has survived a new food, then it is safe for the rest of them. Rats also learn from each other's misfortunes. If a rat encounters a new food, and then meets a sick rat, the first rat will develop an aversion to the new food without ever eating it. It may be stretching the point to wonder whether prudent rats sit around waiting for a gullible companion (ideally not a relative, see p. 154) to test suspicious-looking food!

Protection from predators

The second main package of advantages that can arise from grouping is protection from predators. First, and most obvious, is the enhanced vigilance provided by many pairs of eyes. Creeping up undetected on one rabbit is difficult, but the task is even harder when a whole swarm of them is on the alert. Even on the basis of pure chance, the odds are better in larger than smaller groups that at least one member of a grazing herd of deer will be looking up at a given moment. These odds may be improved, however, if individuals synchronise their activities so that one looks around while the others feed (as occurs in the Patagonian Mara, a guinea pig-like rodent from South America). Furthermore, vigilance is time consuming as well as nerve-racking, and grouping may be a way to share this burden. Among groups of Meerkats (small sociable mongooses from the deserts of southern Africa), the group's total vigilance increases with larger membership, but each individual looks up from foraging less frequently. In this way the Meerkats enjoy greater group vigilance at less individual cost.

Another anti-predator benefit from grouping lies in strength of numbers. Just as the wolves combine forces to overwhelm Musk Oxen, the Musk Oxen form a protective cordon to repel the wolves.

Grouping can also lower the risk of falling victim to an attack. It is probably more difficult for a predator to focus its attack on a milling crowd of prey than on a single victim, so all else being equal, we might expect predators to have to face a seething mass of prey as each potential victim struggles to get to the middle of the protective throng. However, all else is not always equal, in that some individuals have an investment in the well-being of others, so we find that adult Musk Oxen form a ring around their calves, and other armed ungulates similarly defend their young. For example, Apennine Chamois kids tend to congregate in the middle of the flock and should danger approach, the adults tend to behave like Musk Oxen (although less effectively because of their smaller size and less fearsome armaments). Of course, grouping may attract problems too: larger groups

When feeding in a group, each hare devotes less time to vigilance than when feeding alone.

may be inherently more attractive to predators and more easily detected. Nonetheless, on balance it seems to pay to group together at least in open habitats where the only place to hide is behind a companion. (In woodland or scrub, concealment is a better option and herding is rare.) The dangers of open habitats probably explains why deer have become increasingly social over their evolutionary history: primitive deer lived in woodlands, but more recent species spread out into grassland where predator avoidance encouraged herding. A rather unexpected parallel to this idea of seeking safety in numbers is provided by feral horses which are persecuted by horse-flies in summer in the south of France. The flies seem to prompt the horses to form herds, with the outcome that each horse is pestered less as the flies spread out among them. The horses often stand head-to-tail, each using their tail to whisk flies from the face of the other.

The above advantages of grouping seem to apply to many species of mammals, so why do only a minority of species capitalise upon them? The answer is partly that grouping also brings disadvantages (e.g. squabbles over food, increased disease or parasite risks, and social restrictions on breeding), and partly that some lifestyles and backgrounds simply preclude this option or render it unnecessary. For example, lynx have few natural enemies so need not herd for safety. Lynx do very occasionally hunt cooperatively, but then only in pairs. Yet why do they not hunt in packs, like the wolf? The answer may be written in their ancestry. Cats have evolved from an arboreal, stalking lineage, their limbs adept at grappling but not fast pursuit. Dogs, in contrast, have evolved rigid, racing limbs. These two starting points may have predestined cooperative hunting to be a fruitful option for wolves, whereas using solitary stealth and strength is more productive a course for lynx. But foxes, like wolves, are members of the dog family and yet they do not hunt in packs. This paradox is resolved by considering the size of their prey: members of a pack of Red Foxes racing in coordinated pursuit of a single lemming are likely to gain no more than a bruising collision. Of course, if foxes packed together to hunt cooperatively, they could then tackle larger prey, but then they would be thrown into competition with wolves.

Altruism and nepotism

That mammals should join forces to forage, to avoid predators or to cooperate for any other reason is not surprising if each participant improves its fitness by doing so (see p. 36). The benefit of the association is not always obvious, however. There are clans of Eurasian Badgers that cohabit in a communal sett, but otherwise seem to pay little attention to each other (see p. 212). Also, in some social relationships the flow of benefit seems to be very one-sided, for example when among Red Foxes a non-breeding vixen provides food and care for another vixen's cubs. This is a startling state of affairs because, insofar as acting as a nanny causes her to forsake breeding opportunities of her own, the barren vixen appears to be increasing another mother's reproductive success at the expense of her own. Such altruism seems to contradict the central edict of natural selection, namely that individuals are adapted to behave in ways that promote their own reproductive success.

Musk Oxen form a daunting ring, with horns outwards and youngsters encircled, to fend off an attack by a pack of wolves.

A number of solutions exist to this paradox, each showing how altruism can pay (in other words, that it is not really altruism at all, but enlightened self-interest). Perhaps the most far-reaching implications stem from the theory of kin selection, the ramifications of which are anticipated in the time-honoured axiom that blood is thicker than water. The salient point is that evolution by natural selection favours those that leave the most breeding descendants, rather than those that simply churn out the most offspring. In other words, natural selection ultimately operates on the survival of genes, not individuals. Hence an individual that seems to be failing by leaving fewer breeding offspring than it could, is still obeying the laws of natural selection if its actions favour the survival of copies of its own genes produced by its close relatives. Conventional ideas about evolution dictate that parents should sometimes make sacrifices for the sake of their offspring. Indeed, there is one species of gall midge in which the mother serves herself up as food for her larvae, and although no mammalian parent makes such a dramatic donation (at least not as a matter of routine) the end result is much the same: parental investment is repaid with a sort of immortality, as their genes are perpetuated, even multiplied, in their descendants.

The crucial fact that underpins the theory of kin selection is that it is not only parents and offspring which share genes. All relatives share a genetic heritage, and this gives them a vested interest in each other's reproductive output. The value one individual places on the progeny of another will depend upon how closely the two are related. The road to understanding the paradox of the vixen 'helper' is opened with the discovery that such nannies are invariably kin, generally sisters or aunts, of the cubs they tend. A quite different but not necessarily incompatible argument is that helpers gain practice in parenthood, and this apprenticeship will pay dividends when they eventually get the chance to breed.

The help given to cubs by a non-breeding female may appear less nonsensical the closer she is related to them, but surely it would be still better for her to invest in her own offspring? Whether this is the case depends partly on the options that are open to her, and partly on the closeness of her relationship with the beneficiaries of her efforts. As long as her mother or elder sisters survive, a young vixen probably has no option to breed in the territory in which she grew up – more senior females will strive to monopolise the available resources for their offspring and will use their dominance to suppress the subordinate's breeding. If she is to breed she must move out and find a territory of her own, and a mate. Dispersal is very hazardous and often fatal (see p. 264).

The choice, albeit presumably not a conscious one, rests on weighing her chances of breeding directly against those of breeding by proxy. If the nanny's contribution substantially increases the survival of her young kin, and if the chances of finding a mate and a territory of her own are slim, then being a 'maiden aunt' becomes a more attractive option. Indeed, whether she is an aunt or a sister to the cubs will make quite a difference to the calculation involved. This calculation assesses the probability that a particular gene is shared by two individuals, which is just the same as asking about the chances of coincidentally getting 'heads' or 'tails' when you toss a coin. There is a 50/50 chance that an offspring will inherit a given gene from either one of its parents, and also a 50/50 chance that two siblings will share that gene (just as it is even odds that you will get a head each time you toss a coin). However, the odds that the same gene will be shared by aunt and nephew are half as good, the equivalent of getting two successive heads (a 50% chance that the two sisters share the gene, and 50% of that chance that one of them will then share it with the other's offspring). Thus, on average, the non-breeding vixen has a 50% stake in her full siblings and a 25% stake

in her nieces and nephews (yet a further toss of the genetic coin is required for genes to be shared by cousins, with the result that they have a 12.5% relationship – exactly the same as that between grandparent and grand-offspring). These implications of kinship were foreseen in the deservedly oft-quoted remark of the geneticist J.B.S. Haldane who, in the 1930s, observed wryly that he would lay down his life for two of his brothers or eight of his cousins. Had Haldane had an identical twin, his life alone would have merited the sacrifice!

Thus, the behaviour of the 'helper' fox, and many other instances of seemingly selfless behaviour between relatives, might more realistically be seen as making the best of a bad job rather than altruism. Obviously, such nepotism requires a mechanism for avoiding helping the wrong individual. The coarsest way to do this might be to rely on circumstantial evidence, for example, to assume that any offspring in your lair or territory is a relation. (The obvious weakness of this approach is illustrated by the predicament of its adherents among hedgerow birds who find themselves adopting a cuckoo.) The comparative ease with which a wide variety of mammals can be persuaded to adopt orphans illustrates the widespread application of this rule but, in a world rife with promiscuity and cuckoldry, its limitations are obvious. New scientific techniques for proving paternity have revealed that neither cuckoldry (illicit matings) nor multiple paternity are rare. Female Eurasian Badgers may have cubs sired by a male from the neighbouring group, and a single litter of Common Shrews may have at least three fathers. There is little evidence of paternal care in either badgers or shrews, but if there was then males would face a sizeable risk of investing in a rival's offspring. Among ground squirrels a female may mate with up to eight males during one afternoon, and three out of four litters have mixed paternity. Can such a hotchpotch of siblings and half-siblings discern their blood ties? The

Red Foxes are extremely adaptable, their social lives varying to suit local circumstances. Commonly at least one non-breeding vixen (and in some areas up to four) shares the territory of a breeding pair. These barren vixens may tend the cubs and bring them food. The same phenomenon occurs in jackals and wolves, with the difference that helpers may be either male or female. To complete the continuum, helpers in the society of the endangered African Wild Dog are almost invariably male.

question has been raised about one North American species, the Belding's Ground Squirrel, with the answer that, among litter mates full sisters were less aggressive and more cooperative towards each other than half-sisters were (brothers were not so discriminating). How on earth did these females know about their kinship? Perhaps their odours betrayed their shared background, rather like an olfactory old-school tie (see p. 185).

What then of apparent altruism between unrelated individuals? There are several explanations, of which the most straightforward is termed mutualism. This applies where individuals cooperate because together, and simultaneously, they both do better than either could alone. This applies to the cooperatively hunting wolves, or it could apply to cases where females nurse each other's young (as observed in many mammals, ranging from rats to ferrets). It also explains why unrelated male lions join forces to overthrow

A mother Brown Rat allows her young to take food from her mouth; she may even suckle unrelated young. The young rat may learn which foods are safe by taking them from the mother, and this information may affect its feeding habits for the rest of its life.

other coalitions of males and commandeer their lionesses. Male Fallow Deer occasionally occupy rutting stands in pairs, apparently for the same reason. In each case, however, although any ally is better than no ally, the genetic payoff would make it even more beneficial to cooperate with a relative, if one were available.

If the rewards of cooperation are not secured simultaneously by all collaborators, then the spectre of cheating looms as an undermining influence in mammalian society. Social paralysis could arise from the fear that a favour granted would never be repaid. Yet among various primate societies there is remarkable evidence of gestures of reciprocal goodwill. For example, among Olive Baboons oestrous females are monopolised by a dominant male. He is a young animal in his prime that dominates older males which are a bit past it. The only hope for waning studs is to act as a team: one ageing subordinate male solicits the aid of another. One of the team engages the dominant consort in battle while his partner mates with the female. At first it seemed to researchers that the stool-pigeon and the philanderer swapped roles in a system reminiscent of the idiom 'you scratch my back and I'll scratch yours'. But more detailed study revealed that within the partnership the more dominant of the two ageing subordinates almost always got the female. Thus the subordinate is in the cruel bind that alone he has no hope, and in an alliance he has only little hope. However, a little hope is better than none. A male who finds he is always the stool-pigeon in a partnership generally changes partners!

The rewards of cooperating are certainly imperilled by the risk of others cheating, but what rules minimise the risk of being ripped-off? This problem, known to logicians as the Prisoner's Dilemma, can be solved by a rather complicated exercise in logic. The dilemma is how to behave when faced with a situation such that: a) if both individuals cooperate the payoff to each is greater than if neither cooperated, and b) if you cooperate and he does not, you will be worse off than if neither of you did (known ingloriously as the sucker's payoff). The solution reveals that, for individuals who are going to have repeated opportunities to interact, a good strategy is to cooperate on the first occasion, thereby giving the other participant the benefit of the doubt, and thereafter for each individual to do what the other did (i.e. cooperate or not) on the previous occasion. Such a system rests on the participants remembering who did what to whom, and this may disfavour tit-for-tat cooperation in large groups. Just such a protocol exists in the remarkable affairs of Vampire Bats from Central America. Individuals that have gorged on blood will regurgitate to others (who may or may not be their relatives) who have had less fortune in their foraging. If reciprocity is to work, then individuals must recognise churls who renege on deals. Indeed, these vampires give food preferentially to members of their own roost (who will have an opportunity to return the favour due to their shared abode), and individuals are more likely to receive regurgitations from those they have helped in the past.

Another prerequisite for beneficial reciprocity is that the benefit of receiving aid must outweigh the cost of giving it. This condition is met in that donating a small meal has little impact on the well-being of a well-fed donor bat, but receipt of such a meal can buy a lot of time for a starving recipient bat. It seems that the affairs of Vampire Bats, and other cooperative but unrelated mammals, can be described by a scrambling of Old and New Testament doctrines: on first encounter do as you would be done by; subsequently, exchange an eye for an eye.

Resources and territories

In an impish jab at romantic sensibilities, the famous father of ethology Konrad Lorenz once remarked that Vera Lynn's romantic nightingale, singing from its perch on a lamppost in Berkeley Square, was engaged in the same activity as the mongrel cocking its leg below. Both were proclaiming ownership of their territory. With hindsight we might quibble that the scent mark may have other functions (we now know that there is more to social odours than meets the human nose, see p. 185), but it remains the case that many animals expend great effort in the advertisement and defence of territories. Why do they do this?

Before tackling that question it is important to distinguish between territories and home ranges. Almost all mammals occupy a home range, that is the area within which they routinely restrict their activities. Some home ranges, however, are arranged such that they overlap less than would have been predicted if the animals had settled at random in a suitable habitat. In extreme cases home-range borders may neatly tessellate like the tiles of a mosaic. The mechanism for maintaining the spacing of such ranges is sometimes obvious (e.g. aggressive clashes at the borders) and sometimes obscure, but the partitioning of the landscape makes it clear that something is going on; that something is called territoriality.

Factors that determine home-range size

Home-range sizes tend to increase with the body size of their occupants, because larger animals eat more. However, body size is not the only determinant of range size. Consider some pairings of similarly sized mammals: a

Wildcat has a larger home range than a Brown Hare, a Common Shrew a larger range than a Harvest Mouse and a Wolf a larger range than a Roe Deer. In each case predators are thinner on the ground than comparably sized prey, and need a larger area than comparably sized prey to support themselves. The fact that predators' home ranges are larger than those of their prey arises because foliage is always more abundant than flesh (see p. 107). Furthermore, the home ranges of large carnivores are disproportionately bigger than those of small carnivores when compared with the differences in range sizes of large and small herbivores. This is because the prey of large carnivores tends to be especially rare. These generalisations help make some sense of the facts that the Pygmy Shrew ranges over a tenth of a hectare, a Common Mole over a quarter of a hectare and a Western Hedgehog over 20 hectares. All are insectivores, all may even forage in the same place at the same time for some of the same food items, and the two bigger species travel further. All else being equal, the diminishing relative costs of running larger bodies (see p. 60) would lead us to expect that the increase in home-range size with body weight would be less marked in larger species. However, the above examples show that the weakness of such generalisations is that all else is rarely equal. The mole, for example, has access to a three-dimensional world, the hedgehog is large enough to supplement its diet with vertebrate prey such as a nest of baby mice, and the shrew is small enough to face a perpetual energy crisis. Furthermore, at least in some habitats, hedgehogs are not territorial and appear to wander at random, whereas moles and shrews are territorial and exclude all comers from their property except during the breeding season.

So there are enormous differences in the property occupied by members of different species. In the Arctic the lemming scarcely ventures from its burrow, whereas the Polar Bear may wander over an area covering thousands of kilometres. Relative to their body sizes, bats have huge ranges. Their expansive ranges are necessitated by the patchy distribution of their prey, and made feasible by the bats' mobility. A Greater Horseshoe Bat may cover 20 km^2 each night, while a Water Shrew might cover 100 m^2. Similarly, the seasonal needs of foraging and keeping warm prompt Humpback Whales to travel from Greenland to Florida and back annually (small babies with thin blubber require warmer water to survive). It is obvious from these examples that the home-range sizes of different species vary with their requirement for resources and the availability of these resources. This conclusion is emphasised by comparisons of the travels of the same species in contrasting habitats. A Wood Mouse on a cereal farm might cover a home range of 10 km^2, one in woodland might cover only 1.7 km^2. A Red Fox, in so far as it depended on Wood Mice, would need a vastly greater range to satisfy its requirements solely on mice in a cereal field. In fact, Red Foxes in lush suburbia defend territories of about 40 ha^2 (some as small as 10 ha^2), while those on farmland occupy 200–500 ha^2 and those on uplands and moors cover much more than 1,000 ha^2. Similarly, Red Deer in Scottish forests occupy about 250 ha^2, those on moorland, 600 ha^2. Eurasian Badger territories in Wytham Woods near Oxford shrank from an average of 60 ha^2 to 40 ha^2 over 12 years during which changes in farming replaced cereal fields (poor habitat for the badger's earthworm prey) with pasture (rich in worms).

Having ascertained that range sizes are geared to a requirement for resources, we can return to the initial question of why some ranges are defended as territories. The answer is fundamentally to do with shortages and defensibility. Mammals very often require resources (food, mates, lairs) that are short in supply and insufficient to go round. The result is competition, and as soon as competition occurs there will be winners and losers (indeed, this is the meaning of the survival of the fittest, see p. 31). Broadly speaking, there are two ways to compete: a race or a contest. In the first case all competitors scramble for the prize, gobbling up as much as they can. On average, the race will be won by the fastest. In contrast, a formal contest can decide among competitors outside the context of the ultimate prize and the battle will be won by the strongest.

The competition for space is the essence of territoriality. Competitors fight for a plot that harbours the resources they will need, and the winner takes all. Aside from the muddying influence of luck, the strong competitor will triumph over the weak. The disadvantage of a race or scramble competition is that once all the resources are used up, all the remaining competitors, whether strong or weak, face death. By contrast, the winner of contest competition gains reasonably long-term security. In a scramble, the act of exploiting the resource wins the day; in the contest over territory, interfering with your opponents' future access to resources seals their fate. The end result is the same, and in neither case do the meek inherit (or more importantly bequeath) much. The difference between these two types of competition among members of the same species depends on the defensibility of the resources in question. Defending a territory is very expensive – it not only requires a fearful investment in the initial bid for supremacy, but also represents a long-term commitment to patrols and defence. Mammals, and other animals, opt for a territorial system when the resources (food, mates etc.) are so distributed that the costs of defending them are outweighed by the benefits of so doing.

162

Escalating a fight is risky. These Mouflon rams could incur terrible injuries. On the steep slope the prime male (far right) has a marked advantage. The challenging ram risks serious injury if he persists in the attack.

The costs of territoriality determine the size of plot defended. The occupant should defend a territory as rich in resources as necessary, but no richer. We can think of territory holders being bombarded by the have-nots of their society, non-territory holders who float in the population ready to grab any property that becomes available, and ready to overthrow any incumbent that shows signs of frailty. In such a climate, any greedy territory owner whose ambitions lead it to try to monopolise more territory than it needs will be worse off than its more circumspect neighbours because it will be incurring unnecessary costs in defending resources it cannot fully use. Of course, this begs the question of how territory holders decide how big a territory they need. On a realistic timescale (spanning seasonal differences in the availability of food, for example) they probably opt for territories that maximise the returns on the investment they make in property. They might, for example, maximise their daily rate of food intake or minimise their risk of starving.

Having opted for territoriality as a method of competing for scarce resources, with how many occupants should the owner share its domain? Once again, the answer depends on balancing the costs and benefits of being

Humpback Whales swim around a school of fish, releasing bubbles of air to form a bubble-net around the fish in order to prevent their escape.

part of a larger group with those of defending a larger plot, and the solution will depend on the nature of the resources. For a male stoat the resources in question are females. His aim is probably to ensure that his territory overlaps those of as many females as possible, up to a maximum size at which his defensive energies are so thinly spread that he would actually produce fewer progeny if he attempted to monopolise a larger harem. A wolf may benefit from membership of a larger pack because the rewards of increasing pack size outweigh (up to a point) the costs of having to commandeer more land to support its members. For moles, in contrast, it appears that no such compensations exist for sharing (indeed, what could be worse than scuttling down an underground corridor only to find that another occupant had already picked it clean of food?).

Some patterns of resources may permit communal living at minimal cost. For example, in Great Britain Eurasian Badgers prey heavily upon earthworms which they catch when the worms surface to feed and mate. Interestingly, badgers further south in much of France, Spain and Italy for example, must survive without this mainstay to their diet. The worms' tendency to surface, and so to become available as food to the badgers, depends on weather conditions (see p. 101). In the undulating countryside favoured by badgers, one can imagine that there are patches, say on the leeward side of a hill, where it is warm and sheltered and where many worms surface, while on the windward side the chill breeze drives all the worms below. A change in wind direction would cause the whole pattern of worm availability to swap around. Even one badger would need a territory sufficiently rich that it could always find a feeding patch. However, such patches are often thronged with worms, and several other badgers can join in the feast at no cost to each other. In this way, groups of badgers can cohabit at minimal cost, and this may explain why they live communally without seeming to pay much attention to each other, except perhaps that they share the burden of territorial defence. And with whom should the badgers share their territories? Their kin (see p. 157).

Chapter nine

Senses

The diversity of mammalian lifestyles – terrestrial and aquatic, nocturnal and diurnal, predator and prey – imposes hugely varied demands on their senses. The bushbaby, an owl-eyed primate, can see in dim starlight, whereas the Ganges River Dolphin, in waters fogged by swirling silt, has eyes the size of a pea and is one of only two mammals to lack all trace of a lens (the other is the Marsupial Mole, whose vestigial eyes measure only 1 mm across and are hidden beneath skin). Water voles close their eyes under water, but otters can squeeze their lenses to take account of the optical properties of the medium they are in and thereby enjoy equally good vision in air and water (their close relatives, American Mink, cannot do so and lose half their visual acuity under water). Mice are probably not alone in being able to distinguish the scents of individuals that are nearly identical genetically (see p. 193), and many mammals have a special 'vomero-nasal' organ with which they 'taste' smells (see p. 191). Kangaroo rats can hear the low frequency (1–3 kHz) whir of the wind in an owl's feathers. They are able to do this because they have a greatly enlarged ear capsule (auditory bulla) and ear drum (tympanum) with associated engineering to amplify sounds 97-fold – humans in comparison usually magnify sounds 18-fold. At the high-frequency end of the spectrum, the Little Brown Bat uses echoes to 'hear' objects only 0.2 mm wide at a range of 1 m. The Mediterranean Horseshoe Bat can detect a wire only 0.05 mm in diameter at a 20 cm range.

Sight

The big choice in visual systems is between a panoramic view of the world, achieved by having the eyes at the side of the head, or a stereoscopic one, achieved by having the eyes sufficiently to the fore that there is an overlap in their fields of view. The scope for stereoscopic vision varies from mammals like Black Rats, where only 40% of the fields of view overlap between the eyes, and wildcats, where both eyes can see exactly the same field of view. Stereoscopic vision is vital for depth perception, and therefore helpful in jumping from branch to branch, pouncing on prey and, especially useful for uncovering camouflage by differentiating the shape of an animal from its background.

The quest for nocturnal vision has led many rodents, insectivores and bats to forsake 'cones' (the cells in the eye's retina which are sensitive to colour) and instead to cram their retina with 'rods', the receptor cells that maximise sensitivity to low levels of light. Indeed, the need to enlarge eyes for vision in poor light has led to a rearward, tubular extension of the whole eye in some species such as horses, whose night vision is comparable to that of owls. The result is that no space remains in the skull for eye movements. This arrangement is taken to its extreme by the tarsier, a tiny primate which has eyes like soup plates, but can turn its head through 180° to look over its shoulder. Incidentally, no mammals voluntarily move their eyes independently as the chameleon does, for example, and small nocturnal mammals cannot move their eyes at all. Horse's eyes are also immobile due to their light-gathering backward-bulge. This means that the retina-to-lens distance cannot be adjusted to focus the image of near and far objects, but rather the image from the lens falls obliquely on the retina. So, the image is in focus on different parts of the retina as the horse tilts its head. Overall, however, mammalian eyes vary much less in size than do mammalian bodies; there is a minimum size beneath which eyes do not function well, and a maximum size beyond which further enlargement does not improve vision. Therefore small mammals appear to have relatively large eyes, whereas large mammals appear to have relatively small ones: a Blue Whale's eye is not that much bigger than an Elk's.

Those species exhibiting eye-shine in torch light (e.g. yellow or green in wildcats, weasels and seals, and white or blue in deer) do so because they have a tapetum lucidum. This is like a mirror behind the retina, reflecting light that has passed through the sensitive cells back through them again, thereby allowing, so to speak, a double exposure (but diminished picture sharpness). There is another quite different sense in which mammalian vision allows a double exposure. In most vertebrates all the nerve fibres from each eye cross, at the optic chiasma, to the opposite side of the brain. In mammals, however, this crossing (decussation) is incomplete, with some fibres from each eye also going to the same side of the brain. This arrangement is unique to mammals. The result is a stereoscopic view of the world.

The eye is protected not only by eyelids and lashes but also, in many mammals (e.g. all carnivores except skunks), by a nictitating membrane, a curtain drawn automatically across the cornea from front to rear. In the 19th century the interesting but unproven suggestion was made that the nictitating membrane protects Polar Bears and Reindeer from snow blindness. Blue and ultraviolet light reflected from snow damages the retina, so perhaps the Polar Bear's nictitating membrane absorbs these wavelengths, or perhaps, just like sunglasses, it cuts glare.

Sonar

Some bats (Microchiroptera) and some cetaceans (toothed, but probably not baleen whales) have highly developed sonar (echolocation) systems. Furthermore, since most insectivores, some pinnipeds and rodents produce ultrasounds, they too might echolocate. Common Shrews use ultrasound to distinguish burrow openings at 20 cm range (using 'noises' of 25–95 kHz). The bat's voice box (larynx) is enlarged with thin, strongly muscled vocal cords. Daubenton's Bat opens its mouth to emit clicks, whereas the Greater Horseshoe Bat uses its nose as a megaphone to broadcast pulsed sounds. By echolocation, bats can gather information on the size, texture, distance, direction and velocity of objects. Furthermore, it has been suggested that dolphins use loud sounds of this kind to stun their prey. Blind Mole Rats use sound in a different way. Like prisoners tapping Morse code messages between their cells, Blind Mole Rats bash their heads against the roofs of their tunnels to sound war drums to their rivals.

Killer Whales use sonar when hunting. A pod of whales will trawl up a narrow strait searching for, for example, migrating salmon. As they advance in loose formation some make contact calls, each with an individually recognisable voice, so each member of the pod knows its position relative to its companions. Other whales emit sonar clicks, and the echoes from these allow the hunters to navigate, locate each other and locate their prey. At first they use low frequency clicks, which travel further than higher frequencies and produce echoes when they strike anything of the same size or larger than the wavelength of the sound. When they close in on the salmon, they increase the frequency to 500 clicks per second or more, to get higher resolution

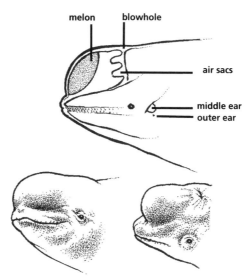

Toothed whales, such as the Beluga, have a protruberant forehead called the melon. This apparatus is thought to enable the whale to echolocate objects. The melon is a waxy lens-shaped structure in the forehead which focuses sounds produced in the whale's nasal passages. These sounds are beamed out and then reflect back to the whale whereupon they are channelled to the inner ear via oil-filled sinuses in the lower jaw. The accuracy of the whole system is improved because the inner ear is isolated from the skull by means of a bubbly foam; this cuts down on any extraneous interference.

information. By hunting cooperatively the entire pod, spread out across the strait, acts as a single sonar collecting dish.

Bats and echolocation

More than 15% of European mammalian species (and indeed about 25% of all mammals) are bats. This comes as something of a shock when reflecting upon the extraordinary nature of their lifestyle. Not only do most bats operate in darkness, but they do so on the wing, sometimes at great heights, and in pursuit of fast-flying, tiny prey that dodge among a profusion of wing-ripping, skull-crunching obstacles. Bats accomplish these startling feats by using what is effectively a sonar system. Sonar is an acronym for a submarine navigational system developed during World War II, and by bats some 55 million years before. The earliest bats probably had nocturnal ancestors and may have remained nocturnal to avoid potential competition with birds in the diurnal niche. Their mastery of aerial nightlife was presumably linked to the development of 'sonar'. Sonar, or echolocation, entails gathering information about the environment from reflections (echoes) of sounds made by the bats. More distant objects return echoes after a longer delay, smaller objects return higher pitched echoes, and smooth objects produce crisper sounding echoes than rough surfaces.

Different species of bat produce different frequencies of sound at differ-ent pulse lengths. In general, high-pitched (i.e. short wavelength) sounds are better for accurate navigation, because lower sounds (longer wave-lengths) cannot resolve finely spaced obstacles. The Noctule produces a 'chonk' several times a second. This frequency of 'chonking' is rather unconversational by bat standards, considering that Daubenton's Bat can gabble out a rapid, but regular, series of clicks at 200 per second as it closes on an insect (while cruising it lets off a mere machine-gun cackle at ten per second). The Noctule flies high above the trees, whereas the Daubenton's flies among them and low over water, and this may explain the different rates at which they gather their stroboscopic image of the world. At 200 sound 'images' per second, the bat's picture of its prey probably has resolution as good as that which we receive from light through sight; at slower click rates, bats might perceive a world of jerking images rather more like a strobe-lit discotheque or early cartoon film.

Most bats' calls are ultrasonic, which means that they are inaudible to humans; this is just as well considering that at a distance of 5–10 cm the calls of the Greater Horseshoe Bat are comparable, in terms of energy, to sound intensities produced by a jet aeroplane (27 newtons per m^2 at 10 cm). The horseshoe bat's calls need to be shatteringly loud because as sound waves spread out (at 340 m per second) their intensity wanes, not merely in direct proportion to the distance travelled from the bat, but to the square power of that distance. That is, the outgoing sound loses volume very, very fast; it then has to hit a small flying insect; and, still losing volume all the way, travel back to the bat again. To have any hope of hearing such an echo, bats need very loud voices and extremely sharp ears. These features pose a problem in combination: a noise that loud would shatter ears that sensitive. Bats get around this by padding their inner ear with fat and blood-filled sinuses, and by having massive muscles attached to the bones (ossicles) of their middle ear, in particular to the stirrup and hammer bones. These muscles tighten to 'dampen' sounds (rather like cupping your hands over your ears) the instant the bat bellows, switching the hearing system on again by releasing in time to receive the incoming echoes – an astonishing feat of synchrony at colossal speed. As a twist to this tale, horseshoe bats do things differently to all other bats: they produce sounds through their noses, the leaves of their gargoyle-like faces functioning like megaphones. Horseshoe bats rely on the apparent change in frequency caused by the relative movement of a sound source and the listener. This change, called the Doppler shift, is the same phenomenon that appears to make the siren of an approaching police car grow higher as it approaches and then deeper as it passes you. By comparing the real pitch of their voice (the pitch at which it was shrieked out through their noses) and the apparent pitch of the echo returning to their ears, the horseshoe bats can calculate the relative speed of a flying insect and their own actual speed relative to a stationary tree. They are very insensitive to the emitted frequency, and exceptionally sensitive to frequencies just above and below it.

The external ears (pinnae) of bats provide directional sensitivity, and the bat's brain is wired for so-called contra-lateral inhibition. This means that stimulation of certain brain cells by sounds coming in one ear briefly switches off sensitivity to the same frequency coming in the other ear, thereby increasing the contrast between the sound intensity perceived by the two ears and helping them to find the direction of the echo.

Daubenton's Bats emit their calls through open mouths, rather than their noses. This generates sound on a front of 180°, rather than the focused 90° cone produced by the horseshoe's nose-leaves. Like other bats, Daubenton's Bats face the problem of distinguishing a profusion of echoes from objects near and far, not to mention from the calls of other bats. Their solution relies on the fact that each pulse of the bat's voice is actually made up of many (frequency modulated) components, and these descend in frequency, like the tail end of a wolf whistle, during each chirp. When the bat hears the returning echo, it knows that echoes sounding like the higher pitched part of its original pulse come from more distant objects than those at lower pitch. This is because the higher pitched part of the chirp or whistle left the bat earlier and therefore must have travelled further in order to come back at the same time.

Long-eared bats, like Natterer's Bat and the Barbastelle Bat are among those whose calls are rather quieter. This may be because their prey take evasive action if they hear bat ultrasounds. Indeed, there has been a remarkable arms race between bats and some prey, such as moths and lacewings. Noctuid moths can sense the distance (judged by the volume) and direction (by comparison of sound reaching the two sound sensors on opposite sides of its thorax) of an attacking bat, and respond by rapid retreat or, in the case of lacewings (Neuroptera), by closing their wings and nosediving. Some noctuid moths have 'stealth' scales that appear to render them invisible to sonar. Some moths may produce ultrasound to jam the bats' echolocation system. Others such as tiger (arctiid) moths are unpalatable and produce ultrasound themselves, possibly to warn bats to avoid them. When they hear

Bats have different shaped wings, depending on how they hunt their prey. Two species fly high: the Noctule (top) and Serotine (below Noctule) may chase fast-flying noctuid moths. Natterer's Bat (centre right) is usually seen around trees and like the Common Long-eared (left) picks insects off trees. Daubenton's Bat (bottom) often swoops low over water to hunt midges.

a bat homing in on them, these moths produce clicks which are remarkably similar to those made by a bat closing on its prey. The bats respond by veering away. Initially, people jumped to the conclusion that the bat mistook the moth's clicks for its own voice, and so was fooled into miscalculating its aim. However, experiments with pipistrelles proved that these bats could distinguish bat and moth clicks. Since the moths are unpalatable, the bats may be pleased to avoid them if they recognise them in time. Perhaps the moths broadcast their identity in voices similar to the bat's own because these are the sounds for which the bats are listening carefully – a split second difference in being recognised sooner rather than later could save the moth's life.

When a bat closes on its prey its calling rate accelerates, as it then needs greater accuracy, and because the risk of confusion from a surfeit of returning echoes is reduced with a very close object. At the last minute it will typically scoop up the insect in its wing or the membrane between its legs, rather like fishing with an umbrella. Smaller insects may be eaten on the wing, and larger ones carried back to a perch. Some bat species fly high and fast and take food directly in the mouth. These bats have reinforced upper palates so that insects splattering on this do not blow the bats' brains out on impact. The Red Bat (*Lasiurus borealis*) turns itself into an animated butterfly net to capture its prey. At the moment of impact, it closes its wings and tail membrane to form a basket and, in a somersaulting movement, scoops the insect from the air. The bat pokes its head into its tail basket to retrieve the prey before flying on.

Although fruit bats have a separate origin to the microchiropterans (i.e. insectivorous bats or microbats), members of one genus (*Rousettus*) also orientate using clicks. However, their clicks are at least partly audible, and are produced by the tongue (the microbats use their larynx).

Electroreceptors and touch

There is no known European example to rival the Platypus' bill: it is equipped with cells able to sense electricity. The Platypus shuts its ears, eyes and nose when it dives so that it may rely on these electroreceptors to find prey. The idea is that voltage changes caused by muscular contractions of shrimps flicking their tails can be detected by the Platypus's bill (an ability that is incapacitated if the water is polluted). Almost as uncanny is the fact that Platypuses use their whiskers to detect water currents set up by their fleeing prey in murky water. Most mammals use their whiskers to some extent to feel their way around. A striking example is the bristly tail of the mole, which allows it to feel where it is going backwards, whereas Ringed Seals use their whiskers (vibrissae) a great deal to chart a safe course in dark waters. Indeed, in Lake Saimora, east Finland, these seals are known to swim in darkness under the ice without using vision at all.

Communication

Western Polecats engage in balletic play (displaying their facial markings) involving complex body movements. The significance of many such signals remain mysterious to human observers.

Sight and sound

Society requires communication. In a herd of reindeer, antlers toss, feet stamp, tails flag on pale rumps, necks arch, males roar, females low, calves bleat, the air is redolent with whispering scents – in short, signals are positively whizzing back and forth. The clacking and creaking of the reindeer's hock bones is even reputedly a mechanism for advertising the herd's whereabouts to stragglers. Even being standoffish is socially demanding – the Common Mole scuttling through its tunnel system is forever monitoring the scents of its neighbours, and steering clear of them, and above ground the Western Polecat is similarly intent on avoiding social collisions. But when they happen, fluffed fur, erect tail and prancing gait all shriek displeasure, as the ringed mask on the polecat's face and white-fringed ears pulse out further visual messages of deterrence. Simply by being seen, the awesome broad-spanned antlers of a master Fallow Deer buck bellow the information to females that his sperm count, not to mention his record as a competitive survivor, is superior to that of the pricket beside him, just as the full beard of a man proclaims the same advantage over the stripling. Mammals reek of information and, rather like spies, each individual gleans the other's secrets while striving to give away only that which suits its own purpose – for that is what communication is: the process whereby signals from one modify the behaviour of others.

It may pay prey to signal to predators that they have been spotted, either because the predator will call off the hunt when it realises that its cover is blown, or because the signal communicates that the individual prey is particularly hale and hearty and therefore pointless to chase. At least the first of these messages appears to be sent by Brown Hares to Red Foxes. Hares feeding in the open remain unflustered by foxes foraging in the vicinity, although they clearly keep an eye on them. However, if the fox approaches within 50 m the hare will stand on its hind legs, openly displaying its white underside to the fox, before resuming its meal. The message is presumably that it would be a waste of time for all concerned if the fox was to attempt to sneak up on the hare. On the other hand, if a fox stumbles upon a hare at close quarters the hare will not flaunt itself, but prepares to make a speedy escape (which is also how they react to dogs, which may have the stamina or speed to course them). Hares probably flaunt themselves at foxes to make absolutely sure the fox realises it has been spotted and thus that an attack is pointless. In most cases this would be an honest signal, in that an adult hare can easily outrun a fox, but it remains to be seen whether a lame or sick hare will stand up in an attempt to bluff the fox!

Mammals communicate through sight, sound, touch and smell (especially the latter, see p. 185), but each of these senses has different qualities. Expressions and postures convey information instantaneously, and with great capacity for subtlety, over short distances under good visibility. However, at least some visual signals, such as fur colour, cannot readily be switched off. This brings possible disadvantages if, for example, flamboyant attire attracts not only mates but also predators. Scent can transmit messages even in the absence of the signaller, whereas sound carries over a great distance. Mammals adapt their communication to their circumstances; some countrymen claim that Roe Deer in dense forests engage in duels of territorial barking, while those in more open country employ visual displays. The physical qualities of different sounds mean that some are suited to particular functions. For example, some monkeys produce calls for communicating within their troop at the same volume as those sending territorial messages to distant neighbours, but the former are at much higher frequency (e.g. 3,000 Hz versus 300 Hz) with the effect that they attenuate much more readily (the same phenomenon explains why you hear the high-frequency crack of nearby thunder, but only the low-frequency rumble of a distant storm). So, despite the similar volume of the two calls, those that need not have a long-distance function do not carry so far, thereby minimising the risk of their being overheard by unwelcome ears such as those of predators.

In terms of both its haunting beauty and its audible range of up to 10 km, the wolf's howl is the ultimate in long-range communication among terrestrial mammals, carrying the furthest of all calls. Surprise encounters between neighbouring wolf packs are very dangerous for all concerned. Not so long ago biologists believed that animals rarely killed their own kind, a belief that was supported by the argument that such behaviour would be contrary to the good of the species. However, in some areas, strife between neighbouring packs is the principal cause of adult wolf mortality, and this accords with modern thinking that individuals act for their own good with general disregard for any consequences for their species (see p. 36). Considering the mortal risks of pack skirmishes, and thus the importance of avoiding chance encounters, one might expect packs to howl frequently to ensure that all parties were fully informed of each other's whereabouts at all

Brown Hares stand up to advertise to foraging foxes that they have spotted them and therefore that a chase would be futile, merely a waste of energy for all concerned.

times. However, precisely because communication is for the signaller's benefit, not the common good, most packs only howl infrequently – perhaps once or twice daily. The problem with howling too often is that, far from minimising conflict, it discloses the howlers' whereabouts to potential rivals (and potential prey). Since strength of numbers is the determining factor in battles between wolf packs, this problem is obviously more pressing for members of smaller packs, and made all the worse by the fact that howling in chorus probably discloses their strength as well as their position. Not surprisingly, larger packs howl more often than smaller ones, whereas lone wolves which have no territory at all generally keep silent while they trespass. The story is full of intriguing paradoxes (for example, why do small packs ever howl?) and prompts the question of how easy is it for wolves to estimate pack size from howling (it is difficult for biologists). Nonetheless, the general rule seems to be that packs only give away their position by howling when they have something important to defend, such as cubs or a fresh carcass. Otherwise it pays to adopt a low profile, keeping neighbours guessing as to each other's whereabouts. Indeed, one study of American wolves reported that when a pack heard its neighbours howling, its tendency to reply depended on whether or not the listeners had recently made a kill. If they had nothing special to defend they generally stole away silently, but they replied on 80% of occasions when they had a fresh carcass, and only 30% of occasions when their kill was largely eaten and hardly worth defending.

The wolf's problem of estimating a rival pack's size from their howls has led biologists to borrow an idea from P.C. Wren's character, Beau Geste. Beau Geste was the warrior who propped up his dead companions with their rifles pointing over the ramparts, and ran frantically from one to the other, firing to give the enemy the impression of a fully manned fort! Perhaps the pattern of howling by a pack is designed to fool the opposition in just this way: howls overlap and make it hard to distinguish individuals, a problem made all the worse because wolves vary the pitch and intensity of their voices during a chorus, and all these sounds echo. Certainly humans struggle to count the voices in a wolf chorus (although they get no selective advantage from doing so!) But why don't genuinely large packs make even more noise to broadcast their size? It turns out that the human brain can only retain five to nine sounds in its short-term memory; if wolf memories are similarly limited they would not be able to hold in their heads the sounds of enough voices to count the members of a very large pack. They would lose count at about ten. In that case there would be no point in either a large pack sounding, or a small one bluffing to sound, bigger than ten members.

Indeed, their line of argument seems rather weak – after all, a lynch mob sounds decidedly different from an angry neighbour, whether or not you can count the individual voices.

Dangerous contests are not confined to wolves; among adult bull Musk Oxen 5% to 10% die annually in battles over females, some 60% of male Narwhals suffer broken tusks during jousts over mates, and about 30% of Red Deer stags face permanent injury during their reproductive lives. The gravity of these risks is reflected in the lengths to which many mammals go to avoid fights. Rival Red Deer stags begin a contest for a harem by roaring. The size of a stag is directly reflected in the depth of his voice, and his stamina is mirrored in the rate at which he can bellow. Duel-by-roaring is very taxing and loosely speaking is the auditory equivalent to a 'press-ups' contest. Contestants may roar eight times a minute during shouting matches which leave the participants badly winded. (On average a stag may roar for several minutes on end and may, breathtakingly, average two roars per

Body language is important in mammalian communication. A subordinate wolf (top left) adopts an 'intention to play' posture and a 'play face' in response to the playful attack-threat coupled with high tail carriage of the dominant animal. As an adult sniffs it (below right), an immature wolf rolls into a submissive posture with its ears back and down and adopts a submissive 'grin'.

minute throughout the day!) As the rut wears on, the stags visibly lose condition and their stamina in roaring matches declines. Roaring ability is such a good indicator of a stag's fighting prowess that most potential fights can be settled without recourse to violence. However, those stags that are evenly matched in roaring then engage in 'parallel walks', strutting along side by side and presumably further eyeing-up each other's fighting prowess. Only after all these stages have failed to resolve the contest do they resort to head-on clashes of antlers, at horrendous risk to both parties.

Why then, do wimpish stags not cheat by roaring more deeply, or why do members of smaller wolf packs not howl at twice the rate (or try ventriloquism) to convince their rivals that they are more fearful opponents? As soon as communication is understood as a tool by which the signaller tries to manipulate rather than to inform the receiver, then the question arises as to why individuals do not cheat. The answer seems to be that signals used in such assessments as fighting ability and attraction to mates have evolved precisely because they are resistant to cheating: a small stag simply cannot roar as deeply as a large one, and an exhausted one cannot roar at the rate of a fit one. Furthermore, it may be that in such contests bluffs are called so frequently that cheats would soon be uncovered. However, their inability to cheat at roaring does not thwart young stags. They opt for a different ruse, imitating females in their posture and behaviour as they insinuate themselves into a harem. Once in among the hinds, they attempt to filch occasional matings from an unwary harem master. Indeed, an increasing number of studies are exposing matrimonial fidelity as a myth among mammals: cuckolding is common among species ranging from Eurasian Badgers to Aardwolves. Ornithologists have discovered many more examples, among which the case of the Pied Flycatcher is particularly entertaining. These birds indulge in so-called polyterritoriality. That is, males may live a dual existence, defending two territories, separated by about 200 m, both containing a female who is said to be unaware of her mate's entanglements elsewhere. However, it is not clear exactly where the last laugh lies, because it turns out that the 'offspring' of polyterritorial males often bear a surprising resemblance to neighbouring males. It seems that the male flitting bigamously back and forth is unable to keep a sufficiently close watch on either mate and so frequently ends up a cuckold himself.

When an animal sends a signal to another, it is likely to be honest. This is because there is a huge cost to being cheated and therefore evolution has fashioned individuals to be extremely discerning when they are evaluating displays so that the risk of them being duped is reduced. For example, a female who was seduced by a male display that was merely a hollow boast

Broken weapons, such as this Narwhal's tusk (above), can be a serious handicap.
A third of Red Deer stags may sustain injury or damage, such as a broken antler (left), whilst fighting for hinds.

would end up with her young sired by a poorer quality individual than a female who was more discerning. Discerning interpreters have forced displayers to come up with specially evolved signals that are both efficient at conveying the message and cannot easily be faked. This is because, respectively, the cost of missing the message is high to both parties, and because recipients simply ignore messages that can readily be bluffed. The roaring of red deer stags is just such a case, because it can only be performed at a high rate by stags that are genuinely robust.

There are thought to be two types of honest signal. One is called a handicap, because it involves individuals showing off in a way that genuinely debilitates them. The idea is that the observer interprets the display on the assumption that only the highest quality individuals can afford to squander their resources (a rich man might impress a girl by throwing a banquet in her honour – the cost is real and makes him poorer, but it would bankrupt a poorer man). The size of a stag's antlers might thus truly reveal the resources they could afford to deflect from muscle-building into ornament. The second type of honest signal is called a revealing signal, because it infallibly calibrates the sender's qualities, but does not do so by the bearing of a handicap. For example, it costs nothing for somebody to show off large biceps, but doing so reveals accurately the capacity to lift heavy weights. It is not always clear whether a given signal is a handicap, or revealing, or both. For example, to the extent that roaring exhausted a stag and thus reduced its fighting potential, it could be interpreted as functioning as a handicapping signal. However, to the extent that only top quality males are capable of roaring, but roaring does not diminish their capacity to fight, it could be interpreted as a revealing signal. Irrespective of the way in which they ensure honesty, signals must be clear. Signals commonly arise from so-called intention movements. If an ancestral Golden Jackal bared its teeth before biting an adversary then it would clearly benefit both parties if they were, respectively, attuned to detecting this signal and to emitting it unambiguously. The result is that a teeth-baring snarl, with no subsequent bite, evolves as a threat. The process whereby movements and structures are modified to improve their communicative function is called ritualisation.

Sometimes calling seems particularly helpful. For example, the gruff yelp of a vixen instantly silences her raucous cubs as danger approaches. One would think that there must surely be a risk involved in shouting out the warning since the act of doing so might well focus the predator's attention on the caller itself. In the case of bird alarms it has long been asserted, although not yet demonstrated, that the physical qualities of alarm calls make them particularly hard to pinpoint in order to minimise this risk. Studies of Belding's Ground Squirrel in North America suggest that raising the alarm against an approaching weasel is hazardous and that the squirrels do it only when they have a vested interest in thwarting the hunt. Females of this species settle near their mother's dens, while males disperse (see p. 264) and keep wandering even after they have fathered a litter. The result is that females spend their lives in the close company of their relations, while males are without family ties. Males rarely raise the alarm, and the tendency of females to do so, rather than simply ducking for cover, depends on whether or not they happen to have relatives living in the neighbourhood. In a related species, males give alarm calls before but not after dispersal. This suggests that the heroism of the sentinel is tempered by the reward it can enjoy due to its neighbour's survival (the reward being paid in genes snatched back from the predator's talons). Of course, in some societies it is easy to imagine that even if the signal is aimed at kin, in practice a mixture of relatives and strangers will pay heed to an alarm, for instance when a rabbit stamps its foot or flashes its rump, or when a Red Squirrel chatters, or a chamois whistles. But this benefit to non-kin may be only accidental rather than altruistic. In contrast, warning unrelated animals in a group could be adaptive if it starts a stampede which confuses the predator and lowers the warner's chance of being eaten. Equally, there may be advantages to giving the alarm that overwhelm kinship considerations, such as attempting to reduce the overall success of a predator in your district, so that it transfers its attention elsewhere, or simply broadcasting to the predator that the caller has spotted the danger and is too alert to be caught. On the other hand, the idea that individuals might raise the alarm on a tit-for-tat basis, each helping others in the long-term expectation of the favour being returned, seems implausible in that such a trusting arrangement would be prone to corruption by cheats. Such tit-for-tat cooperation can work if there is a high chance of retaliating on a cheat to keep him honest, but that is not an option if you were eaten while the cheat prospered. Incidentally, in some social species alarm calling is highly coded – Vervet Monkeys have different calls to specify avian versus terrestrial, and grave versus trifling dangers. Ground squirrels and various mongooses similarly call differently to distinguish aerial and ground predators. The importance of reliability of signals is emphasised by experiments in which taped Vervet calls were played out of context – thereafter the individual whose voice had been played and which then appeared to be giving the false (artificial) alarms was no longer trusted by other members of its troop.

Some mammalian communications are beyond the range of our hearing. Infant rats, displaced from their nests, produce ultrasonic squeaks which prompt their mothers to carry them to safety. Shrews also produce high-frequency, pulsed calls whereas their distant relatives the Madagascan tenrecs are said to use the echoes of their clicking calls as a crude pathfinding

Alarm signals take many forms: the Roe Deer buck barks (right); the European Beaver smacks the water's surface with its tail (below).

A Greater Mole rat communicates its territorial occupancy to neighbours by drumming its head on the roof of its tunnel.

system. It is uncertain whether the baleen (mysticete) whales use their calls for echolocation, but the toothed (odontocete) whales certainly do (see p. 169). The baleen whales produce complex underwater sounds; the song of the Humpback Whale is famous for its remarkable complexity of frequency and structure. On arrival at their breeding grounds, male Humpback Whales start singing, generally in shallow coastal water (20–40 m deep) with smooth sea beds which may help their voices to carry. The song is unique to each whale and can be heard more than 30 km away (depending on the water layer in which they are swimming). Each song may last half an hour, and there appear to be dialects characteristic of whales originating from particular regions. Whale sounds have great communicative potential. Long-finned Pilot Whales have seven categories of whistle, some of which may identify the caller, but at least two of which indicate mood. The clicks produced almost continuously by Sperm Whales swimming at depths of greater than 200 m may signal precisely the reproductive prowess of the caller, rather like a peacock's tail or stag's roar (see p. 179). Each click, audible at least 30 km away, actually contains a succession of pulses of sound. These arise because of the structure of the melon apparatus in the whale's head: as the click is emitted from the whale's mouth it also echoes back through the head until it hits bone, ricochets forward and makes the second pulse within the click. The interval between the two pulses (the click and its echo) are directly proportional to the length of the Sperm Whale's head, and thus of its overall size. This information might be decoded by a listening whale miles away. Perhaps competition between males or selection of males by females has led to big-headed whales: not only are male Sperm Whales bigger than females, but their heads are proportionally much bigger, as are those of several other whales suspected of having a polygynous mating system.

How a sound is heard and perceived is equally important as how it is emitted. To humans, the Humpback Whale's call seems incredibly slow: to whistle through one verse of the song takes half an hour. But who knows how the whale perceives the sound – considering the slow metabolism that comes inevitably with the Humpback's giant body, half an hour may seem like an instant, and the verse of its song may sound to listening whales much like one stanza from a canary sounds to us (or possibly like one stanza from a canary sounds to another canary). It is intriguing to consider the implications of the fact that while some processes happen at similar speeds in large and small bodies (e.g. the speed at which nerves transmit messages), other things happen at size-dependent rates.

Both the Pygmy Shrew and the African Elephant experience about the same number of heartbeats in a lifetime (approximately 800 million), but the shrew's whir past in a year while the elephant's heart ticks along for 70 years. Does this mean that the shrew perceives life racing past whereas time drags interminably for the elephant? If humans think that the Humpback Whale takes its time over a verse of its song, just imagine what it would sound like to a shrew!

Scent

The glands of the skin are at the very root of mammalian success. Some glands are modified to secrete oils which protect the hair, some produce sweat, and both functions facilitate endothermy (see p. 58). Other glands produce milk (see p. 75). The revolutionary success of mammals also owes much to their communicative powers and these too, rather unexpectedly, can be traced in large measure to skin glands. The smelly products of skin glands have been grist to the evolutionary mill which has fashioned them into messages, the so-called social odours.

The contemporary mammalian body is a veritable perfumery, with a nose-bombarding profusion of glands tucked into a surprising array of bodily nooks and crannies: under the chin of male rabbits, in pockets beneath the eyes of most deer, under the dark ellipse of bristles on top of foxes' tails, in the genet's perineal pouch (between anus and genitals), in a large cavern beneath the badger's tail, along the flanks of water voles and Pygmy Shrews, in a pouch encircling the mongoose's anus, on the cheeks of Wildcats and Grey Squirrels, the salivary glands of Wild Boar, the prepuce (foreskin) of beavers, the underside of the Stoat, the tarsus (heel) of the White-tailed Deer, the feet of the Golden Jackal, beside the eyeballs and in the tear ducts of hamsters and hares, the lips of lemmings, the base of the tail of male Wood Mice and white-toothed shrews, the rump of Field Voles and the eyelids of Common Shrews. The anal regions of many mammals (all European carnivores for example) are a hotbed of odorous glands. In foxes, weasels, martens and otters these form paired flask-shaped vessels, one opening on either side of the anus, their contents either coating droppings or being dripped out voluntarily. In otters the glands produce a viscous jelly left at sprainting sites (latrines), and in polecats they have been enlarged to produce a foul-smelling repellent to predators (few predators would choose to tangle with the osmic barrage produced by skunks, which have taken the polecat's approach to an extreme). These many and varied glands surround their bearers in a penumbra of scent laden with messages to which, for the most part, we are oblivious. When a horse snorts at you, for example, it is actually showering you with the odours produced by glands nestled in its nostrils.

The existence, far less the function, of these odorous clarion calls in the wind are largely lost on people due to our hopeless noselessness. Sensitivity to scent is roughly indicated by the surface area of the scrolled membranes coating the nasal turbinates. In humans, unfolded and ironed out, these measure about $5 \, cm^2$, whereas from a dog's nose they measure $200 \, cm^2$. This difference goes some way to explaining why dogs can smell, for example, vinegar at one millionth of the concentration at which people can do so. Of course, the comparison may be slightly unfair if dogs have been selected for some special reason to be sensitive to vinegar (it might be a similar smell to the acids characteristic of foetid meat). Indeed, even among people there are great differences in sensitivity: women are about one thousand times more sensitive than men when it comes to detecting particular musky odours similar to those derived from men's sex hormones (most men cannot smell them at all), and this sensitivity depends on the stage of a woman's reproductive cycle.

Transmitting information about reproductive condition is a widespread function of social odours. Other messages may include individual and group identity. Members of a clan of badgers, especially the dominant males, press their bottoms against each other in a sort of olfactory kiss which leaves on the recipient a shared community scent emanating from a whitish goo produced in the sub-caudal pouch. Similarly, just as the dialects of whale calls may differ regionally, so the olfactory 'fingerprint' characteristic of populations of, for example, water voles differs.

Mammals produce scents from every nook and cranny, as illustrated by these deer. The preputial tuft of the Fallow Deer (1) is soaked in urinary fragrances. The muntjac (2) rubs the secretions of its frontal glands on the ground. Axis Deer (3) thrash the vegetation, which doubtless makes a visual and olfactory landmark, while rubbing with its frontal glands in a posture known as 'preaching'. A Fallow Deer (4) rubs the secretions of its ant-orbital glands on its companions. The Red Deer (5) wallows in a mud bath of urine, and probably, ejaculate. An anxious Reindeer with tail aloft (6) wafts scent from its caudal glands and leaves a trail with its pedal (foot) glands. The faeces (7) of all these species probably also convey messages. Many deer have tarsal glands (8), the hairs of which are specially structured to disperse scent and can be erected during social encounters.

Eurasian Badgers have a large pocket of scent beneath their tail. The copiousness and colour of this secretion varies with the season, and between the sexes. As well as using this to mark their environment, badgers 'bum-press' to smear the scent over fellow members of their social group.

Many scent glands appear to be involved in courtship, as evidenced by their great enlargement during the mating season. For example, the skin gland situated on the top of Red Foxes' tails (about 10 cm from the base) swells up in males during midwinter at the same time as their testes become active. In this case it may be no accident that many encounters between foxes involve lashing and arching of the tail, movements which may well waft scent from this so-called 'violet gland' under the nose of an adversary or a mate. Indeed, in this case not only is the gland marked with dark guard fur and sprouts of yellowish bristles specially designed to disseminate the odour, but the end of the tail is often flagged with a white tip which presumably accentuates its movements in the gloaming. The preputial gland of male Fallow Deer is active only during the rut, and male rabbits also have a gland whose activity seems to cycle in phase with their sex hormones. In rabbits this gland is under the chin. Males rub their chin glands on objects throughout their territories. Since male rabbits contribute minimal direct paternal care, their main contribution in a polygynous society is to bestow upon their offspring their competitive prowess (see p. 255). Thus, for the female, choosing the best quality mate is crucial. The quality (and quantity) of their scent may be a reliable indicator of male fertility, because the sex hormones that stimulate the glands are hard to fake. Among rabbits, and many other mammals, the most dominant males tend to have the highest levels of circulating (in the bloodstream) sex hormones, and this is reflected in their production of both odour and abundant sperm. (House Mice, as well as rabbits, can be distinguished as dominant or subordinate on the basis of the quality of their odours alone.)

Male rabbits have chin glands, and females mate with males with the most active glands. This may be because the sex hormones that determine a male's status are also involved in the development of its scent glands, and therefore copious secretion is an indicator of high status amongst males.

Everyone who has cohabited with a bitch on heat, and thus experienced a siege of male dogs, will be aware of the power of female odours to signal reproductive status. The signal may be a particular chemical, and one such has been identified in the urine of oestrous vixen Red Foxes. However, in the Brown Rat, although the perfumes of the haunch contain no such single sexual totem, the blend of scents does change to give a subtle signal of the female's receptivity. This changing blend is a chemical 'image' reminiscent of the difference between a friendly and a hostile face, the message being communicated by the complete face (or the complete smell) rather than the minute individual changes of eyebrow and lip. The whole character of the perfume of a female rat's haunch is different when she is sexually receptive.

In addition to messages coded in the quality of scent, a different signal of oestrus may lie in the quantity of perfume produced by Brown Rats. Rat skin contains oil glands which produce sebum (the stuff of adolescent pimples and greasy hair), and the flow of sebum is affected by the concentration of the hormone oestrogen in the blood. It seems that high levels of oestrogen, associated with the female being on heat, switch off the flow of sebum from the haunch but, if anything, have the opposite effect on the shoulders. This gives rise to the possibility of the self-calibrating rat: a male rat detecting a difference in the quantity of secretion from head to tail as he ran his nose along a female's body could know that she was on heat.

Females selecting a mate may take note of the quality of his odours, but this may be an insufficient guide to his potential. The luck of the draw is such that even some well-endowed males may fail to hold a territory, and such tenancy may be the only important indicator of a male's desirability to a female. This probably explains why female rabbits, when presented with a choice between otherwise similar males, will select one whose odour matches that of scent marks in the vicinity. This matching process may be her guarantee that she has selected the rightful territory owner, rather than some interloping poseur. Indeed, in a wider context, such scent matching may be the basis on which scent marking functions in territorial defence. We know that most itinerant individuals are unlikely to fight most territorial residents, despite coveting the latter's property, because such a challenge is likely to be very dangerous. Territorial occupants are, almost by definition, high-quality combatants with a proven record, and with so much to lose that they will fight with no holds barred. Therefore, as an interloper trespasses it is important that it should be able to recognise, among those of its kind that it meets, the territory owner from other passers-by. Such recognition may hinge upon comparing the scent marks that permeate the territory with the odour of the owner when met face to face (or nose to gland).

Just because a mammal makes scent marks in its territory is no reason to presume that the scent has a territorial function. After all, in territorial species, individuals spend almost all their time on their 'property' and so if they are going to deposit scent marks for whatever reason, they will inevitably place them in their territories. Nonetheless, the idea that scent marks are territorial signposts has so caught the popular imagination that it is commonplace for people to talk of scent marking and territory marking as synonymous, and to imagine that intruders will respond to the olfactory signature as they would have done to its author had they met in person. This conclusion is quite unwarranted, and observations of an intruder simply sniffing a scent mark and turning on its heels as if having read a 'no entry' sign, are rare (although it has been recorded in wolves and Red Foxes). It may well be that one among the many functions of some social odours is territorial defence, but this may more often operate by affecting the intruder's behaviour when he or she (although it tends to be males) meets the owner rather than by affecting his or her behaviour at the moment he or she smells the mark. Nonetheless, the absence, or waning of scent marks may rapidly signal the absence or enfeeblement of a territory's occupant. For example, for most of the year male and female moles defend territories, each of which supports only one tenant. The moles' tunnels are heavily daubed in the scent of their preputial glands, which is smeared along their burrows as they travel. If a resident mole vacates its territory, neighbours readjust their borders after a delay of some 24 hours. This interval may be prolonged to three or four days if secretions from the occupant are experimentally renewed in its absence. It seems that the presence of the scent postpones, for a day or so, the moment at which the remaining moles notice their neighbour's absence. So in this case scent does serve a territorial function.

Social odours are carried not only in the secretions of glands, but also in bodily excretions: urine and faeces. Sometimes urine is applied to the signaller, sometimes to the recipient, and sometimes to the environment. Goats lather it into their beards, Red and Fallow Deer squirt it onto their undersides and, as do Elk and Bison, they urinate into a mud bath in which they then wallow to coat themselves in a perfumed mud-pack. The most specialised urine-wafting apparatus is found on Musk Oxen, whose name

Scent is crucial to communication amongst most mammals. Many not only sniff lightweight, volatile molecules, but also suck heavy molecules into a cavity in the nasal cavity, called the vomero-nasal organ, where it is tasted. This young male wild goat is shown in 'cut-away', drawing a female's urine (shaded black) up the duct into this organ. Male ungulates adopt a particular lip-curling expression, called flehmen, when sampling in this way. Male Goats often squirt urine forward to splatter on the beard which thus becomes an odorous, as well as visual, statement of their status.

pays tribute to their osmic pre-eminence. Displaying male Musk Oxen can evert their prepuce to form a 12 cm long tube fringed in a curtain of special urine-soaked hairs encrusted with urinary salts. This censer is swished from side to side as the males posture at each other, the resulting sprinkling effect soaking the skirt of hairs that hang like a pelmet around the oxen's underside. Meanwhile, Musk Oxen rub their preorbital glands (in front of the eyes) against their knees to release another scent. A similar principle is adopted by camels, who soak their tails in urine and then wag them at their companions, and female tamarin monkeys who, when in oestrus, flirt by rubbing their tails on the urinary fragrances of their genitals and then flaunting the perfumed flag beneath the males' noses.

Male Red Foxes and male rabbits are among those who urinate upon their mates, possibly a cheaper approach to the same goal that motivates a man to buy his favourite perfume for his mate. Male rabbits mark prospective mates by leaping over the female during a ritualised dance, and sprinkling the scent as they pass overhead. But by far the most common deployment of scent marks is in the environment. Many rodents dribble urine along their runways, male members of the cat family spray it backwards in a fine aerosol onto regular marking sites, and squirrels urinate on places where they have gnawed a visual marker on tree bark. Droppings are similarly deployed, often on visually conspicuous landmarks and at convenient nose-height to catch passing air currents. Badgers may do handstands to get their scent marks aloft. Otters leave their spraints (droppings) on top of boulders, and sometimes return so often to the same site that they accumulate their own mini-manure heaps which develop into the well-grassed otter 'seats' found, for example, on the west coast of Scotland. Indeed, spraints are such special signals that an otter may squeeze out as many as 30–40 tiny droppings in one day, rather than wasting all that communication potential in one large dropping. Fox droppings are also generally found on top of tussocks of grass or molehills. Badgers, in contrast, create latrines that comprise a collection of up to 35 small dung pits, which form cordons around the border of their territories and around their setts. The question arises as to why badgers ring their territories with latrines, whereas foxes opt for blanket coverage of droppings throughout their territories. The answer may be that only group-living mammals, like badgers, can collectively generate enough droppings to ring the whole perimeter. Indeed, perhaps the number of droppings in a latrine is a statement to neighbours about the collective territorial strength of the local occupants. Making a show of urination is linked with dominance: the dominant male and female wolves in a pack will do most of the urine marking, ostentatiously cocking their legs to leave many scent tokens along their trails. By contrast, subordinates squat to evacuate their bladders in one large puddle. Lone wolves depart from travel routes whenever they need to urinate or defecate, anxious to avoid detection. In some cases it seems that wolves urine-mark at a higher rate when near their territorial boundaries, so increasing the likelihood of an intruder stumbling upon a mark.

House Mice have such a highly developed system of scent marking that it enables them, in effect, to see in the dark. Mice live in territorial family groups in which a breeding pair and their adult offspring all mark extensively with urine. This network of marks coats every object in their environment, and allows them to negotiate, in total darkness, narrow bridges and to sense, through their noses, precipices. Theirs is the world of the scent-scape. As they breathe in across the stinkorama, little olfactory stalagmites are scattered amidst the general veneer of odour. These olfactory beacons may stand 3 cm tall, and arise where repeated urinations bind with dust to form a solid monument. These stalagmites are marked especially by the dominant male and breeding female. It seems they serve to pronounce the presence of the territorial animals to their offspring and their neighbours, the males broadcasting their dominance, the females their breeding status. This information has far-reaching effects on its recipients (see p. 194).

Mice provide proof that odours disclose individual identity. Some strains of House Mice have been bred so selectively in captivity that they are now genetically identical. It is as if all the mice of such a strain were identical twins. Among the genes of mice (and other mammals) there is a set concerned with immunological mechanisms, and these are called the Major Histocompatability Complex (MHC) of genes. The genetic make-up of these mice is known in such detail that it is possible to say that out of all the tens of thousands of genes that make up the identity of a mouse, two mice differ by only one gene in the MHC. The point of this remarkable story is that a mouse trained to recognise other mice by the smell of their urine, can distinguish the scents of those individuals that differ by only one gene! Although nobody knows whether wild mice ever make such fine distinctions in nature, the experiment shows that they have the potential to do so. Considering the almost innumerable ways in which normal mice (i.e. not artificially bred populations of 'twins') differ genetically, we can safely assume that mammals that can distinguish individuals that differ by only one gene, smell a veritable blast of identity and personal information in each other's odours.

Scent also plays an important role in interactions between species, between predator and prey for example – Brown Rats have an innate fear of the scent of Red Fox urine. Hedgehogs may borrow the protective smell of unpalatable toads – they have special digestive enzymes to digest the poison produced by the toads' skin which protects them from most other predators. Hedgehogs actually chew on the skin, and then froth at the mouth while they spread the saliva over their spines. The smell of toad, and the poison itself, may protect the hedgehog from predators such as badgers, which can otherwise easily overcome the defensive spines. Another possibility is that the toad poison kills some of the fleas and ticks that nestle safely in the prickly sanctuary where the hedgehog cannot groom.

Hedgehog anointing: olfactory camouflage or insecticidal shampoo?

Primers

The powers of suggestion exerted by some odours would gladden the hearts of Orwell's Thought Police. Perfumes work not just on the nose, but on the ovaries and testes. Just a whiff can be enough to throw the reproductive activities of some mammals into overdrive, or even into turmoil. Scents which influence behaviour indirectly, through their effects on reproductive physiology, are called primers. They have the potency to switch oestrus on or off, and even to terminate a pregnancy.

A young male House Mouse, developing under the shadow of scent from an adult male's urine takes longer to reach puberty than it otherwise would, even if it never meets the older male face to face. Similarly, a young female who might normally mate at 37 days old will not do so until she is 57 days old if she lives in an atmosphere laden with the scent of an adult female. In contrast, an adolescent male House Mouse's progress to puberty is hastened by the seductive whiff of a breeding female in the air. Similar effects have been noted in rats and many other mouse-like rodents, and in sheep and goats, but the pervasive influence of perfumes is probably far more widespread. For example, among the many traits shared by mice and humans is that the oestrous periods of females cycle in synchrony when they live together and, at least in mice, this synchrony can be induced by odour alone. What are the advantages of breeding synchrony? In some cases it provides the opportunity for communal care of the young, in others it may reduce the risk of predation to each infant by so swamping the predators with defenceless young that they cannot eat them all at once. In some complicated mammalian societies breeding synchrony ensures that youngsters have playmates with which to socialise, and will grow up with contemporaries with which they may form coalitions in adulthood.

The smell of an adult male House Mouse, in breeding condition, kick-starts the female mouse's reproductive system – between 48 and 72 hours after exposure to the male's urine, she will exhibit sexual behaviour (solicit male courtship) and come into oestrus. This effect on the female depends on the testosterone levels of the male, so there is a tangled web in which the odours of one sex affect the sex hormones and nervous system of the opposite sex, which in turn produces fragrances that affect its mate, and so on. Since the odours are made up of airborne molecules of scent, and since the sex hormones are molecular messages carried in the bloodstream, it is not too fanciful to envisage a continuum of molecular messages between the reproductive organs of individuals, some of which are conveyed within their bodies and some of which pass between them.

Perhaps the most dramatic primer effect involves termination of pregnancies. Collared Lemmings and Wood Mice are among the many rodents whose pregnancies terminate if the pregnant female finds herself in the odorous ambience of a new breeding male. That the body odour of a strange male can provoke a female to abort her pregnancy is graphic evidence that in some species the battle to win females is not over at fertilisation. If a new male usurps the original mate then it is not too late to abandon the pregnancy and start again. One of the first things a victorious male might do is saturate his range with his scent marks, which may explain why male urine alone is sufficient to terminate the pregnancies of rats, mice and lemmings. Furthermore, the female may face an even worse alternative – if the new male perceives that the infants are not his he may withdraw paternal care or worse. While male Collared Lemmings tend the pups they have fathered, they often kill those they have not. The latter course of action not only eliminates the progeny of rivals, it causes the female to return to oestrus after 21 days, rather than the normal 28 days. By terminating pregnancy when she senses the smell of a newcomer's success, the female may simply be hastening the inevitable and preparing to put time and energy into some young with better prospects.

Pregnant female mice and voles differ somewhat in their susceptibility to male odours. Mouse-like rodents are spontaneous ovulators (see p. 74) and their females terminate pregnancies when exposed to the odour of alien males (this phenomenon is widely referred to as the Bruce Effect). However, this post-fertilisation mate-selection only functions up until the time (about four days) at which the ova implant in the mother's uterus (see p. 71). Voles, on the other hand, are induced ovulators, and although males' urine is sufficient to accelerate a female's maturity, it is less effective at blocking her pregnancy. However, a strange male's presence can cause female voles to

*Male Collared Lemmings tend pups they have
sired, but kill those sired by other males.*

resorb (dissolve) their foetuses, and, unlike mice, this effect operates even
after the foetuses have implanted.

Producing the scents that are so influential in the sex lives of male
mammals has a cost, and a measure of that cost can be seen in the testes.
Essentially, testes have two components, the seminiferous tubules which
produce the sperm, and the interstitial cells and so-called Leydig cells which
produce sex hormones, notably testosterone. The balance of these two
components varies markedly between different species. In the testes of
some, such as House Mice, the great emphasis is on sperm-producing tissue,
whereas in the testes of others, such as the European Mole, hormone-producing
cells predominate. The hormone testosterone stimulates the growth of
specifically male characters, such as some scent glands. For example, the
size and activity of the Red Fox's testes vary seasonally, and as the male's
testes expand in preparation for the midwinter mating season, so too does
the volume of his violet gland (an elliptical patch of scent-coated bristles on
top of the tail, near its base). Ultimately, therefore, the costs of producing
some scents can be seen in the proportion of the testes devoted to producing
the hormones that catalyse their manufacture. Inevitably, energy is in short
supply, and so natural selection has the opportunity to cause the design of
males to differ depending on whether it pays them to emphasise prolific

sperm production at the expense of, for example, muscle building or pumping out influential odours. Which of these options will pay the best reproductive dividends depends on the mating system of the species in question – those that engage in sperm competition (see p. 227) will have testes built largely of seminiferous tubules. Why the mole has opted for the other extreme is uncertain, because the nuances of male rivalry and female choice in mole courtship are unknown, but it may be that life in a subterranean tunnel system has put a huge emphasis on scent in seduction and rivalry.

Even individual males within a species may differ in the allocation of resources between the two components of their testes, depending on their social status and therefore their likely relationship with females. This is the case for male capybaras, sheep-sized rodents of which several may live in a strict dominance hierarchy within mixed-sex groups in South American wetlands. Capybara males flaunt a preposterously carbuncular scent gland aloft their snout, and the most dominant male in the group has the largest such gland and the largest testes. However, the larger testes of dominant males owe their greater bulk entirely to extra interstitial cells, presumably because these top males put all their energy into producing extra testosterone because their goal is to monopolise the female to the extent that even a relatively small quantity of sperm will be sufficient to guarantee a fertilisation. Subordinate males, in contrast, can sneak only fleeting access to females, while the dominant is distracted; each may get only one shot at the target and so opts for a scatter-gun approach, turning a greater proportion of its testicular workspace over to producing as many sperm as it can in order to maximise the chance of successfully fertilising the female on the rare occasions on which it gets a chance.

PART THREE

MAMMAL REPRODUCTION

Chapter ten

Breeding

Why have sex?

The question of why mammals, or any other animal, mate at all has no obvious answer when the huge advantages of reproducing asexually are considered. If an animal has survived long enough to reproduce, it clearly has a successful set of genes. In asexual reproduction an individual simply replicates itself, passing a full complement of that successful set of genes on to all of its offspring. In sexual reproduction, the individual produces eggs or sperm that contain only a half set of its genes, thereby throwing away half of a proven recipe for success, and splices them with another half set from a different individual. This might be all right if each sexually reproducing individual produced twice as many offspring with half sets of its genes as it would have done if it had produced whole sets asexually, but they do not. Because a female's eggs provide all the yolky nourishment needed for the embryo (the sperm provides none), there is a limit on how many eggs a female can afford to churn out, and that limit is the same whether she is reproducing sexually or asexually. The result is that, in comparison to asexual reproduction, sexual reproduction halves the chances of any given gene getting into the next generation. Since reproduction is all about genes maximising their chances of getting into the next generation, the existence of sexual reproduction is a puzzle.

The first really convincing explanation for the evolution of sex was proposed in 1980 by one of the greatest biological theoreticians of the 20th century, W.D. Hamilton of Oxford University. Observing, as any farmer knows, that livestock fight a continual battle with parasites, Hamilton realised that the life cycles of these agents of disease were hugely faster than those of the creatures they afflicted. During the lifetime of a farmyard rat, the toxoplasma that afflicts it will have been through countless generations (see p. 34). The result is that parasites can evolve very much faster than can their hosts, and thus in the battle of adaptation and counter-adaptation to fend off infection, the host is always out of date. By having sex, animals reshuffle their genes at every generation, making obsolete all the adaptations parasites had just evolved to attack the previous generation. The extent to which we mammals are outrun by pathogens is neatly illustrated by the fact that the bacteria resident in each human body are likely to go through well over a million generations during the three score years and ten of their host's life. In contrast, in the seven million years since we shared an ancestor with chimpanzees there have been only 200,000 generations. In the sanitised societies of western Europe people all too readily forget the horrendous impact of parasites on the lives of people in the Third World, but we are reminded of the force of parasites by the example that in Europe many sheep farmers must dose their lambs against gut worms every three weeks if they are to grow sufficiently to reach market.

If the purpose of sex is to give your offspring immunity from parasites, it will be important for females to select parasite-resistant mates. A strain of males that is especially resistant to viruses in one generation is thus likely to father most males in the next generation. Their commonness is likely to give parasites plenty of opportunities to crack their defences, leading to a situation where the most disease-resistant strain of males of one generation may be the most susceptible in the next generation. Thus, by choosing the healthiest mates of their generation, females would be keeping one jump ahead (but only just) in the evolutionary war against marauding pathogens. This reshuffling of genes does not happen with asexual reproduction, in which genes that perform poorly in one generation go extinct when their bearers die. In contrast, in the genetic reshuffling of sex, genes that are temporarily obsolete (because a virus has cracked their code) may be tried again at subsequent reshufflings (matings) until they again come into fashion. As Hamilton wrote in 1990, 'The essence of sex in our theory is that it stores genes that are currently bad but have promise for reuse. It continually tries them in combination, waiting for a time when the focus of disadvantage has moved elsewhere.' That disease-resistance is relevant in fact as well as theory is indicated by female laboratory mice, which, when given the choice, select to mate with males whose disease-resistance genes are different to their own. Disease might also put a limit on life spans, in that lives would gain little from being longer than it takes a parasite to adapt to defeating their defences.

Hamilton's idea (that sex evolved to outmanoeuvre parasites) is unproven, but the fact that female mammals are constrained to produce a limited number of eggs, whereas males deploy their energies in other ways and produce huge numbers of sperm, has far-reaching consequences for their reproductive lives. Males are forced into intense rivalry as they compete for females and their scarce eggs. Females, safeguarding the fate of their expensive eggs, are forced to be extremely choosy about males. The result is a process called sexual selection (see p. 220).

When to give birth

In Europe's temperate climate, conditions vary widely between the seasons. Birth and infancy are precarious times in a mammal's life, times that place heavy demands on both parent and offspring. The mother must secure a good food supply to sustain the demands of lactation. Common sense, bolstered by the fact that almost all European mammals do it, suggests that it is advantageous to be born in spring or summer when the climate is clement and food at its most abundant. But this coincidence in the breeding seasons of everything from bats to bison becomes more remarkable on consideration of the difference (up to eight-fold) in the durations of their pregnancies. The Whiskered Bat mates in midwinter, the badger mates in early spring, the 210 g stoat has a pregnancy of nine to ten months, its 35 g cousin the weasel has a 34- to 37-day pregnancy. Yet they all give birth at roughly the same time.

How is this remarkable seasonal synchrony achieved? If the aim is to produce young just when conditions are ideal, then the safest bet might be to wait until there is tangible (or better, tastable) proof that food supplies are burgeoning. This appears to be exactly what the Montane Vole does: within 24 hours of eating green sprouting vegetation, females come into oestrus and the testes of males swell into spermatogenesis. However, the need for a long pregnancy rules out this approach for most European mammals, especially the big ones upon whom size imposes a long pregnancy; a bison waiting for the first flush of buds to trigger its rut would find itself giving birth sometime during the next winter! Even if the ultimate determinant of the breeding season is food supply, the need to set reproductive wheels in motion far in advance of spring often makes it necessary for the immediate (or proximate) trigger to be a predictor of future food supply rather than the food supply itself.

How might mammals anticipate the correct time to reproduce? There is an important clue in the regional variation in breeding seasons within species. Bank Voles in England generally start breeding in April, while those in the north of Scotland postpone their nuptial activities until May. Similarly, in Arctic Norway, the Common Shrew, the Northern Red-backed Vole and the Root Vole all end their breeding season in August, whereas further south they breed through September. Furthermore, Fallow Deer transported from England to New Zealand shifted their rut from September/November to March/May. Facts such as these point towards environmental (i.e. exogenous) triggers of reproduction, which may override calendars built in (i.e. endogenous) to the individual. However, lots of environmental indicators of the seasons vary together, and this makes it hard to diagnose the important ones. For example, the Bank Voles in Scotland might have suffered colder temperatures, less nourishment, shorter nights and stronger winds than their Sassenach cousins, and changes in any or all of these might indicate the passage of the seasons. The fact that Brown Hares, wherever they are in Europe, start breeding almost immediately after the shortest day of the year, suggests day length as a cue. The story is complicated, however, by exceptions to every rule: Red Deer in zoos throughout the northern hemisphere calve at much the same time irrespective of latitude, whilst those in the southern hemisphere calve six months later.

Exploring the details of seasonal timekeeping requires ingenious experiments. Through laboratory manipulations varying the proportion of each 24 hours allocated to light and dark, the role of day length (i.e. photoperiod) as a trigger for breeding in many mammals has been proved. For the Field Vole, as winter days lengthen into spring, their hormones switch into reproductive gear as day length reaches 12–14 hours. Female Field Voles kept under a regime of 12 hours of light alternating with 12 hours of darkness are some 42 days old before they mature; those under a regime of 14 hours light to 10 hours of darkness reach the same state of sexual readiness in only 17 days. This discovery begs the question of how these animals measure the time, and what feature of the day/night pattern they measure in assessing the passage of the seasons. From studies in other contexts, mammals are known to have internal clocks, such that even when kept in complete darkness their activities will follow a daily cycle (called a circadian rhythm) of approximately 24 hours. It seems that the Field Voles use their internal clocks to measure not the quantity of daylight, but its timing. That is, by exposing the voles to doses of daylight of different durations at different times it emerged that they were setting their internal watches at dawn (or what appeared to be dawn under experimental conditions), and then checking whether it was daylight during a sensitive period about 12 hours later. Only if the light was on at that critical time did the Field Voles' reproductive system 'believe' that spring had come. If the voles were exposed to a total of 12 hours (or even more) of daylight, but in bursts that happened to miss the critical 12-hour check-up, then they failed to breed.

Each species faces a particular set of problems in this timekeeping. Fallow Deer, for example, mate in October and/or November, so their problem is to detect shortening days, rather than lengthening ones (mammals like this are termed short-day breeders, in contrast to long-day breeders like the vole). The Golden Hamster is not only nocturnal, but also hibernates and so is 'asleep' at the very time it needs to assess the day length. Generally, hamsters use dwindling day length (less than 12½ hours) to switch off their reproduction and trigger hibernation and then towards the end of, but still during, hibernation their reproductive hormones reactivate spontaneously. However, their internal clock can be overridden even when they are hibernating: if increasing day length is artificially accelerated, the hamsters respond by coming into breeding condition sooner. Once the reproductive time-fuse has been lit, it cannot be snuffed out: having been exposed to the sexually arousing long days, no amount of short days will switch off the reproductive organs for the next three to four months.

This raises the question of how hamsters measure the day length while snuggled in a burrow with their eyes closed. Mammals and other vertebrates have a light-sensitive organ in the brain (the pineal organ), and this might be involved, not least because it produces hormones (a notable one is called melatonin) that appear to have the effect of inhibiting breeding. In early vertebrates the pineal organ was a functioning third eye that peered upwards from the middle of the forehead. This eye was still open in the mammal-like reptiles but, mercifully for milliners, is now firmly locked inside the mammalian skull. It used to be thought that the pineal gland was affected by light penetrating the skull, but it turns out that it is actually stimulated by nerves running from the eyes. What then of the somnolent hamster? At least in the case of Turkish Hamsters, it turns out that they awaken every four to eight days for a peek at current lighting conditions.

Another problem is how the mammal's internal clock distinguishes between a day length that heralds the onset of spring and an identical day length, some months later, that signals the passing of summer. It seems that Field Voles, at least, get around this by re-setting the sensitive period of their clock as the season progresses.

Clearly the whole mechanism is very intricate and made all the more so by the fact that day length is not the only determinant of breeding seasons, as witnessed above by the Montane Vole's response to fresh greenery. In that case it seems that the vole responds specifically to a chemical found in young plants (with the rather challenging name of 6-methoxybenzoxazoli-none). Other mammals are known to respond to other plant chemicals in this way. House Mice respond to gibberellic acid, which is a plant growth hormone. The mechanism is pleasingly elegant. The herbivore, using its ability to sense growth hormone surge in its food plants, can anticipate any forthcoming flush of vegetation. It can thus time its breeding accordingly. One theory is that the synchrony in breeding of voles and lemmings during their population cycles (see p. 127) is triggered by such plant hormones.

The litter sizes of Red Foxes that feed on these rodents also increase during the explosion in numbers of their prey. Intriguingly, these larger fox litters are conceived in January or February, when the vixens ovulate, whereas the voles only become available in May, raising the question of how the predator anticipates the increasing numbers of its prey. The same question applies to stoats which, due to delayed implantation, ovulate during the previous season (see p. 210). One ingenious suggestion is that the foxes respond to the circulating hormones in the bodies of the voles they are eating. During the vole cycle, winter reproduction occurs only when their numbers are increasing towards a boom year, and thus it is only in such winters that vole bodies hum with hormones called gonadotrophins, which regulate their own ovulation rate. The idea is that the vixens get an extra dose of gonadotrophins through eating flourishing voles. The sceptical response to this theory is that hormones are surely digested and, anyway, it would be a precarious business to let one's breeding life be tossed hither and thither by the things one ate. However, it turns out that suckling rats can absorb active hormones from their mother's milk through their guts, and of course women take the pill orally. But neither of these cases involve hormones made of the glycoproteins, which make up the vole hormone and is definitely digested by people. Furthermore, the crucial glycoprotein hormones (Leuteinising Hormone and Follicle Stimulating Hormone) have different molecular compositions between species, so it is not likely that vole hormones would work on foxes. So, unless the foxes have done some nifty evolutionary footwork with their digestive systems, the theory is looking a bit shaky and the mystery of how they anticipate the vole-peak remains.

If breeding is triggered by a switch thrown by day length, then the problem arises that day length differs with the onset of spring, which varies with latitude. For this reason, the Australian marsupial mouse, *Antechinus*, fine tunes its reproduction to the rate of change of day length: southern populations ovulate when day length changes at a rate of 127–137 seconds per day, but northern populations, being nearer the equator, ovulate when day length shifts by only 97–107 seconds per day. This reflects the fact that the difference in day length from one day to the next increases towards the poles. Thus, when stoats moult from white to brown, or vice versa, the transition is slower at lower latitudes.

Delays

Polar Bears are born between late November and early January, which is the harshest part of Arctic winter. Bear cubs are partially weaned and ready to go out onto sea ice by the time their mother breaks out of the maternity den between March and May (depending on latitude). This coincides with spring and abundant seal pups for food.

Brown Bears are born early in the New Year; their arrival is also timed so that their eventual emergence from their mothers' hibernacula will coincide with a flush of food for both mother and offspring. Meeting this deadline is inconvenient in that, taking account of the bears' three-month gestation, it would seem to require mating during October when males and females alike are in fact hibernating in separate lairs. Similarly, hibernation is an impediment to the courtship of most European bats. The bats and the bears have solved the conundrum differently.

Delayed fertilisation

With the exception of Schreiber's Bat, all European bats exhibit a phenomenon called delayed fertilisation. Males produce sperm in the autumn. They then mate with both immature and adult females, whereupon their testes regress, but viable sperm are stored for up to seven months in tubes within storage organs (*cauda epididymis*) which are attached to the testes. In the spring, these stored sperm can be used to fertilise any females missed during the autumn matings. In some bats, including Daubenton's, males awaken in winter and mate with females – it is uncertain to what extent the females are torpid and thus oblivious of the quality of their mate. Meanwhile those females that mated in autumn store the sperm in their uteri throughout hibernation. During this time the females' ova are nourished by Graafian follicles (a sort of cellular support-staff), which in these bats are

A male Daubenton's Bat awakens briefly during hibernation to prospect for females.

especially large and well supplied with nourishing glycogen. Fertilisation takes place as soon as the mated females wake from hibernation. The advantage of this system is presumably that it allows an immediate start to pregnancy when time is short, re-scheduling the time-consuming and debilitating business of courtship to a more appropriate moment.

Delayed implantation

Brown Bears, Schreiber's Bat and quite a few others, have opted for a different solution to the incompatibility of sex and sleep. Bears mate in May or June and the ova are fertilised immediately and begin development. However, the blastocyst (i.e. the embryo at the stage of implantation in the uterine wall) then falls into a state of suspended animation until some five months later, well into the mother's hibernation, whereupon it implants in the uterine wall and continues its development normally. This mechanism is called delayed implantation. By suspending its growth at such an early stage, the embryo has minimal nutritional requirements. The embryo therefore imposes minimal burden on its mother during the winter sleep, until it is necessary to reactivate growth in order to keep its appointment with the world, at birth. It is important that baby bears are born early in the year, so that they have time to lay down sufficient fat reserves to sustain their first winter of hibernation.

Delayed implantation is known in some 47 species in six placental orders: Carnivora, Pinnipedia, Chiroptera, Insectivora, Artiodactyla and Edentata. Some, like badgers (but only in the far north) and Schreiber's Bats, hibernate, but others such as walruses and wolverines do not. Most, however, seem to face some difficulty in the timing of their breeding. Roe Deer give birth in May or June following a true pregnancy of five months. Implantation of their blastocysts is in December, but the nutritional demands of midwinter (when they are less territorial and form herds) make it a poor season for mating, and they have brought this forward to July or August. In this case, why Roe Deer move the time of mating to midsummer, rather than autumn

like the mouflon and chamois, is not known. The Roe Deer may be bound into this compromise by its small size. Red Deer, with their larger body weight, have longer pregnancies and so can mate in September and still deliver their calves on time without any delay in their development. So more than half the Roe Deer embryo's 42-week 'pregnancy' is spent in limbo, while the Red Deer embryo is developing throughout its 32-week gestation.

Other delays

Some rodents and marsupials, including Europe's Red-necked Wallaby, keep one embryo simmering in reserve (a condition known as embryonic diapause) until its development is triggered by the weaning of the previous infant. One final dodge in the timing of birth is not shown by any European mammal, but is the prerogative of the New World Natalid Bat in which pregnancy is slowed down to ensure that the young is not born at an inconvenient time.

The need for birth to be timed to coincide with abundant resources in the European spring or summer is pretty obvious, but what considerations determine the best time for mating? On the grounds that females can increase their fitness by selecting mates of the highest quality (those quali-ties then being passed on to their offspring), one suggestion is that mating should be timed for a period when male competition and female choice can be exercised strongly. This could apply to the annual calendar of most seals, which congregate on dry land only once a year at their pupping grounds. It is advantageous to pup and to mate at the same time in order to free themselves to feed without interruption for the rest of the year, and to minimise exposure to predators on land. During the annual haul-out, males can compete for harems in a post-partum or post-lactational orgy. However, the true pregnancy of most seals and sea lions is eight months, so a two- to four-month delay in implantation postpones the pregnancy to keep their reproductive lives on its annual schedule.

The weasel family provokes many questions about delayed implantation. Martens invariably show a delay (the longest known is the American Fisher at 300 days), as do wolverines, but not polecats. The American Mink is paradoxical: it mates in spring and its pregnancy varies between 39 and 76 days (the gestation is shorter when the mating is later). It is not obvious why the mink needs delayed implantation. Perhaps it is an heirloom from an ancestor that lived under different conditions. The European Otter has conventional pregnancies, while the strikingly similar North American Otter has delayed implantation. But most debated of all the paradoxes is the fact that the closely related and often sympatric weasel and stoat differ.

Weasels have a conventional 42-day pregnancy following spring mating. Stoats mate in June or July and give birth 280 days later, in the following spring. Speculation on this contrast is varied, but shares the theme that the evolution of burrowing rodents in the Pliocene (and their massive population explosions) set the evolutionary stage for small weasel-like predators that could churn out young fast to capitalise on a glut of prey. Weasels, with their smaller body size, can produce two litters in a good season without the head start provided by delayed implantation (see p. 208), whereas stoats may have opted for getting their single litter born as early as possible in spring.

Another idea is that stoats have retained the ancestral habit of delaying their implantation (which weasels have abandoned) because it brings advantages in concert with another remarkable reproductive trick: extreme precocity. Infant female stoats mate in the nest, even before weaning (indeed, their reproductive systems may even be switched on by oestrogens circulating in their mother's milk since she comes into oestrus while nursing them). All the infant females mate *en masse* with their mother's current mate (which is highly unlikely to be their father of the previous year). Observations of male stoats carrying food to litters of young that were unlikely to be their own offspring make more sense if they are following up their paedophilia by investing in the infant (but pregnant) mothers-to-be of their unborn offspring. The effect of nestling mating is to double the number of litters an average female stoat can squeeze into her lifetime, so the combination of delayed implantation and precocity in stoats that live about two-and-a-half years produces the same doubling of lifetime reproductive output that small body size allowed the weasel to achieve by producing two litters per season. However, in the wild, average age at death for weasels is less than one year, and for stoats less than one-and-a-half years. Stoats also

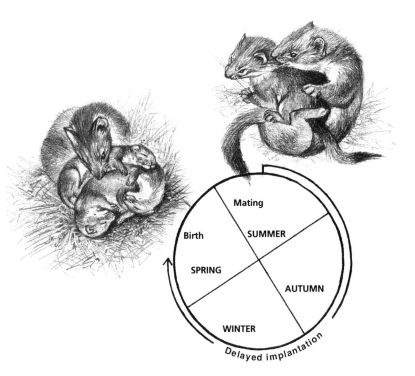

The female stoat is pregnant for most of the year, but only during the last three to four weeks do the eggs implant and the embryos develop. Males may mate with both a female and her nursing daughters. The likelihood of a male surviving two breeding seasons in an area is low, so it is unlikely that the nestling with which he mates will be his daughter.

keep their options open with their high ovulation rate, which makes it possible for them, too, to react to vole cycles by varying intra-uterine mortality (i.e. number of miscarriages).

Mating systems

Red Deer stags roar and fight to win harems of up to 60 females (an average harem might be closer to 8–12 hinds) upon which they force their ardour. If the harem moves to a fresh feeding ground the stag follows, shepherding the hinds to keep them away from other males. Fallow Deer bucks leave their bachelor herds to display at traditional rutting stands at which they groan, urinate in mud scrapes, thrash the vegetation with their antlers and generally behave in an attractive way. The result is that they are visited by does which bestow their favours as they choose (see also p. 256). Roe Deer bucks patrol territories that encompass between two and six smaller territories of females, while the male muntjac occupies a 15 ha^2 territory that

Male muntjac deer are associated with only one or two breeding females.

overlaps one or two similarly sized territories of females; some muntjac may even be monogamous. These are all closely related species, with much in common in their lifestyles, often living and courting in the same place at the same time, yet conducting their affairs in totally different ways. Why?

The same questions might be asked about the differences in mating systems of other groups of mammals. Red Foxes, badgers and stoats are all carnivores and may all coexist in the same habitat, but differ in many aspects of their courtship and family life. Foxes (Red or Arctic) show broad-minded variability in their matrimonial arrangements: sometimes they live as monogamous pairs, sometimes a male may consort with two breeding vixens (which may or may not share a communal den), and sometimes a single breeding female may have several non-breeding female helpers (see p. 156). In each case there is only one breeding male in the family, and he will be a diligent father, providing his cubs with food.

Badgers (who may even share a den with foxes) do things differently. Their social lives vary radically between habitats, with pairs forming in the heat of Spain and the cold of Sweden where food is sparse, but with larger social groups living in a communal den or sett where food is more abundant. The largest such social group so far discovered numbered 29 individuals, but eight to ten adults of both sexes might be closer to the average. One breeding male probably monopolises most matings in each group, but other males certainly secure a proportion of matings too. Within Britain, the breeding habits of females within these groups vary with latitude, doubtless because food is less abundant (and thus territories are larger) further to the north. In the lap of southern luxury up to four adult females may breed within one social group of badgers, whereas in the austerity of the north of Scotland only one female breeds in each group. The factors that determine whether or not a particular female breeds may also vary between populations in different circumstances. In a high-density population in Gloucestershire, the fattest females in autumn go on to be the successful breeders, whereas in parts of Scotland female breeding hinges solely on social status, which is likely to be determined by age and body size. One population, in Oxfordshire, has been studied in particular detail. There, badgers live at a population density of some 17 per km^2 and, during the study, all female badgers of three years old or older became pregnant with some 58% going on successfully to lactate. However, a greater proportion of those in larger groups failed to complete their pregnancies successfully when compared with those in smaller groups, suggesting that in badger society too much company is a bad thing, especially amongst females. It would appear that competition amongst females limits their breeding success and applies a tighter tourniquet when more females cohabit. This competition bites most severely before, or around, the time of birth. It seems the heat goes out of the rivalry by the time a female has got her young to the stage of sucking, however, because few die between then and weaning.

The badger is one of those species exhibiting delayed implantation (see p. 208). They have two oestrous periods, one in spring and one in autumn, and the embryos of both matings (which do not necessarily have the same fathers) implant and develop during the following winter. Thus cubs born in the February of one year were conceived under whatever conditions prevailed in the spring or autumn of the previous year, and during the intervening winter the female has largely fasted and lived off her fat. In the Oxfordshire population, the factors determining females' breeding success each February varied depending on the weather the previous summer. Dry summers are bad for earthworms, which are the badgers' staple diet, whereas wet summers bring out the worms in profusion and the badgers grow fat. Following a dry summer, all adult females got pregnant, but only the fattest successfully completed their pregnancies, and females in larger groups were the most emaciated and thus least likely to give birth successfully. Suckling infants is very expensive for female badgers at the best of times, as evidenced by the radical loss in weight of nursing mothers. Indeed, females that have nursed young are at greater risk of dying than are their barren contemporaries. It was discovered, by ultrasound scanning pregnant female badgers, that some mothers resorb all or part of their litters. Thus it may be that following a failure in the summer earthworm harvest, those females with insufficient fat reserves resorb their litters – cutting their losses because the costs of carrying them to full term are just too great.

Following a wet summer and consequent bumper crop of earthworms, things are very different in the badger community. All adult females are sufficiently corpulent to breed, but again only a proportion do so. This time, however, their portliness is no predictor of future breeding success. It is only the largest and probably the most socially dominant that successfully wean cubs. Although it remains unproven, it seems likely that under these circumstances the dominant females kill the newborn of subordinates. In those summers when the living is easy, the biggest females (which are probably the most socially dominant) also maintain exclusive foraging enclaves within the group territory, and are able to monopolise particularly fruitful habitat patches. Such exclusivity is too expensive a luxury when times are lean, when all females, large or small, dominant or subordinate, quest everywhere in search of any available food. Thus, depending on the weather, competition between females adjusts the group size of badgers to the available food supply in two different ways. Indeed, irrespective of whether their mother's fat, or her status, determined their survival to weaning, it will be autumn rainfall (and thus the supply of worms) that will determine whether weaned badger cubs survive to their first winter.

If badgers, like foxes, live in groups within which some or most adult females fail to rear cubs each year, why do not badgers, like foxes, have a system whereby non-breeders help raise the group's young? One suggestion is that group living is a rather new phenomenon for badgers, and anyway one that predominates only in a fraction of their geographical range, namely the rich and undulating farmland of Great Britain. Probably pastures rich in earthworms, which facilitate the formation of badger groups, only emerged with the agricultural revolution. Perhaps badger numbers also built up with the decline in wolves as people felled the wildwood. Thus far it seems that female badgers may suppress the reproduction of others in their sorority because there would be insufficient food to go around all their offspring, but do not do so in order to coerce them into acting as wet-nurses or baby-sitters, as in some other species. However, non-breeding female badgers have been seen guarding cubs, albeit infrequently, so perhaps they are starting down the evolutionary road to cooperative care of young nieces and nephews as a device for making the best of a bad job in a society where not everybody can breed (see p. 156).

The home ranges of all members of badger (and fox) groups generally overlap tightly. This is in contrast again with the stoat's approach, wherein solitary females occupy small territories, two or three of which are embraced by the larger territory of a male. The male stoat mates with the territorial females (and their daughters), but does relatively little by way of conventional paternal care (in common with male badgers, but in contrast to male foxes). Wildcats operate spatial arrangements similar to those of stoats, and their males follow a similar 'love them and leave them' approach to courtship.

The three mating options are monogamy, polygamy or promiscuity. The monogamous option involves the formation of a bonded breeding pair (possibly in association with other non-breeding individuals). Longer-term monogamous unions may be an advantage, insofar as studies of some sea birds have shown that established pairs have better breeding success than newly formed pairs. Polygamy can work both ways: one male mating with several females (polygyny) or one female mating with several males (polyandry).

The great majority of mammals are polygynous, and monogamy is thought to be rather rare. A commonly quoted figure is that only 3% of mammalian species are monogamous, in contrast to birds in which apparent monogamy is more common. Having opted for a polygamous mating system, the question arises as to which sex is more likely to desert the other to seek further mates. The general answer is that the sex which initially invests more is the less likely to desert. In mammals this is a foregone conclusion since females face long pregnancies and only females can lactate, so it is inevitable that males will be the gallivanting sex. However, this is not a universal rule, and in some fish it is the female which deserts. Female sea horses have evolved a fake penis which they use to insert eggs into the male's pouch. The male then adds sperm to them and is left holding all the babies while the female devotes herself to other dalliances. In this astounding case, each sperm is almost as big as an egg, so the male's initial investment is as great in total as the female's.

Promiscuity describes the system in which both males and females mate with more than one individual of the opposite sex. The flavour of Bohemian randomness associated with the word promiscuity should not be taken to indicate that species which opt for some form of this system (ranging from Brown Rats to mink) have abandoned the competitiveness and quality assessment that underlies other mating systems. On the contrary, these species have merely shifted the competitive arena from outside to inside the female (see p. 232).

Monogamy or polygyny

Whether an animal will be monogamous or polygynous is really determined by its ecological circumstances. Natural selection determines that both males and females behave in ways that maximise the numbers of their descendants in future generations. Despite this unity of purpose, the battle of the sexes still arises because the way in which males can maximise the number of their surviving offspring differs from the strategy females must adopt to maximise theirs. All else being equal, males are more likely to achieve their end by mating with as many females as possible, whereas females are more likely to achieve it by mating with the best males they can find (see p. 220). In short, because a female has only a few eggs (relative to a male's capacity to produce sperm) and because she is lumbered with them inside her, she is constrained to be fertilised by only one or a few males and so all she can do is make sure she chooses good ones. But the species' natural history sometimes means that all else is not equal. For example, if food or other resources are distributed in such a way that females are widely spaced out, it may be impossible for a male to monopolise more than one female (and all the more so if the females' oestrous periods are synchronised). In such circumstances a male leaving one mate to search for others would face a high risk of being cuckolded while he was away gallivanting. In contrast, if resources are organised into clumps then females will also be clumped, so that one male can monopolise several females, then polygyny will ensue (assuming that the females' oestruses are not too tightly synchronised – such synchrony would make it impossible for the male to defend one female while

The male Alpine Marmots that defend the best burrows gather the largest harems.

mating with another). Similarly, if the dangers of predation force females into groups, then polygyny is facilitated.

Monogamy may also be advantageous if the nature of the food supply or predator pressure, combined with the demands of the young, puts such stresses on a single-parent family that the male's paternal help becomes a necessity. Among canids, such as Golden Jackals and foxes, the tendency to monogamy and the father's diligent provisioning of food is interpreted in this light. If the father did not help, he would end up with no offspring. Similarly, in marmosets (small South American monkeys), the fathers are needed to help carry the twin babies through the trees. Indeed, among these little monkeys, two males (the father and an assistant) are indispensable if the twins are to survive. However, among species whose food is seasonally superabundant (such as fruit or seed eaters) one parent may scarcely be worse off than two in the task of providing for the young, and this situation pushes the balance towards polygamy. In other words, monogamy is probably generally advantageous to the female, but it is only advantageous to the male when he rears more offspring by behaving monogamously than he could do by behaving polygynously.

There are circumstances when polygyny can be the best of two bad options for a female, however. If male quality is translated into territory quality, so that a female faces the choice between mating monogamously with a male holding a poor quality territory or polygynously with one holding an excellent territory, then there will be a point at which she may do better to opt for polygyny. This option would be even more attractive if her sons inherited the polygynous male's capacity to secure good territories. This argument may apply to the Alpine Marmot. Male marmots defend a burrow and associated grazing lawns, and males with the best quality burrows gather the largest harems. However, there is evidence from related species that each female's reproductive success may fall with increasing harem size. The tradeoffs to be assessed by the female are even more complex because her annual reproductive success may increase as she ages and gains status. While she might do worse in the larger harem of a high-quality burrow in her early years as a subordinate, she may regain this lost output over her reproductive lifetime in comparison to her lifetime production of offspring in a smaller harem resident in a lesser quality burrow. Certainly, female status can be an important ingredient of reproductive success, albeit less dramatic than the differences wrought by status among males. For example, dominant female rabbits may have four-fold higher mating success than their subordinates, whereas dominant Red Deer stags produce 11-fold more calves than their subordinates.

Leks

Variations on the polygynous theme can all be fitted into three categories. Either the male defends a group of females, as with the Red Deer and most pinnipeds, or he defends the resources that will bring the females to him, as with the marmot. Either way it is the male's capacity to control resources economically that enables him to secure a harem. A third system, the use of leks, is rare among European mammals, known only in some populations of Fallow Deer and perhaps a population of Sika Deer in the Czech Republic. Leks are display grounds where males congregate, maintaining a honey-comb of mini-territories of as little as 10 m diameter. Females visit these territories, and mate *en masse* with the males in a brief but orgiastic period. In that minority of Fallow deer populations where the males form leks, the most successful individuals may mate with 50 does within a two-week rut. Indeed, each male is unlikely to retain his territory for more than five consecutive days before being worn out by almost continuous fighting and mating, and the struggle of shepherding his herd of does within the confines of his mini-territory. This strain contrasts with the less frenzied reproductive efforts of Fallow bucks in other populations where conventional territories are generally held throughout a month-long rut.

Males form leks under a particular set of ecological circumstances: where females are quite numerous, but where males cannot easily monopolise a harem or the resources which might attract them. In the case of Fallow Deer, these conditions apply where females move unpredictably in herds of unstable membership. That females must be numerous to make lekking effective is illustrated by comparing the changing mating tactics in two populations of deer: in one parkland population of Fallow Deer in England the bucks changed from dispersed rutting stands to leks when the popula-tion increased from 120 to an astronomical 185 deer per km^2. In contrast, a population of Czech Sika Deer abandoned lekking in favour of conventional territories when their numbers fell from close to 3 per km^2 to fewer than 1 per km^2.

A widespread idea is that leks evolved in roughly the manner of a débutante's ball: the female deer congregate to inspect clusters of eligible bucks from which they pick the best of the crop, making it socially cata-strophic not to be on the guest list. Once females begin to choose partners at a lek, males would have little choice but to join such clusters to have any hope of being amongst the chosen few. The idea that females' evaluation of males drives leks is almost opposite to the explanation of the forces thought to foster other sorts of polygyny, which arise where it is economically possible for a male to defend a disproportionate share of females. Furthermore, there is actually scant evidence to support the notion that female choice is the driving force behind lekking. An alternative, and more convincing, suggestion is that females select leks as safe havens from the maelstrom of chaotic courtship. When a doe Fallow Deer in the herd comes into oestrus she is pursued relentlessly by every male that catches her scent. Because these herds have unstable membership there is no policing via a dominance hierarchy amongst the males, who harass the females anarchically. Each attempted mating is likely to be interrupted by the interventions of rival suitors, and with antlers flailing such skirmishes are hazardous for all involved. On the lek, the male seeking to corral does within his mini-territory shoulders the exhausting burden of repelling a miscellany of suitors. Females may also gain safety from predators on the lek, partly because by grouping they have increased vigilance, but also because males may site leks in places which are anyway safe havens (with short vegetation for example).

Once they arrive at a lek, females may congregate in a particularly safe mini-territory. For example, in one population they preferred territories with clumps of sedges which they used as obstacles when trying to dodge the unwelcome attentions of males. They also favoured males which were particularly large, or which groaned frequently. Finally, an added incentive to join a particular male is apparently the sight of him copulating, which is perhaps some endorsement of his credentials as a potential stud. However, these factors are all secondary in determining the disproportionate success of some males on the lek, which hinges largely on the greater ability of the most successful males to keep rivals at bay. A male Fallow Deer may have to chase off a rival as often as once a minute. If his mini-territory is so situated that he suffers a higher than average bombardment, or if his stamina wanes so that his defence is less effective, his females will be more and more harassed and will move *en masse* in search of a less chaotic haven. The females seek out the males that currently have the largest harems. In this way, success breeds success, presumably because females congregate on the assumption that conditions must be preferable in a place where their sisters have congregated. Furthermore, females may also be attracted by the prospect of hiding within the larger herd, both from predators and from unwelcome males. None of these factors has much to do with the selection of a particular male by discriminating females. Rather, it suggests that particular males happen to benefit incidentally from putting themselves in the right place at the right time in a highly structured arrangement which enables them to cash in on the females' search for sanctuary from anarchic attentions of other males. By analogy, females might try hiding amongst bushes from rapacious males, but it does not work, so instead they hide amongst spatially disciplined males, which does work. From the females' viewpoint it does not matter much whether they are bushes or males. However, from the males' viewpoint, forming leks results in securing matings, and so they form leks.

Overall, the sex lives of different species form a pattern determined by their ecological circumstances. Red Deer hinds grazing on flushes of grass can form herds, and it may pay them to do so in order to bring many pairs of eyes to bear on the problem of spotting danger. The result is that it is possible for a stag to monopolise a large harem. Muntjac, in contrast, select highly nutritious titbits and finding these necessitates intimate knowledge of a large area. Female muntjac therefore defend territories to keep other females away from their favoured browsing spots, consequently males can only monopolise one or two females. Under an extreme set of ecological circumstances, it pays Fallow Deer to form leks. In each case, society is a mirror of ecological circumstances.

Sexual selection – female fashion or good genes?

Whatever social system they adopt, it is clearly important for females to choose the best available male to sire their young. Males would thus be at an advantage if they had traits which either made them attractive to females and/or helped them defeat rivals. Darwin referred to any character that gave males an edge in the romantic arena as sexually selected. The functioning of some such characters is obvious: hugely muscular males can defeat wimpish ones. This in itself can lead to males getting bigger and bigger, and in so far as females exert any choice at all, they can base their selection on a very direct test of male quality by letting them fight it out. Indeed, in order to sort out the men from the boys, female mammals regularly engineer circumstances that bring rival males into direct conflict. Sometimes, however, females appear to select males on the basis of indicators of their prowess, for example deep voices or massive horns. In this context, the fact that females appear to perceive bigger as better is thought to explain some extraordinary male regalia, of which the peacock's tail is the most oft quoted example. A huge tail or unwieldy horns would seem to be terrible encumbrances that threaten the survival of their bearers, but if, through the vagaries of female choice, they secure a glorious but foreshortened reproductive career then their bearers will prosper relative to unadorned but

The physical differences that distinguish this Sika Deer stag from the hinds, such as the antlers and muscular neck, are the result of sexual selection. Amongst other costs, the male has to consume five times its normal daily intake of calcium to grow these antlers.

longer-lived contemporaries with no sex life. In this way, female choice could lead to ever more exaggerated male adornments.

Three ideas may explain how female choice directs the evolution of gaudy, and seemingly absurd, male ornament. Once females begin to select a feature, such as big horns, it is obvious that horns will evolve to be bigger and bigger until some other force (such as that they get tangled up in the branches) puts a stop to female fancy. But why should females prefer big horns, or in the case of peacocks' flamboyant tails, in the first place. One possibility is that runaway selection operates on a chance fashion such that females prefer big horns because females prefer big horns. That is, any female who goes against the fashion and mates with a small-horned male is likely to have sons with small horns who will find it difficult to attract mates (because most females like large horns). Thus the genes that produce big horns in males and that cause females to like big horns will soon be found together in the offspring of fathers with big horns and mothers who were attracted by them, and these proclivities will spread through the population. A male's adornments have, in this case, evolved as a female's fashion icon. The whole argument hinges on females selecting mates with characters that will be an advantage if inherited by their sons.

The second theory for how female choice works involves females selecting males on the basis of indicators that both their sons, and their daughters, will have good qualities. In this case the starting point would not be some whimsy on the behalf of females, but rather females would select males on the basis of signals that genuinely indicated their health and vigour (see handicaps and revealed signals, p. 181) and thus the likelihood of these useful qualities being passed on to their offspring. One of the most important things a female could look for in a male is the capacity to resist parasites and diseases (see p. 202). This led to the idea that elaborate ornaments, like the peacock's tail, were indicators that allowed females to check that a male was disease free. A poor quality male would either be unable to afford to grow the adornment, or would be unable to disguise that it was tatty and parasite ridden.

Both the runaway effects of female fashion and the search for honest, cheat-proof signals of male quality could lead to a spiralling exaggeration of male adornments, ranging from the male Mandrill's multicoloured face to the Fallow Deer's sweepingly palmate antlers. Similarly, exaggerated traits may be favoured by the straightforward need to make signals as conspicuous as possible when it is vital, irrespective of their quality, for males to be noticed by females. Striking male adornments are commonplace amongst birds and seemingly few amongst mammals. However, this may be an illusion, because mammals are so dependent on scent signals; it remains to be seen whether robust males shimmer within an aura of ornate perfumes, but it is certainly the case that dominant males often have very exaggerated scent glands and mark at a very high rate.

Mirror images

A male Barbary Macaque signals its superiority over a rival by yawning at him, and flaunting a pair of ominously dagger-like upper canine teeth. In the quest for foolproof indicators of male quality, female primates may select the males with the biggest teeth. They may also have corroborative evidence that big teeth signal good quality in the surprising fact that amongst monkeys with polygynous societies, males with the largest canine teeth also have the most perfectly symmetrical ones. Similarly, there is evidence that Fallow Deer bucks with the largest antlers have the most symmetrical antlers, and that greater symmetry is associated with dominant status. Psychologists have shown that people are perceived as more attractive the closer the two sides of their face are to mirror images. More remarkable yet, male lions whose facial whisker patterns are more asymmetrical have shorter life spans than those whose whiskers more closely approximate a mirror image on either side of their faces.

The challenging yawn of a male Barbary Macaque may reveal not only the size, but also the symmetry of his canine teeth.

An astonishing fact of life is that if an individual endures stress while it is developing, its body when adult will be less perfectly symmetrical. The stress can be either environmental (such as a heavy parasite load) or genetic (such as a mutation). Asymmetry in human babies is affected by their mother's smoking habits, and asymmetry in numbers of bristles on either side of a fruit fly's head is an indicator of how inbred it is! A fashionable idea is thus that females may use fluctuations of asymmetry in male adornments as an uncheatable signal of the males quality: the idea is that only the very healthiest males will have adornments that are both large and symmetrical. Symmetry is too expensive for unhealthy individuals. This idea gained a lot of credibility because male swallows with the longest tails had the most symmetrical forks, and greater symmetry was associated with higher mating success. Growing a long tail is a sort of handicap (see p. 181), and only the best males can afford to grow really long ones; the fact that these long tails are the most symmetrical may be further verification of the bearer's good health. It happens that female swallows are directly impressed by the symmetry of a male's tale, but even if she had been attracted only by tail length, the fact that long tails and symmetry (and thus good health) are bound together reveals that the female is selecting males on the basis of a true indicator of their quality, and not merely a whimsical liking for long tails. Another striking example is that female Japanese Scorpion Flies prefer the smell of males with more symmetrical bodies, even when they cannot see them. Furthermore, there is mounting evidence that the asymmetry in sexually selected traits, such as antlers, is five to ten times more variable than in most bodily traits, providing plenty of scope to distinguish more or less asymmetrical individuals. In principle the same idea could apply to lots of mammals – the symmetry of a badger's facial stripes might reveal weaknesses in its character, and symmetry in antlers could be read like a medical record. For example, a deer that breaks a foreleg develops a kink in the opposite antler. Furthermore, amongst male Common Shrews, a mysterious fact is that the more symmetrical are their flank (scent) glands, the greater is the proportion of their offspring that survive to adulthood! However, there are few mammalian cases where this idea has been tested, and it has some problems. A major criticism is that the bigger the ornament, the greater the torque caused by an asymmetry, and hence the greater the need for the ornament to be symmetrical. Thus the laws of physics could demand greater symmetry of larger antlers; female deer might indeed choose males with larger antlers (although it is not proven that they do), but their symmetry may be incidental. However, that would not explain the preferences of the Japanese flies, so the notion that symmetry can be read as a medical record remains an enthralling possibility.

Alternative strategies

In this world of the mighty stud or the diligent father, what of the meek and the feeble? The general case in mammalian mating systems is that meek males far from inherit the earth. Rather they, and more significantly the genes they carry, drop out of the evolutionary race. There are, however, some exceptions to this gloomy prospect. Young male Northern Elephant Seals in the New World have no hope of securing a harem in a fair fight with a gargantuan adult. So while biding their time until their muscles mature, some of them behave like females and thereby insinuate themselves into a harem where they surreptitiously try to sneak matings. Young Red Deer stags similarly steal matings from the prime stags in this way. Indeed, thieving from a tender age is almost a prerequisite to the success of males of both these species: as infants they steal milk in their desperate race to grow larger than their competitors. In the case of elephant seals, after four weeks of nursing, the spherically obese infants are deserted by their correspondingly slimmer mothers who set off to sea (after an orgy of copulation during which many pups are accidentally crushed by adults reckless with passion). Most pups then face ten weeks of fasting before taking to the sea, but about 10% become dedicated milk thieves, pilfering from unwary mothers at great risk. More than three-quarters of these sneaky suckers are male. Other young, also predominantly male, opt for a different strategy from the outset by seeking out a bereaved mother. By gorging from mother and foster mother, such pups may grow from their 50 kg birth weight to 227 kg at weaning. This is twice the average weaning weight and an advantage that doubtless launches them forcefully along the road to adult splendour, not to mention sub-adult cuckoldry.

There may be a rough parallel to the surreptitious matings of Red Deer and elephant seals in the behaviour of male stoats. Fully adult male stoats tour the countryside seeking receptive females with whom they stay for about a week, while younger males may stay in a large home range, perhaps using their local knowledge to steal a few matings before the itinerant Casanovas cruise in.

There are only a few reports of alternative mating strategies in mammals to those discussed here, but considering the high stakes involved, we may expect to discover even more ways of making the best of a bad job. Certainly, in one population of Fallow Deer some bucks defended harems, others defended mating territories, others lekked and others simply raped passing does. Nonetheless, mammals are moderately limited in the scope of their alternatives (due to their specialised reproductive systems and lactation), whereas some other vertebrates are more extravagant in their deviations from traditional sex. Some male fish, finding themselves as puny youngsters facing hot competition, will change sex to become females. The Coho Salmon actually produces two distinct types of male: large fighting machines called hooknoses that take a long time to mature, and wimpish sneaks known as jacks that mature a year earlier. The success of each type depends on the prevalence of the other, with the result that evolution has favoured a mixture of the two.

Alternative reproductive tactics may arise amongst males for two reasons. First, some males may find themselves permanently disadvantaged

Amongst Common Shrews, 'settler' males may enjoy greater mating success when courting females in their parish due to the females' greater familiarity with them.

and thus have no option but to make the best of a bad job. Second, younger males may adopt a different policy to courtship than their seniors because competitive abilities change with age. The first case can be illustrated by Common Shrews, the second by Grey Squirrels.

In southern Britain male Common Shrews become sexually mature in March, at which time they rapidly gain weight, begin to moult and their testes swell until they form a visible bulge at the base of the tail. Their testes are surprisingly heavy for such small animals, which may hint that producing abundant sperm is a priority for male shrews. Females in a locality come into oestrus in synchrony, generally during the second half of April, and may produce up to three litters by late autumn. Few adults survive the breeding season, and none survive the winter, so each spring the entire breeding population is composed of first-time breeders of similar age. Female Common Shrews occupy exclusive territories, but males adopt two distinct tactics. Having established exclusive territories (of about 30 m diameter) in March, in April wayfaring males set out on a series of long distance excursions to visit female ranges. In contrast, in March other males, the settlers, establish larger home ranges, which overlap to a variable extent with those of other settler males and of several territorial females. During March, the wayfarers are rather inactive, moving less than the settlers who are already scuttling about, building relationships with the females in their parish and doubtless carefully monitoring the females' scents for any sign of oestrus. However, during April the wayfarers' wanderlust leads them to frenetic activity, sometimes travelling as much as 200 m to visit a female before retreating to their enclave. The two approaches have different rewards. Each settler, on average, inseminates more females and sires more young than does each wayfarer. Indeed, in one study settlers inseminated between zero and four females and fathered between one and nine weaned offspring, whereas each wayfarer inseminated none or one female and sired between zero and six weanlings. Not surprisingly, the settlers did best when courting females in their parish, in whose territories they probably felt confident, and with whom they probably enjoyed a tolerance built on familiarity. In contrast, wayfarers scored their romantic successes with isolated females whose territories were closest to their small March enclaves.

Once the breeding season is in full swing, there is no difference in body weight between wayfaring males and settlers, but early in the season the wayfarers are consistently lighter. This probably means that the tactic a male will adopt for its entire reproductive career is determined by the time at which it reaches sexual maturity. The settlers are individuals that mature early, presumably due to the circumstances of their births – a silver spoon effect. They become members of the reproductive male community, a sort of men-only club, and are so well entrenched in that role that by the time late developers have matured they have missed the opportunity for membership. Thus late developers are destined to wayfaring in order to make the best of a bad job. However, wayfaring male shrews have developed another tactic in their effort to overcome their disadvantaged social standing. Although their testes do not differ in size from those of settler males, the wayfarers had more sperm in their epididymides (the storage vessel where sperm are retained prior to ejaculation). It seems, therefore, that in anticipation of having only few mating opportunities, and those few being with females likely also to be inseminated by other males, wayfarer's invest more sperm in each mating.

Within one population of male shrews the two categories of male, settlers and wayfarers, may consistently produce ejaculates of different size. This would be adaptive if wayfarers are generally likely to mate at a less optimum moment in the female's oestrus than are settlers, or if wayfarers can only sneak the occasional mating because settlers keep them at bay. Wayfarers are, in effect, either shooting at a smaller target or have fewer shots, or both, and therefore they give their all on each occasion. Most female Common Shrews mate promiscuously with several males during one oestrus (see p. 231), so the sperm of several males will be racing for the eggs. Wayfarers start with the odds stacked against them due to poor access to females, so it makes sense for them to try to regain the advantage by fielding a larger team of sperm for the race.

Although sperm are so often said to be a throw-away commodity for males, in comparison to the high value, limited edition eggs of females, males can nonetheless only produce them in limited numbers and at a measurable cost. Males investing too many or too few sperm in each mating will lose in competition with males that apportion their reproductive resources optimally. Thus, males of species in which double mating is likely to lead to those of one male racing against the sperm of a rival, tend to produce relatively larger ejaculates than males of species in which a female is only likely to mate with one male per breeding season. That Common Shrews are firmly in the former category may explain their relatively large testes. Furthermore, amongst rats, individual males may dole out sperm in parcels that vary in size depending on the risk of double mating. A male rat who mates with a female he has accompanied continuously for five days ejaculates about some 29 million sperm on the first occasion he mates with her. In contrast, if after a similar period of abstinence, he mates with a female who has spent the previous five days in the company of another male, he will ejaculate some 52 million sperm (a somewhat probing piece of research reveals that the same trend applies to men who have been in the company of, or away from, their partner). Presumably, in the first case, when the male rat has kept an eye on the female for five days, he can be confident that no other male has entered the race, and therefore can afford to pace himself.

The case of the rat's ejaculate is even more remarkable because it reveals that the behaviour of sperm may also vary depending on the likelihood of their being a race for the eggs. One idea, known evocatively as the kamikaze-sperm hypothesis, is that sperm come in several different types. The suggestion is that only a minority (perhaps only 1%) are destined to be egg-getters. The remainder have various suicidal but useful roles. Some may speed high up into the uterus to kill the sperm of other males that have a head start in the race, others may seek to disadvantage late-coming competitors, either by blocking up the openings of the uterine horns or by forming a so-called copulatory plug, which acts like a bung in the vagina. This idea, which is fairly controversial but stems from the mysterious fact that sperm come in many shapes and sizes, leads to the prediction that individuals that are likely to be the first in a series of mating males should load their team with blockers, whereas those likely to mate at the end of a queue should build a team of hunter-killer sperm (this could be a distinction between dominant and subordinate males). Remarkably enough, exploration of female reproductive tracts about 20 minutes after mating revealed that in the case of the male rats which had kept company with the female for five days prior to mating, only 28% (8.2 million) of the 29 million sperm had made their way close to the finishing line high up in the uterus. In contrast, when the female had been unchaperoned by the mating male, but in the company of another male, 64% (33.2 million) of the 52 million sperm had reached these inner regions. In both cases a similar number of sperm lurked lower in the female's vagina. Furthermore, sperm in different locations had different appearances. More than half of those making up the copulatory plug had no heads at all (the same applies in the copulatory plugs of bats), whereas those that were close to the finishing line had bigger heads than those that remained lower down the track. Why the seeming winners of the race were big-headed is unknown, but their great number high up the track is in accord with the prediction that hunter-killer sperm would predominate where there was a risk that another team had got a head start in the race. Whether or not the kamikaze idea is correct, it appears that the form and function of sperm, in addition to the numbers of them unleashed at a given mating, depend on the prevailing sociological circumstances.

Grey Squirrels illustrate the case where differences in the prowess of young and old males lead to the two age classes adopting different mating tactics. The female squirrel's oestrus lasts just one day, during which males come from far and wide (up to 600 m away) to congregate around her. Because females in a locality come into oestrus on different days, all the males in the vicinity can concentrate on one female at a time. As many as 34 males have been seen around one female. Older, pugilistic males wade right into the contest: if one male mounts the female another pugilist will seek to disrupt their moment of bliss by flinging himself at the couple, knocking the rival (and sometimes the female too) clean off his perch. These unwelcome interruptions put a premium on mating quickly, and so Grey Squirrel matings last only 21 seconds on average, which is much shorter than the mating of species of squirrel with more sedate courtships. While pugilist males throng around the female, other males dispersed through the canopy spectate keenly. Every so often a female breaks away from the admiring pugilists, darting hither and thither through the branches to escape her entourage, and takes sanctuary in the foliage close to the ground. There she sits stock still. Now the search is on, and pugilists and spectators alike scour the trees to find her. A spectator with a keen eye has just as good a chance of finding her as has a pugilist, and the prize in this game of hide-and-seek is that the female mates with the first male to find her. Females mate with up to eight males (generally three or four) during the day, and after each mating a successful male tries to guard her – presumably to give his sperm a good start in the race. About 20% of copulations are interrupted by another male, and about 40% come to a premature conclusion because the female pulls away – which may suggest that she fans the flames of competition amongst the pugilists. About a third of males opt for

Sexual selection may be the principal reason why the male American Mink is much larger than the female, but a consequence is that male mink can easily hunt relatively large prey such as rabbits.

the pugilistic approach, while the remaining two-thirds spectate. Overall, pugilists each secure more matings than each spectator, but because spectators are more numerous than pugilists, each female receives matings from the two types of male in roughly equal proportions. Pugilists have a complete monopoly on the 70% or so of matings that occur in the throng, but spectators secure most matings (in direct proportion to their greater numbers) following games of 'find the female'.

Spectator squirrels are youngsters. They have no hope of success in the frenzy of pugilists, so they make the best of a bad job by trying an alternative tactic. Around the time of their third birthday, with another two to three years of reproductive life ahead of them, spectators graduate into pugilists. But why should the female behave in a way that gives the spectators a chance? Most probably it is not her intention at all to help these stripling males, but simply to escape the physical danger of the fighting throng. The pugilists often corner a female high in the canopy, from which she may fall at peril in the skirmish; females can be attacked by over-zealous suitors attempting to dislodge a copulating rival, and some get badly wounded. Her attempts to escape these hazards incidentally offer an amorous opportunity to younger males which would otherwise remain as voyeurs.

Even paired males seek to increase their reproductive output: in one case study of Red Foxes, a paired male made a swift excursion from his own territory to another where he was seen mating with another vixen, whose cubs were later tended by the presumably cuckolded dog-fox in her territory. Similarly, genetic studies reveal that badger cubs are not infrequently fathered by a male from an adjoining clan.

Manipulating males

The adaptation of females' oestrus to manipulate males is illustrated by the American Mink. Female mink are stimulated to ovulate by the vigorous act of mating (see p. 74), and they have four receptive periods during the spring, each period separated by six to twelve days as a new wave of ovarian follicles ripens and sheds its eggs. At each period of receptivity the female may be courted by more than one male, and from one ovulation she may produce a litter with more than one father. Even if she is fertilised during her first period of receptivity, she continues with the subsequent ovulations. During any one ovulation, the last of a series of males to mate with her secures the largest share of the offspring. After a succession of ovulations, the males that mated later father more of the eventual litter than those with whom she mated in the earlier periods. Apparently the last dose of sperm ejaculated into the female displaces the previous sperm and has the best chance of fertilising her eggs. Clearly it is an advantage for an early male to thwart the mating attempts of a queue of late-comers, and his efforts to monopolise the female include matings that may last three hours, during which the male may ejaculate several times.

It is clear that each of several males may be eager to mate with a single female, but does the female gain anything from multiple mating? In the case of the mink, where the male is twice the female's size, she may not have much choice in the matter. However, the likelihood is that a male mink, having mated with the female may attempt to guard her, and will thus only be displaced if a stronger male challenges him. In this case, if her first mate turns out to be weaker than a subsequent mate, from the female's viewpoint it is no bad thing if he is replaced – she will have had her cake and eaten it by both ensuring that she does not miss the opportunity of breeding altogether due to being too choosy at the outset, while also keeping open her options in case a better male happens along. Thus the repeated oestrous periods of female mink may give her several opportunities to find the best quality mate. She could also benefit from multiple mating if it were advantageous to have a diversity of fathers for her offspring, each bringing its own particular genetic strengths. However, insufficient is known about the sex lives of American Mink to be sure whether the female benefits from multiple matings, or merely has them inflicted upon her.

The case of the Common Shrew reveals that a female's perspective on multiple mating is likely to be affected by the distance over which she and her brothers disperse from their birthplaces. Female shrews give birth to litters of between five and eight babies, and members of one litter may have up to six different fathers. Shrews do not disperse far from their birthplace (on average they settle, as adults, only one-and-a-half home-range diameters away), and so there would seem to be a high risk of inbreeding. Inbreeding is generally damaging to the viability of offspring. In one population of Common Shrews one-third of matings were between adults who were as closely related to their mate as they would be to their offspring – in other words brother–sister matings were common, as were matings between cousins. Furthermore, the offspring of inbred liaisons were smaller at weaning, and were less likely to survive the winter than were the offspring of outbred partners. Clearly, it is to a female shrew's advantage to mate with a male that is not her close kin. If she is unable reliably to identify kin, and as the risk of inbreeding is high, it would be in the female's interest to minimise the risk by soliciting mating with several males, hedging her bets so that at least some of her offspring are likely to be sired by a suitable male. It may well be that the female shrew could not prevent several males mating with her even if it were to her advantage to do so, but where the risk of inbreeding is high it is actually in her interest to be promiscuous and to stop any one male (even apparently the best of them) from monopolising her.

In the context of such competitiveness surrounding mating, it seems paradoxical that a group of male rats may be seen amorously consorting with a female and showing no apparent aggression as they take turns at mating with her. The same startling lack of animosity typifies the several males that may mate in succession with female domestic cats. The explanation appears to be that males may sometimes abandon the attempt to compete directly for females, but rather rely entirely on their sperm to run the race. Males inseminating the female with more sperm may secure a greater proportion of the offspring. Indeed, as a glance at a large male rat reveals, males of species with promiscuous females tend to have disproportionately large testes. Males must decide how to deploy their limited energy between investment in muscle, with which to fight for females, and in sperm, with which to swamp them. The pugilistic Grey Squirrels go for a compromise, but male rats put a greater premium on mating more often and producing more sperm which compete through sheer weight of numbers. By analogy, all else being equal, a player throwing lots of darts at a dartboard is more likely to hit a bull's-eye than one throwing few. The difference between rat and squirrel hinges on whether it is too costly even to try to keep other players from the board. Similarly, among primates, those that live in multi-male societies (e.g. the Barbary Macaque) have disproportionately large testes, with disproportionately spacious storage potential, in comparison to those (e.g. gibbons) that characteristically live in single-male groups. One might guess, in this context, that since the testicles of a Right Whale weigh more than a ton, these males are unlikely to be monogamous. Once sperm competition has arisen in evolution and so become important in determining reproductive success, it will itself encourage female promiscuity in cases where her choice includes several finalists. Then, the best way of sorting out the competition is to mate with all of the serious contenders and let the best man win.

The timing of mating may be crucial in the competition between a female's rival suitors. In the American Mink the last male to mate is at an advantage, in Golden Hamsters and rabbits the first male is at an advantage, whereas in Brown Rats order appears irrelevant (although it may be significant that in laboratory rats the most dominant tends to mate more often and to be the last of a series to mate). The critical factor for the male is to be in the right place at the right time, so that his particular mating coincides with ovulation. The rams of Bighorn Sheep and male Black Rats mate more frequently with females that have recently mated with other males, presumably in an attempt to swamp the competitor's sperm. The Bank Vole and many other rodents and bats opt instead to forestall further competition by including in their ejaculate a gluey secretion from their accessory gland which forms a plug in the female's vagina, thereby hindering further matings. A rather more personalised form of plug is the copulatory tying of wild canids, which prevents other males mating for up to 20 minutes in Red Foxes, minutes that may represent a vital head start as the sperm race towards the eggs. It seems obvious that the successful male fox benefits from the tie, by keeping competitors at bay, but it is less obvious whether the female gains from it.

Mammalian mating ensures that sperm have a secure start in their journey to the egg. Amongst members of the dog family, such as these Red Foxes, mating (left) is prolonged because the pair 'tie' (right), the male's penis being locked in the female. The two individuals may remain 'tied', facing in opposite directions for many minutes. This may be a device, on the part of the male, to prevent competing males mating with the female while his sperm gain a head start in their race to fertilise the eggs.

Chapter eleven

Birth and reproductive potential

For any family the questions of how many offspring to have and how to space out their arrival are critical. A human family might make its decision on the basis of its resources, and the likely consequences of spreading its investment in care and attention between a smaller or larger number of offspring. Similar albeit unconscious considerations have, on an evolutionary timescale, affected the litter sizes and frequencies of breeding of all mammals. Common Shrews may have ten offspring in a litter, but many have only one litter in a lifetime (although some, those in mixed woodland in the Netherlands for example, have up to three litters). Small insectivorous bats also generally have only one offspring each year, but they may continue to do so for ten or more years. The Sei Whale and the Walrus both bear offspring one at a time (as do almost all Cetacea and Pinnipedia), and may continue to do so at intervals of two or three years for half a century. These are clearly different approaches to parenthood, and each approach has hugely different consequences for the lifestyle and populations of its adherents. For example, by the time an elk gives birth to its first, single young (they tend to have twins when older), a Harvest Mouse born on the same day as the parent elk would have been dead for three years and potentially could have left more

The female elk is limited to producing only a few, relatively large, slow-growing young in her lifetime.

than ten thousand descendants (but see p. 123). What determines these remarkable differences in life history?

Realising that natural selection favours individuals that leave more descendants (see p. 36) one might jump to the conclusion that, within a species, parents of larger litters would be at an advantage over those of smaller litters. Extending that line of thought, one might also conclude that species, such as the Common Shrew or Harvest Mouse, characterised by larger litters would prosper relative to those, such as a whale or the elk, for which small litters are typical. Both conclusions would be wrong, but for different reasons.

First, the key to evolutionary success is leaving surviving offspring, or more particularly breeding offspring. Thus it would be counterproductive for either a shrew or a whale to, say, double its litter size if the net result was that each offspring received such poor treatment that the chance of survival was halved or worse. After all, there is only a limited supply of milk to go around (and lactation is more expensive than gestation), only limited time to devote to teaching the young, and only a limited amount of food to feed them. There comes a point at which resources spread too thinly are simply

236

squandered. This line of thought led to the suggestion that the litter sizes characteristic of a species have evolved to maximise the number of surviving offspring. If so, then overambitious individuals that bore extra-large litters would be so stretched that they ended up rearing fewer offspring: a case of counting your chickens before they hatch! Producing young that perish is an expensive waste of resources and opportunity. The optimum litter size will rarely be the maximum litter size.

Hedging their bets against the uncertainties of the natural world, mammals must adapt their litter size to that which gives them the best chance of rearing successfully as many young as possible in their lifetime. Females of species with the potential for long lives (a female elk might have a reproductive life of 10–15 years, while the female Pygmy Shrew is spent within a season) face repeatedly the substantial energetic demands and wear and tear associated with breeding. Therefore, we might expect these longer lived species to opt for litter sizes that are a bit smaller than those determined solely by instantaneous considerations of the tradeoff between infant survival and litter size; long-lived species have the option of pacing themselves early in the race to reproduce, and thereby may tot up a higher score in the end. At one extreme, producing no young in one year can be advantageous if it means young can be reared more successfully in the future when resources are more abundant. For example, Red Deer mothers produce heavier calves if they were yeld (barren) the year before; milk hinds (i.e. nursing mothers) do not show the summer peak in body weight and fat reserves characteristic of yeld hinds. Overall, 90% of yeld hinds conceive in the rut, whereas just 30% of milk hinds do so, hence calving in one year greatly reduces the chance of doing so the next. Furthermore, milk hinds that conceive do so on average one week later than yeld hinds. This web of effects shows that merely pumping out more calves is not necessarily the route to producing more surviving calves in a lifetime. So, remembering the first of the two incorrect conclusions, namely that larger litters lead to more descendants, we see that it is flawed because it confuses quantity with quality. A larger litter is only an advantage up to the point at which further additions diminish overall survivorship through straining the parents and their resources too much.

The case of yeld and milk hinds among Red Deer illustrates an unrelenting truth, that all life histories are a compromise. You cannot have your cake and eat it. To a milk hind, the ultimate cost of breeding is that she is more likely to die the following winter than a yeld hind. If she survives, she is less likely to breed the following spring than the yeld hind. Similar facts of life apply to very different species. For example, amongst badgers, females that rear cubs at the earliest opportunity (as two-year olds) suffer higher mortality than their contemporaries that postpone motherhood until their third year. These are the tradeoffs from which natural selection charts the optimal life history. The payoff, measured as the total score of surviving young over a lifetime, depends not just on the immediate result of breeding now, but on the consequences of doing so for future breeding opportunities. Evolution has adapted animals to manage their lives so that their family planning aims to maximise the summed total reproductive value of present and future breeding. This actuarial gamble takes into account the likelihood of surviving and breeding in the future. In the case of the Red Deer, these likelihoods are affected by many things: seven-year-old hinds have a good chance of surviving the winter whether they calve or not, but among 13-year-olds, one in three milk hinds is likely to die that year, whereas comparable yeld hinds have a 99% chance of surviving. Competition, as reflected in population density, also affects the gamble. At low population densities, yeld and milk hinds alike have a 90% chance of breeding the next spring, but this plummets to 20% for milk hinds in crowded populations, whereas the probability for yeld hinds is unaffected by crowding.

The second flawed conclusion, namely that, all else being equal, a species producing larger litters and therefore more offspring would out-compete another species producing smaller litters, is invalid because all else is invariably not equal. Some niches impose traits, such as small litters, on their occupants. Just as it would be impossible to design a satisfactory pig with wings, it would be an impossible task in biological engineering to design a whale or a walrus that spawned litters of 18 or so young annually. This is because tradeoffs limit the possibilities for evolution: a whale, in opting for being big, forgoes the ability to breed prolifically. In the absence of such tradeoffs, evolution could theoretically produce a demon creature that lived forever and produced an infinite number of offspring at infinitesimally small intervals! Before investigating the restrictions on life histories, let us first consider some of the things that affect mammalian family size.

Litter size

The availability of resources in Europe varies seasonally, and mammals adapt their litter sizes accordingly. Bank Voles breeding in winter have smaller litters on average than those breeding in summer. Similarly, as the year progresses, Wood Mice litters average 5.5 in spring, 6.0 in midsummer, and fall again to 5.0 in autumn; while Field Vole litters peak at an average of 7.5 in May, almost twice the September average of 3.9.

Litter size can also be affected by the mother's age. Bank Voles and Red Foxes are among the species that bear larger litters as they mature. But older Red Foxes (more than five years old) along with older Common Shrews have smaller litters than prime ones. In the case of the shrews, this is due to greater mortality among the unborn young of older mothers. In the case of Red Foxes, litter sizes depend on the combined influence of the numbers of eggs produced by vixens and early deaths in the womb, both of which are partly determined by the age of the mother. The number of eggs produced by the mother increases steadily with age (by 28% per annum in one study), whereas partial litter loss declines annually until vixens are four years old and then rises again. The net result is a fall in litter size in elderly mothers. One study of the numbers of uterine scars (examined post mortem, these scars show how many unborn cubs had been attached in the placentae) of urban Red Foxes in England showed that litter sizes rose annually for mothers of up to four years old and then fell by 55% into their fifth and sixth years.

Population size affects how much food there is to go around amongst expectant mothers. A study in America showed that Red Fox litters increased from 4.7 to 7.2 per female during three years of intensive fox control (presumed to reduce competition for food among the survivors). The influence of population pressure is illustrated by House Mice, which average litters of 5.1 when living under crowded conditions, but 6.2 when at low density. Litter size in rabbits falls when they grow old, which they rarely do!

The Common Mole demonstrates that there is also regional variation in litter size. Litters in both Britain and Germany average 4.0, those in Italy 5.0 and those in the Ukraine 6.0. These differences probably reflect variations in food supply. In the north of Norway, districts vary in the quantity and quality of elk winter food: the heavier the elk the earlier they breed in the spring and the greater the likelihood of having twins. Wood Mice and Bank Voles breed earlier when their food supply is good. The crucial hurdle for male Wood Mice is 21 g. If they reach this weight in February the females will soon be pregnant, but if the males fall short of this target in February females will not be pregnant until March or April. Variations in food supply clearly have a marked effect on the litter sizes of Red and Arctic Foxes. For example, while Red Foxes over much of Europe average four or five cubs, those of the same species in Ontario, Canada, average between six and eight. Similarly, Red Foxes in the south of Sweden, where food abundance is rather stable, tend to have litters averaging 6.4, but those further north, where vole numbers undergo violent cycles (see p. 127) have litters varying between 3.4 and 4.9 depending on current prey availability. Similar factors probably explain why Arctic Foxes living in Iceland (where lemmings and ptarmigan fluctuate wildly) may average litters of as many as 10–12 cubs in good years (and occasionally over 20). In this boom or bust situation the bad news in the Arctic is that in lean years for lemmings, the foxes may fail to breed altogether.

The reproductive system of female stoats accommodates the fluctuations in food supply caused by vole cycles. They ovulate many eggs (between 8 and 10, up to a possible 19) but not all of them develop if voles are scarce. Stoats can only adjust their litter size by reduction, since their commitment to delayed implantation (see p. 208) means that mating occurs nine to ten months before birth. Litter size is controlled by a mixture of abortion of unborn young and nestling mortality. In Britain 20% of the loss occurs before the embryos implant in the walls of the uterus, and a further 5% between implantation and birth. Fascinatingly, a similar overall percentage loss occurs in New Zealand where the stoat was introduced. There, however, pre- and post-implantation losses are almost equal (12–13%). The stoat's litter size is determined by a cause and effect relationship between food supplies and death in the womb. Good years are few, and when one occurs it pays the stoats, like the Arctic Foxes, to take a boom or bust approach to reproduction.

For some prey species, but generally not their predators, litter sizes increase at higher latitudes. This effect has been found in rabbits, some voles and, in North America, White-footed Mice. The breeding season is short at high latitudes, and females must base their reproductive strategy on their lifetime, as opposed to immediate, prospects. The limited time available for breeding in the far north means that, relative to more southerly individuals, a Meadow Vole in the Arctic would be best advised to invest in fewer but larger litters, even if this imposes a cost on its life expectancy (which is already rather poor, so perhaps it does not have much to lose). The Mountain Hare may package its young into one large or several small litters, depending upon latitude (and altitude). In Russia Mountain Hares produce an average of 2.4 litters per year at 57° North, with 3.6 leverets per litter; this corresponds with 8.7 surviving young per female. Further North, at 66°, 1.1 litters are produced, with 5.8 leverets per litter, corresponding to 6.4 surviving young per female.

Packaging offspring

Just as the number of offspring in a litter is important to their mother, so too is the way they are arranged in her womb. Pygmy Shrews, for example, have two horns to their uteri into each of which an ovary sheds eggs. The two ovaries shed eggs independently of each other, and it is also a matter of chance which eggs are fertilised. In the same way that somebody tossing a coin sometimes gets a run of heads or of tails, we might expect that sometimes more embryos would develop in one horn of the uterus than in the other. However, remarkably, female Pygmy Shrews, and quite a few other mammals, generally end up with approximately the same number of embryos on each side of their uterus. It seems that the mother has three ways of balancing her embryonic load: she can resorb the surplus on one side, or she can cause a fertilised egg (blastocyst) in the crowded horn to migrate around to the other horn, or, and this is thought to be rarer (although it is known to occur in sheep), the blastocyst may migrate through the wall of the crowded horn and make its way through the body cavity (coelom) until it arrives in the less crowded horn. All these mechanisms are thought to be controlled by the mother's body, although how they are controlled is a mystery. The phenomenon of a balanced distribution of embryos in the two sides of the uterus is most common in species that need to be especially quick and agile in escaping predators, or have especially heavy babies, or small litters. This suggests that balancing the embryos is an adaptation to prevent a female's agility (in the face of danger) deteriorating into an ungainly wobble when heavily pregnant. The imbalance would be especially punishing for species with litters of only two (according to chance both members of 50% of such litters would be jammed into one horn, causing an extreme list to one side). Not only is the likely effect of an imbalance greatest for species with small litters (a heavily pregnant bat with both embryos lodged to starboard would face aerodynamic disaster), but the percentage of embryos that must switch sides (or be resorbed) to rectify the imbalance is highest in small litters. This is because the larger the litter, the less likely it is that, by chance, all the babies will be in one horn, just as the more tosses of a coin you make, the less likely it is that they will all fall head-up). To rectify the chance imbalance in litters of two would, on average, require 25% of embryos to switch sides, whereas in litters of ten only 12.3% would on average have to swap.

Mothers may wish to spread their embryos out between the horns of their uteri for reasons in addition to minimising the handicap on their agility. The unborn infants may squabble amongst themselves, and it is in the mother's interest to reduce this antagonism by spacing them out. In rabbits, for example, crowded embryos suffer high mortality, presumably due to competition between them. Furthermore, there are cases where embryos of one sex, generally male, lead to the deaths of embryos of the opposite sex if they implant side by side in the womb (see p. 71). Unborn infants may also interfere with each other's adult sex lives in ways that the mother would benefit from preventing. For example, female House Mice that were sited between two brothers in their mother's uterus grow into butch adults with delayed puberty, longer oestrous cycles, and poorer production of young in comparison to their sisters which were not next to males in the womb. Indeed, female mice growing from embryos that were sandwiched between two males grow up to be more aggressive towards males, and less attractive to them, than females who were not exposed before birth to the masculinising company of their brothers.

In contrast, male House Mice that, as embryos, were not next to other males grow up to be less aggressive towards other males as adults, and less paternal towards their offspring than other males. Male mice that are sandwiched between two brothers in the womb grow up to scent mark at higher rates, and to mate more vigorously than their more effete brothers who grow up between sisters. It would certainly seem to a mother's advantage to arrange her unborn babies in ways that controlled these effects of uterine position, but amongst House Mice there is no evidence that they do so. However, in the 5th century BC, Hippocrates made the remarkable assertion that male embryos were usually on the right, and females usually on the left horn of the womb. Nobody paid much attention to Hippocrates' statement until it was noticed that in the uteri of Mongolian Gerbils (amongst which the masculinising effects of being sandwiched between two male foetuses cause adult females to have only half the lifetime fecundity of other females) 55% of male babies were indeed located in the right horn, and 58% of females were located in the left horn. A small but important difference with the consequence that baby male gerbils in the right uterine horn and baby female gerbils in the left uterine horn were less likely to find themselves next to a member of the opposite sex than were, respectively, male babies in the left uterine horn and females in the right horn. Considering the radical social and reproductive effects in later life of uterine placement in these rodents, there is clearly great pressure on mothers to manipulate the juxtaposition of their unborn young in the womb. Exactly how they achieve this is unknown, but the clustering of males in the right horn and females in the left horn of the gerbil's uterus is sufficient to lower the odds of inappropriate sexual influences on each baby.

The mechanical consequences of pregnancy impose limits on litter size for agile species such as this Flying Squirrel which cannot afford to be too heavily weighed down with unborn young.

So litter size is an adaptive trait, like sharp canine teeth or camouflage, and the question of how many young to have in a litter is inexorably linked to the question of how to package them. The young can be born pink, squirming and incapable (altricial) or furred and frolicking (precocial). Precocial young might seem a better bet, being far from helpless, but to produce them generally requires longer pregnancies leading to larger (essentially older) babies. Because, weight for weight, female mammals have approximately the same internal space available for their total litter, opting for precocial young inevitably means smaller litter sizes. For example, members of the squirrel family have heavier babies, but fewer of them, than comparably sized members of the mouse family. Leverets are born to mother hares in trios, hairy and with their eyes open, following a pregnancy of 41 days. Rabbit kittens are born five at a time, naked and blind, after a 30-day gestation. Similarly, Wolves produce about five altricial young, while Roe Deer bear a couple of precocial ones. Actually there is a geographical cline (i.e. gradient) in Wolf litter sizes (e.g. from 4.0 in the Northwest Territories of Canada to 6.5 in Alaska). The choice, in evolutionary terms, between altricial and precocial young depends on whether the particular species' lifestyle makes it safer to nurture the young inside or outside the mother.

The need for arboreal athleticism and the laws of aerodynamics probably respectively explain why both the Barbary Macaque and Common Pipistrelle have single, altricial young. A single baby bat weighs 20% of its mother's weight at birth, while members of a litter of ten mice might each weigh 4% of their mother's weight. Agile species cannot afford to be weighed down by pregnancy (although the mother macaque is still burdened by carrying her infant). Tree-climbing Pine Martens have litters averaging three young, while ground-dwelling stoats have an average litter of nine. However, a female stoat drops her infants in a burrow as soon as possible, because pregnancy ruins her figure for burrow hunting.

How often to breed

Having considered how many young to have and how they should be packaged, the next question is: how often to have them? The options are to breed once or more than once. Breeding once in a lifetime (semelparity) is found among mammals only in the mouse-like marsupial genus, *Antechinus*, and a handful of similar Australian species. Male *Antechinus* mate many times in one breeding season and then expire before their first litter is born. Some species of shrew are almost as extreme, living for only one breeding season but squeezing in the production of more than one litter. Most mammals are markedly iteroparous (produce several litters). What are the pros and cons of these two approaches? The all or nothing approach of *Antechinus* can only pay off when the survival prospects of each young into the following year exceed those of each adult. One might normally expect the reverse to apply: adult survival being higher than that of juveniles, due to their greater experience and proven survival skills. The more an adult's chances of surviving to breed again exceed a youngster's chances of surviving to breed at all, then the greater the payoff for producing several litters rather than one. The fact that this differential is usually great is evidenced by the fact that only four genera among all 1,000 or so genera of living mammals are semelparous.

Life histories vary hugely both between species and, in some respects, between populations of the same species. Some breed often, some breed once, some have large litters, others have one offspring at a time; young may be born helpless or they may be up and running within minutes. But these characteristics are not displayed by mammals at random. Large litters of highly precocial young is an unheard-of combination. The necessity for compromise offers only the options of more, smaller offspring versus fewer, larger offspring. Life-history traits tend to come as a package deal, but what determines which package a particular species opts for? The answer has three parts: life histories are determined by ancestry, the laws of physics (i.e. physical limitations) and the environment.

Ancestry

Animals have only a finite amount to invest in their offspring, both in terms of their bodies and in parental care. The harsh reality is thus that opting for offspring with a protracted childhood forces a parent into rearing only a few of them. Alternatively, if a species opts to produce many offspring, then it has to sacrifice parental care. This is a pretty obvious case of not being able to have your cake and eat it. The options open to mammals are greatly curtailed by the inescapable consequences of bearing live young, nourishing them with milk and being homiothermic. For example, the choice of abandoning parental care for the sake of producing copious young (an option favoured by many fish, amphibians and turtles for example) is not really open to mammals.

Physical limitations

One physical limitation on life histories is size. This is because the offspring of larger mammals tend to take longer to develop than those of small mammals. This is for two reasons. First, the litters of larger mammals are born at a relatively smaller proportion of their adult weight, which means that they have more growing to do. Second, because of their larger size and consequent proportionally slower metabolisms, they do that growing more slowly. The need for longer parental care for the slow-growing babies of big mammals can be reduced by packaging the litter into a few larger offspring rather than many tiny ones, each with even more growing ahead of it. This is why smaller litter sizes are common among larger mammals. It takes a mother Brown Bear up to four years (but more often one and a half years) to educate her twin offspring, and it takes a Red Deer stag six to seven years to grow the musculature and antlers that allow him to compete for mates. Smaller species have faster metabolisms in proportion to their body weight and their 'souped up' engines drive their bodily processes faster, which includes growing faster. For example, although they are close relatives and similar in many respects, the offspring of a 100 g water vole will double their weight faster than the offspring of a 1.4 kg muskrat. The result is that larger mammals have longer intervals between generations and a lower potential for increasing numbers from one generation to the next. This conclusion, which reverberates from the rate of chemical reactions in each mammalian cell, is at the heart of their population dynamics. It takes a Norway Lemming a minimum of 14 days to grow to a size at which it can bear its first litter of six young; it takes a Musk Oxen two years before it can produce its first single calf. Mammalian species with fast, expensive metabolisms have a greater capacity to produce young than those with slower metabolisms, so they are pre-adapted to population explosions.

These physical facts of life affect the ways in which mammals can cope with different environments. Environments vary: they may be constant, seasonal, unpredictable or ephemeral.

Unstable environments

Some environments favour those species with a capacity to breed explosively. In unpredictable environments the supply of resources may sometimes exceed the current demand for them; when conditions improve the survivors of a period of stricture may find themselves in a land of plenty. Similarly, in an ephemeral environment the first immigrants may be free of shortages. Then, reproductive success of immigrants is unrestrained by their competitive ability or by population density. There will be plenty to go around and the best way to capitalise upon it is to churn out lots of young as fast as possible while the going is good (and to produce plenty of emigrants before the going gets bad). Such changeable environments are called r-selecting, and species whose lives follow this pattern are said to have been r-selected by evolution (the enigmatic name 'r' comes from an equation in the theory of population dynamics, where the term r stands for the potential for population increase). In Europe, mammals such as the microtine voles and members of the mouse and rat family are r-strategists, with explosive reproductive rates. At least intermittently, they achieve very high population densities, but often poor individual survival due to, for example, heavy losses to predators.

Some of the predators are so closely linked to these prey that they have the same characteristics. Weasels are a good example of a species adapted to exploit unpredictable prey. Here again the link between body size, speed of growth and reproduction may play a role: stoats and weasels both hunt voles and are similar in many respects. However, weasels are smaller and their long, thin diminutive physique is a bodily design that is expensive to heat (which may partly explain why their metabolism runs even faster than might be predicted from their small body weight alone). The result of their small size is that weasels can breed twice or even three times yearly (uncommonly fast among carnivores) and a young female can have her first litter in the same year as she was born. Therefore, weasels can capitalise much faster on a sudden increase in voles or lemmings than can stoats, which are locked, by delayed implantation, into producing only one litter annually (see p. 210).

Stable environments

In contrast to the breathless rush to reproduce imposed by environmental uncertainty, mammals in a stable or seasonally predictable niche will utilise every nook and cranny. In these circumstances supply and demand will have reached a balance, and populations will be limited by the availability of food and other resources. The need to compete for scarce resources puts a premium on individual prowess, with the emphasis on quality and not quantity. Parents will secure more descendants in the long run if they invest heavily in a smaller number of offspring, cosseting each as they groom it for entry into the competitive fray. Equally, the young are heavily dependent on their parents' competitive ability, so parents under these circumstances must also invest heavily in their own muscle power. Such species are said to be K-selected ('K' being from the same equation as the r (see above), and referring to the carrying capacity, in other words the maximum number of individuals that the environment can support). K-selection promotes individual success under conditions where individuals are living in a population at the carrying capacity of its environment.

The difference between r- and K-selection, and the life histories each imposes, is a bit like the two ways of playing golf. In 'match play', players compete hole by hole and the one who wins the greatest number is the victor. In 'stroke play' both competitors tally the total number of strokes played over 18 holes and the one with the best score wins. In both r- and K-selection, and stroke and match play, the ability to survive the course ultimately decides the winner, but the best tactics to employ to achieve victory are quite different. In one case (K-selection and match play) the yardstick is a battle between individuals (and only indirectly involves their total score against the adversities of the course), while in the other (r-selection and stroke play) the battle is directly with the course (and only indirectly with the other competitor). In both cases the ultimate challenge is the same: staying alive to breed (or keeping the ball in play). In both cases the rewards are the same: maximum lifetime reproductive success (or glory), but the tactics for competing are different due to the different circumstances. For animals living in a stable population, the evolutionary winners are those with the highest score in their lifetime reproductive success, and it does not matter when in their lifetime they accumulate that score. In contrast, under boom-or-bust (r-selecting) circumstances, it is crucial to produce offspring today in case there is no tomorrow, and so it is advantageous to breed prolifically while young, even if doing so leads to premature death and so lowers the possible lifetime score.

In comparison to the care lavished on their young (and themselves) by K-strategists, r-strategists appear to treat their offspring (and themselves) as throw-away commodities. Mammals in stable environments tend to produce small litters of advanced young that are indulged with protracted parental care. Because they live in stable environments they must be K-strategists (good competitors), therefore they must be long-lived, and therefore they must be big. Being big is laden with consequences such as a proportionately slower metabolism. This brings us back to slower growth and longer pregnancies, compounding the necessity for heavy investment in young in K-selecting environments.

Alternative lifestyles

We have seen that a basic fact of mammalian life (homoiothermy) and a law of physics (the relationship of area to volume, see p. 62) not only has implications for body size, but even more far-reaching consequences for life history and therefore for populations. The maximum life span of a 10 g mammal is likely to be a year; that of a one tonne mammal may be closer to a century. However, the one tonne mammal may take ten years to mature, whereas the 10 g one takes only a month. Mammals that have grasped the opportunity to grow big or small in order to occupy a given niche (such as the Harvest Mouse or the elk, see p. 61) may find themselves locked into a particular life history due to the consequences of their body size. To clamber on an ear of wheat, the Harvest Mouse must be minuscule, and we might speculate that the fact that it can produce large litters at short intervals is a spinoff from, rather than a motive for, its small size. However, rapid churning out of offspring is also a trait that fits them well to the short life of a wheat field. In some species small size is a means to achieve mass production, favouring many undeveloped young over fewer precocial ones (see p. 238). For example, the high reproductive potential of voles and lemmings is a key to their success in unpredictable

The tiny female Harvest Mouse can produce many large litters of small but fast-growing young in her lifetime.

environments – success bought with small body size, and paid for through their high metabolic rates which permit rapid growth. Thus, r-selected mammals tend to be small. Among small mammals, some have especially souped-up metabolisms, apparently to adapt them to extremely r-selected lifestyles. The high metabolism of a female lemming enables her to have her first dozen offspring by the time she is 42 days old. To achieve this her metabolism races in comparison to that of the comparably sized, but relatively K-selected, Wood Mouse which, with a conventional metabolism for its size, produces litters of four to seven young once or twice (to a maximum of four times) a year. The demands for high productivity on the Brown Lemming are colossal, their population peaks exceeding the troughs by 125-fold (see p. 127). The metabolic rate, and thus the need for frenzied fuel consumption, is somewhat less in the Varying Lemming whose population cycles vary only 38-fold.

The association between metabolic-rate and life-history strategies is strong – the life expectancy of most species is about 800 million heartbeats (or 200 million breaths). However, there are exceptions. For instance the Virginia Opossum has a short life (18 months), a low metabolic rate but a very high capacity to churn out offspring. Cases such as the opossum have caused the most recent thinking on life histories to shift away from emphasising metabolic rate as the driving force and propose instead that reproductive effort is scaled to life span. Whatever the emphasis, a short life demands living (and in particular breeding) at a fast pace to squeeze a full life into the allotted span.

The r-versus-K distinction is a relative one: a Brown Rat is r-selected relative to a Minke Whale, but K-selected relative to a Field Vole. Similarly, different populations of the same species can be arranged on this continuum. For example Bank Voles living on Skomer, an island off Wales, grow larger and have smaller litters than those on the mainland; that is, the island population behaves in a more K-selected manner. In the light of the idea that reproductive effort is linked to life expectancy it seems likely that Skomer's voles live longer than their mainland counterparts. Indeed this is probably the case, because Skomer voles are free from predators.

With this link between size and life-history strategy, it is not surprising that the r-versus-K distinction affects the process of population limitation (see p. 120). Habitats associated with r-selecting uncertainty tend to be inhabited by populations limited by density-independent factors, whereas species living in K-selecting habitats tend to be limited by density dependence.

Some mammals are born to lifestyles that demand a spurt of growth. Young shrews and seals alike may not be weaned until they have reached a higher weight than that of the average sub-adult of their species – both have taxing lifestyles ahead and need to build up reserves of fat before tasting independence. Pinnipeds generally grow at a dramatic rate and circumstances dictate that nursing is brief (see p. 76). Most European seal species are weaned within six weeks; the Walrus is an exception by being weaned at 18 months. Marine mammals need to grow fast and lay down lots of fat before facing oceanic waters that will not only drain heat from their bodies, but also present serious challenges to their novice foraging skills. Other lifestyles also demand rapid growth: small insectivores, such as the Pygmy White-toothed Shrew may double their birth weight in just four days. The Common Pipistrelle weighs 1 g at birth and flies at 25 days by which time it weighs 3.5 g (the adult weight of about 4 g is attained at 50–60 days).

A final restriction on the options open within a mammal's life history is its ancestry. Some options simply are not open to particular types of animal. It is no good wondering whether the Wild Boar, faced with massive migrations, might be better off if it could fly – pigs simply do not have that option.

Chapter twelve

Family planning

Which sex?

Not only do mammals vary in the sizes of their litters, the development of their young at birth and the number of young they produce in a lifetime, but natural selection has also produced variation in the sex ratio of the newborn. Individuals of each species have evolved to maximise their own reproductive success, that is, maximise the number of descendants they leave (see p. 36). So when we discover that more sons than daughters are born to wolves living at higher population densities than those at lower densities, to Grey Seals pupping earlier in the season, to House Mice bred in laboratories and African Wild Dogs under most circumstances (the ratio is about 3:2 in favour of males in wild dog litters), then we must ask whether these skewed sex ratios increase the parents' fitness.

The explanation of these exceptional sex ratios becomes clear if we understand why most mammals produce equal numbers of sons and daughters. The explanation was spotted by biomathematician R.A. Fisher in 1930, and represents one of the most elegant ideas of the century. Since every individual has one mother and one father it follows that the average reproductive success of each sex must be the same, irrespective of whether they specialise in fidelity or philandering. Therefore no individual parent will gain by producing a predominance either of sons or daughters. For example, a lineage that produced a surfeit of sons would leave their descendants in a world with a shortage of females, putting the parents of daughters at an advantage: thus every departure from a 1:1 sex ratio would prompt a self-correcting demand for the rarer sex, with the result that the average parent would, over a lifetime, produce equal numbers of sons and daughters. This reasoning hinges on the assumption that offspring of each sex are equally costly to produce, and equally rewarding in terms of the grandchildren they spawn. It is the departures from this assumption that explain why it is sometimes adaptive for parents to produce a predominance of one sex or to invest differently in their sons and daughters.

Unequal sex ratios

There are two ways in which parents can favour one or other of the two sexes of their offspring: the numbers produced of each sex, and the investment devoted to each. Consider, for example, the case of the Coypu.

Coypus, like many mammals, live in polygynous societies. That is, one male monopolises several females. In this system the number of females with which a male can mate depends greatly on his competitive prowess. In these circumstances, rearing sons that are stronger than the average can make a great difference to the number of offspring they eventually produce as grand-offspring for their mother. Since most females breed irrespective of their fortitude, the quantity rather than the quality of daughters is most

The Coypu represents a rare case of an alien species (introduced to Britain from Argentina) which has been successfully eradicated. During its brief but tenacious residence in Britain, post mortem studies of the victims of the eradication campaign revealed an intricate system of sex-ratio manipulation in the unborn litters of females.

important in maximising the number of grand-offspring through the female line. On average, female Coypus in early pregnancy carry equal numbers of sons and daughters. However, some females become pregnant with larger or smaller litters than the average, and some with litters with more sons than daughters or vice versa. Coypu mothers also differ in their physical condition, as indicated by their fat reserves. When circumstances combine so that chubby mothers in good condition are pregnant with a small litter which includes a preponderance of daughters, they selectively abort the whole litter. Soon afterwards they will become pregnant again. It is odds-on that the replacement litter will be larger than the smaller-than-average one just jettisoned. The result is that females in the best condition produce most sons (because they jettison litters laden with daughters). Because the mother's condition affects her ability to nurture her offspring, the young of a corpulent mother grow stronger and her sons may be expected to sire more offspring than the more feeble sons of leaner mothers. Thus, for the healthy female Coypu, the opportunity of producing strong sons is too good to miss.

Similar lines of thought, though not necessarily the same mechanism, may serve to explain why the sex ratio of American Mink born in smaller litters is skewed to favour males (a few high-quality sons being a more profitable investment of maternal resources than a few high-quality daughters or a swarm of lower-quality sons or daughters). Intriguingly, a preponderance of male offspring is born to high-ranking spider monkeys and presidents of the USA (of which 42 have yielded a total of 90 sons and 60 daughters.

It is fairly straightforward to grasp that there are circumstances under which natural selection can favour females that produce unequal numbers of sons and daughters, but it is awe-inspiring to think of the complexity of the mechanisms that might permit them to do so. Perhaps the female Coypus monitor the hormonal condition of their embryos in order to ascertain their sex. Golden Hamsters achieve the same result by a different mechanism. Amongst hamsters it is also the case that the larger the litter, the greater the proportion of young that will be female. On average 70% of baby hamsters in litters of three are male, whereas only 37% are male in litters of 18. A similar link between litter size and sex ratio shortly after birth exists in Mongolian Gerbils. Surprisingly enough, quite a lot of gerbils have been delivered by Caesarean section, and this revealed that immediately before birth there was no such tendency for small litters to be predominantly male. This suggests that the mother gerbil, and probably hamster too, is manipulating the sex ratio of her young once she has had a chance to count them. People who keep pet hamsters have long since discovered that they

Female Romanian Hamsters occasionally eat their babies, which may be part of a mechanism to foster sons in small litters and daughters in larger ones.

have a tendency to eat their babies, and dismissed this as an aberration of captivity. However, killing and eating female babies in small litters and male babies in large litters may pay off. If putting all her efforts into a few sons will lead to them growing up to be disproportionately successful studs, then cannibalising daughters in small litters could yield the female a net gain in numbers of grand-offspring. Similarly, a lone male baby in a large litter might have no prospect of the pampered body-building infancy necessary to turn him into a successful suitor, and so the female might as well cut her losses and recycle him into milk for her daughters. Such macabre speculations are unproven, but they fit the facts.

Another theory about biased sex ratios arose out of a study of African bushbabies (wide-eyed nocturnal primates), which give birth to a preponderance of sons. Bushbabies live in loose-knit communities of males and females which feed on gum and fruit. The idea stems from the observation that their food is patchily distributed, and only a few patches are sufficiently rich in food to sustain a nursing mother during the period when her offspring shackle her to a small area. If a female is to breed, she simply must have access to one of these bountiful patches. In fact, females often share these oases of fruit and gum with their daughter or sister. Males, on the other hand, range widely and never depend upon these special patches. Thus, closely related females are thrown into fierce competition of a type that is irrelevant to their brothers. The result, for a mother, is that while her son's fitness is unlikely to depend on the sex of his siblings, her daughter's fitness is likely to dwindle the more sisters she has. Mothers, so the theory concludes, are thus better off producing more sons under these conditions of local resource competition among related females. The same argument can be adapted to explain why more sons are born to White-tailed Deer and Wolves in crowded populations – that is in conditions when competition between female kin may escalate.

Male versus female strategies

Many mammals live in polygynous societies, and many of these are sexually dimorphic (i.e. the sexes differ in size). For example, male American Mink are 75% heavier than females. The fundamental difference between males and females is the underlying reason for sexual dimorphism: sperm are much cheaper to produce than ova. A single ejaculate of a male Brown Rat may contain 44 million sperm. He is ready to mate again after four to eight minutes, and continues to bombard the eggs six to ten times during the next hour until he is sexually exhausted. However, if at that stage he meets another attractive female he will start again with undiminished ardour, having kept a reserve of some 700 million sperm. Incidentally, and to emphasise the point, the Wild Boar's ejaculate contains more than 78,000 million sperm.

In contrast, a female rat sheds a mere 3–18 eggs (the average is 10) each time she ovulates. Each egg is 1,845 times the size of a male rat's spermatozoon. If she is not mated, it will take her another week to generate another clutch, and once she is mated the female is left holding the baby. During pregnancy her reproductive machinery will be tied up for 20–23 days until she gives birth to a litter of seven to nine young which, since males cannot lactate, she will have to nurse for a further 21 days. During pregnancy the female rat will be storing fat for the siege ahead, and she will mobilise some 60% of her bodily fat reserves when it comes to paying for lactation (at the same time she will also have to increase her food consumption by half). The inequality in the reproductive opportunities open to the two sexes is potentially immense. Males can most readily maximise their reproductive success by mating with many females. Females, in contrast, are caught in a cruel bind and are greatly constrained by the costs of eggs (which take time to replace), pregnancy and lactation, so they can only mother a relatively small number of young. They can best increase their fitness by investing in the quality, rather than the quantity, of their young. Females can do this by their direct care of young, and by selecting the best father. In this way, competition between males, choice of mates by females, sexual dimorphism

255

and favouritism for sons become entwined in an aspect of natural selection known as sexual selection.

In many species, one consequence of the evolutionary pressure on males to mate with many females is that males that have mated to satiation with one female are swiftly aroused by a new female. This is called the Coolidge Effect after the American president of that name. The story goes that during a tour of a farm, Mrs Coolidge saw a cockerel and asked how often it mated with the hens. When she was told that the answer was dozens of times a day she requested the poulterer to tell this to her husband. Shortly afterwards the president was shown the cockerel and told about its mating habits. 'Same hen every time?' he enquired, to which the poulterer replied, 'Oh no, Mr President, a different one each time,' whereupon the president said, 'Tell that to Mrs Coolidge.'

Male competition and female choice

Because eggs are more limited in supply than sperm, females could be thought of as a resource over which male mammals compete. A big male will defeat more rivals, win more females, and thus sire more offspring. If his competitive prowess is inherited by his sons, they too will prosper. Therefore females, with an evolutionary eye to maximising the number of their descendants, will select the winning males as mates. While male–male competition may impose the 'choice' of winner on the female, it is also true that good quality males are a resource for which females may compete. In the face of these sexual inequalities, females hold several trump cards.

First, they may be able to choose with whom to mate, which may lead to males evolving alluring secondary sexual characters such as full manes, long beards, loud roars, or even specially potent scents. Second, they may organise themselves as a limited resource, grouping together to increase competition between males. This leads to the evolution of large male body size and armaments such as the antlers of Red Deer or the neck pads of Elephant Seals. Indeed, among ungulates, primates and seals, the males of species in which females form harems are larger than females relative to the average membership of the harem. The larger the harem, the larger the males. This need to compete for or attract females is why males cannot afford to be small in polygynous society. It is also the reason why, especially for females, feeble sons are worse than useless. This takes us back to Fisher's argument about parental investment in offspring of each sex (see p. 251). One way of investing differentially in the sex likely to leave most grand-offspring is to give birth to more of the favoured sex. The other way, having produced a litter, is to invest more heavily in the upbringing of the favoured sex. The reproductive success of individual offspring is often likely to be affected by the amount of parental investment they receive, but the influence of this investment may not be the same for sons and daughters. In polygynous mammals, the reproductive success of males is greatly influenced by their size and strength. The adult size attained by many mammals is influenced by their growth rate as youngsters. Therefore sons are likely to benefit more than daughters from extra food while young. For this reason, parents in polygynous societies are likely to invest more in individual sons than in individual daughters.

Favouritism

The Red Deer is a polygynous species. Hinds pregnant with male calves prolong their pregnancies in comparison to those bearing daughters, and newborn male calves are typically about 0.5 kg heavier than newborn females. Subsequently, sons nurse more frequently than daughters. Such favouritism may not be alien to our own species, in which historical records reveal that in many societies élites pamper their sons more than do other classes. In the case of the Red Deer, this favouritism appears to cost the mother dearly, because the mothers of infant stags tend either to miss the next breeding season altogether or to give birth later than hinds that bore hind calves. Calf birth weight varies widely between years and between individual mothers. Small hinds consistently produce calves weighing 4–5 kg, heavier hinds have calves of 7–8 kg. Larger, more dominant hinds produce a higher proportion of male calves than smaller hinds do; hence mothers produce more female calves at the beginning of their reproductive life, less when older and higher up the pecking order. The payoff for this extra burden of rearing sons is potentially enormous if the care lavished on the young stag weighs the odds in his favour when he eventually joins battle. The stag may be six or seven years old before his sex life begins (although sexually mature at two years), and it may last only three or four seasons, since fighting success, harem size and mating success usually fall rapidly after ten years old. During this brief but orgiastic career, a successful stag may repay his mother's investment with the better part of 50 grand-offspring. A less successful male, leaving none, will become an evolutionary dead end. There will be many more dead ends than successes because a tiny minority of stags father the great majority of the next generation. We might pause to marvel at the fact that average male reproductive success is actually the same as that of the average female, so that the huge imbalance in the mating success of different stags has no effect whatsoever on the overall sex ratio at birth.

There are circumstances, however, which counteract the forces promoting sexual dimorphism and polygyny. Where the food supply is spread out, or the need for paternal care very great, a male may be unable to monopolise more than one female. For example, the solitary, ice-breeding Crabeater Seal forms monogamous pairs and is not sexually dimorphic (whereas the fur seals are polygynous and highly dimorphic). Furthermore, some lifestyles are incompatible with having differences in body size between the sexes. For example, tree-dwelling species tend to be less dimorphic than ground-dwelling ones, presumably due to the demands of arboreal gymnastics. Similarly, constraints imposed by lifestyle may explain why rabbits and hares are not dimorphic. Although males are generally as large or larger than females in most species of mammal, this is not a universal rule. Females are invariably bigger among birds of prey, and generally so among insects. Among mammals, females are larger than males in many species of mongoose, bat and mysticete whale. Female bats produce large babies, so the demands of airworthiness may require them to be large in order to stow such heavy cargo. Female whales have to withstand a massive drain on their energy due to the rapid growth of their foetuses and subsequent lactation. Further, they need to survive losing blubber as milk while they migrate back from their tropical breeding grounds to the polar feeding grounds. Perhaps that larger size might help the famished mother with depleted blubber to withstand the cold when she arrives in polar water.

Chapter thirteen

Life strategies

Conflict and care

Parents are wonderfully generous to their offspring. The mother Grey Seal, for example, stores up 68 kg of fat prior to producing her 14 kg pup. During three weeks of lactation, the mother loses 3.6 kg per day, while the pup gains 1.6 kg per day. By the time the pup is weaned, the mother has lost 65 kg of her fat, retaining a mere 3 kg for insulation. Fathers may also may work hard – dog-foxes diligently feed their cubs – but among mammals mothers generally shoulder a greater burden of caring for their young than fathers do. Why? The answer may be slightly different for monogamous and polygynous species, but in both cases the governing principle is that parents of both sexes are adapted to maximising the number of descendants they leave. The two sexes can best pursue this same long-term goal by behaving differently, however.

Monogamous parents

In a strictly monogamous pair both parents have an equal stake in the welfare of a given litter and so should invest in it equally. However, only females can lactate, so fathers must deploy their energies differently. In some cases the lifestyle of the species offers the father opportunities to contribute directly to his young. For example, male wolves and jackals can regurgitate food for their family and Arctic Foxes carry prey back to the young and their mother. In other cases opportunities for paternal invest-ment are necessarily indirect: there is no reason for a male herbivore to carry leaves back to a fawn that can readily browse unaided, but the father can devote his time and energy to keeping a lookout for predators and defending the territory that will sustain his family. This case describes exactly the circumstances of the Mara or Patagonian Cavy, but does not apply to any European mammal because there is really only one monogamous European herbivore. This is the Beaver, which does not need to carry food to its young. So fathers invest their parental care in whatever way is most profitable, and thus there is a sense in which they become involved with the infant directly only when they have nothing better to do. A commonly quoted example of this comes from two species found outside Europe. Gibbons are apes from South-east Asia, and they are invariably monogamous. The males of one species, the Lar Gibbon, are so preoccupied by the demands of territorial defence that they have little time for direct care of their young. In contrast, the similar and equally monogamous Siamang Gibbon appears less belea-guered by intruders, and males take over most of the non-lactating care of the young. The difference can probably be traced back to the Lar Gibbon's more specialised diet, which means it needs to defend a larger territory; patrolling probably takes up the time it might otherwise have devoted to carrying its infant.

Polygynous parents

For polygynous mammals things are rather different. The greater limi-tations on the number of offspring a female can ever produce mean that each offspring looms larger in her reproductive life than it does in its father's (see p. 216). After all, while a mother is bearing one litter, a father may be siring several. The result is that mothers may best promote their fitness by tending their infants (and by persuading the father to stay and help her), while in certain circumstances fathers may best promote their fitness by striving to mate with more females. Considering this from the viewpoint of our own species whose circumstances in the western world push us towards monog-amy, we might be tempted to apply a judgement that a highly polygynous male abdicating direct paternal responsibilities is behaving churlishly while his mate behaves selflessly. On the contrary, in evolutionary (as distinct from moral) terms, both are pursuing the same goal, namely the highest possible representation of their offspring (more specifically their genes) in the next generation. It is simply that ecological and physiological circumstances mean that different approaches have a better payoff for each sex.

There is another reason why mothers tend to invest more in their offspring than fathers, and it applies particularly to species with promiscuous mating systems (see p. 215), such as the American Mink, amongst which males take turns at mating with a single female. The fact is that in all species with internal fertilisation, females can be certain that they are the mothers of young they bear, whereas males can never be sure. This uncertainty devalues the significance of any given young to its putative father relative to the certainty enjoyed by its definitive mother. Consequences of this state of affairs may explain the variable behaviour of male Hoary Marmots (an American relative of the Alpine Marmot) depending on their social circumstances. Some populations of Hoary Marmots live in large colonies with many adult males and a consequent high risk of cuckoldry. In these colonies males exhibit no paternal behaviour, and devote themselves energetically to promiscuity. Elsewhere, their food supply dictates that Hoary Marmots live in isolated family groups, in which a pair associate with their adult daughters. In this case opportunities for cuckoldry are minimal, and male marmots devote considerable attention to their offspring. However, as is so often the case, this explanation is just one possibility. Another is that male Hoary Marmots with isolated harems nurture the future of their lineage more effectively by caring for existing young than by seeking out more females.

The relationship between parent and offspring would seem to be an unusual instance of perfectly shared goals. Both have their eggs (almost literally) in the same basket, since the evolutionary success of both depends on the offspring's survival. This coincidence of self-interest can be seen in the behaviour of mother and nursing infant. Among domestic sheep (and presumably also mouflon), the ewe produces more milk than her lamb can drink during the first two weeks of its life, so the only limit to the lamb's intake is its appetite. If the mother should have twins, this period of milk on demand is prolonged to about three weeks and the ewe ensures fair play by only allowing the twins to suckle when both are hungry. (Indeed, a hint that the coincidence of interests is not perfect has crept into the scene by the time the lambs are a month old, whereupon the mother may often reject their strenuous requests for milk.) However, although we look for harmony between parent and offspring because of their shared genes, the fact is that they only share some of their genes. Indeed, because an infant mammal has inherited half of its genetic make-up from each parent, it is only half as interested in the well-being of either parent as it is in itself. Furthermore, because each litter represents only a part of the female's lifetime reproductive

As they grow, mouflon lambs seek to suck more milk from their mother than she provides. This is part of an increasing divergence in the self-interest of parent and offspring.

success, she has to balance the demands of the present lamb against those of future lambs, that is against her own future reproductive potential.

Thus, the fact that parents are genetically different from their offspring, and that parents may maximise their lifetime reproductive success by having subsequent offspring, leads inexorably to conflict between parent and offspring over the appropriate balance of give and take in their relationship. Care of an infant costs a parent time and resources, both of which might otherwise have been devoted to producing other offspring.

Parent–offspring conflict is most conspicuous when mothers attempt to wean their young. A Wild Boar sow that lies down to prevent its piglets nursing, or a lynx that cuffs its demanding kitten, is not merely nudging her offspring along the unfamiliar road to independence – she is displaying a real conflict of interest between them. A hungry fawn's bleatings are not mere petulance, but an expression of a genuine disadvantage. Initially, while the mother's care is indispensable, the offspring's interests are inseparable from its mother's. But natural selection will favour mothers who wean their young at the point when the benefit from nursing them further is outweighed by the cost of doing so. That cost is measured in lost opportunity to invest in other young. The infant also has a stake in those other siblings, through the genes they probably share. However, that consideration would prompt it to volunteer for weaning only after it had enjoyed twice the benefit of maternal investment its mother deemed appropriate, because it is only at most half as related to its siblings as it is to itself. This probably explains why young chimpanzees resort to violence in the attempt to interrupt their mothers' mating, thereby seeking to postpone the arrival of a competing infant. A more arcane conspiracy is that of juvenile Japanese Macaques (relatives of the Barbary Macaques of Gibraltar), which interrupt the nursing of their younger siblings. Such interruptions tend to bring the mother back into oestrus and so lead to the production of a new sibling. This suits the interests of older juveniles, who have outgrown the rewards of their mother's direct care, and benefit most from her producing more of their brothers and sisters. In contrast, new additions to the family are a disadvantage for younger macaques, which are still trying to postpone weaning because they are still young enough to benefit directly from maternal care. Interestingly, elderly Red Deer hinds appear to invest more heavily in their offspring than do younger hinds (as judged by the condition of the fawns in winter relative to that of their mother), and older Olive Baboon mothers postpone weaning their young and so avoid the turbulent weaning typical of younger mothers. This is probably because these older mothers have limited future reproductive potential and so it pays them to put all their

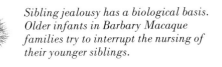

Sibling jealousy has a biological basis. Older infants in Barbary Macaque families try to interrupt the nursing of their younger siblings.

efforts into the young in hand, rather than planning for the welfare of future unborn.

Vested interests can prompt strife or harmony in the family. Parents benefit from their young behaving altruistically towards each other, just so long as the benefit derived from the recipient of the altruism is greater than the cost to the donor (because parents are equally related to all their offspring, they tend to treat them equally, see p. 36). But for an offspring to benefit from promoting the well-being of its sibling, the beneficiary's prospects must be improved by twice the cost to the benefactor (since full siblings share only half their genes). Therefore it may pay egocentric youngsters to behave badly towards their siblings, whereas parents will intervene to prevent this.

Dispersal

When mammals reach maturity, they usually leave home. Although some individuals of all European mammal species disperse eventually, there is wide variation in how they go about it. Coypu disperse in their first year, but beavers bide in their parents' lodge for two years. Male Red Foxes disperse as yearlings, but on average travel different distances in different habitats (the longest record in Britain was 52 km, while in Sweden it was 500 km). Conversely, some vixens never leave the territory in which they were born. Most badgers of both sexes never disperse and those that do so wait until they are more than two years old. Thereafter, males disperse alone, but in some populations groups of two or three related female badgers may disperse together. It seems that they work as a coalition to overthrow a resident female and take over her social group. In Wolves and Golden Jackals both sexes of youngster may be equally likely to emigrate, but in most mammals males are more likely to disperse than females. When they do disperse, males tend to travel over longer distances than females. However, in a minority of cases (the African Wild Dog is an example) dispersal is a female prerogative. Why do these differences exist between species, between the sexes and between individuals? But first, why disperse at all?

Why disperse?

Most mammals seem to leave home voluntarily, rather than as a result of being physically chased out (although relationships within the family may have deteriorated before emigrants take the decision to go). Generally juveniles opt to disperse when their prospects (essentially of breeding successfully) are better elsewhere. They may be prompted by competition for food, shelter or mates at home. Such emigration may simply take a youngster out of the frying pan into the fire, however; competition may be just as tough in the outside world. Another, and perhaps crucial, reason to emigrate is the risk associated with inbreeding. Inbreeding can be dangerous because it increases the risk of an offspring inheriting a double dose (one from each parent) of some dangerous, but rare, gene. In contrast, the likelihood of two unrelated parents sharing the same hereditary disability and both passing it on to the same offspring would be low. Dispersal may not be due to one factor alone, an individual leaving its family home may simultaneously be avoiding competition with dominants, minimising competition with its kin, or avoiding inbreeding.

Ecologically, the most obvious consequence of dispersal is that it can lead to colonisation of new habitats. Therefore we might expect dispersal to be a conspicuous aspect of the natural history of species living in unpredictable environments, where there is a good chance that the grass really will be greener on the other side. This appears to be the case: Brown Rats, for example, make a mass exodus from cereal fields at harvest, and roam widely looking for new resources.

Avoiding inbreeding

Zoos often have to deal with small breeding stocks and this, unfortunately, puts them in a position to demonstrate that inbreeding really is risky. The general rule to emerge from these studies in zoos is that infant mortality is a third higher among the offspring of parent–offspring and full-sibling matings than it is among the offspring of unrelated parents. For example, inbred reindeer and muntjac suffered, respectively, 43% and 37% higher mortality in zoos. However, there are exceptions, and some species seem to tolerate inbreeding better than others.

Quite apart from the risk that inbreeding will throw up a bad penny, it also cuts down the variability between offspring, and thus reduces the chance of any one of them happening to be well equipped to survive a sudden environmental change. Investing in inbred young is much like gambling on raffle tickets that all bear the same number.

Some wild mammals actively seek to avoid inbreeding, but as it happens the best examples come from outside Europe. Adult female Prairie Dogs (a species of North American ground squirrel) sometimes live in the same 'coterie' as their parents, but fathers and daughters rarely mate; however, the daughters solicit the attentions of their father's rivals from neighbouring coteries. Most female Prairie Dogs breed in their second year, by which time their father will have left the family group. However, there are always some who breed in their first year, and these precocious females are generally the daughters of fathers that have died or otherwise disappeared early from the group. In another North American ground squirrel, the Belding's Ground Squirrel, males that have already bred successfully are more likely to disperse than those that have not. This is rather unexpected in so far as they seem to be quitting while they are winning. But social organisation of these squirrels is such that successful breeding males live in the company of increasing numbers of their adult daughters, and thus dispersal may be in order to avoid inbreeding. Two to six male lions join forces in coalitions that dominate prides of lionesses. The pride males would not normally relinquish their hold on their harem voluntarily, and certainly would not normally transfer to a pride with fewer females. However, they do volunteer for just such a transfer when they have occupied a pride for sufficient time that their daughters are approaching sexual maturity. Similarly, female Olive Baboons avoid mating with males born within their troop, but seek matings with immigrants. The same mechanisms may explain the fact that people raised communally in the same Israeli kibbutz tend to seek sexual partners outside their childhood peer group. This may indicate that, in evolutionary terms, it is a safe rule of thumb that you may be related to those with whom you grow up.

The power of the avoidance of inbreeding as a force promoting dispersal is clearly supported by the Australian mouse-like *Antechinus*. Male *Antechinus* die after a frenzy of mating, and therefore never see, far less consider incest with, their daughters. Nor, of course, can fathers compete posthumously with their sons. Nonetheless, all young male *Antechinus* disperse. Competition cannot be the explanation, because the place of the emigrants is filled by equal numbers of immigrants. Even only-sons disperse, and they have no brothers with which to compete, and their fathers are dead before their birth. Therefore, competition between males cannot be the impetus for their dispersal. The only remaining explanation is that sons, if they did not disperse, could face the risks of inbreeding with their sisters. So, in the case of *Antechinus*, dispersal alters the genetic make-up of the community, but not its competitive milieu.

While inbreeding may have its genetic hazards, so too may mating with a total stranger. One idea is that mammals mixing in the same population are adapted to the same circumstances, and to mate outside that community is to throw away a long history of shared adaptations and compatible lineages, rather like spoiling a well-tried recipe by introducing an unpredictable ingredient. This thought prompted the unproven notion that not only is it advisable to avoid inbreeding, but also that there is an optimal level of outbreeding – it may pay to disperse, but not too far.

There are, however, species that appear to pay no heed to inbreeding – for example, it is commonplace for Bat-eared Foxes to mate with their parents or siblings. It may be that some species, such as Naked Mole Rats, are actually adapted to inbreeding, having done it for so long (perhaps due to the constraints of a closed social system, or perhaps as the result of developing from a small isolated population of founders) that they have already bred-out any fatally dangerous genes and become, as it is termed, homozygous (this means that individuals are remarkably similar genetically). Golden Hamsters in captivity are the prime example of a successful and highly inbred species, since they are all descended from one female and her 12 young. Cheetahs are an example from the wild of an intriguingly genetically uniform species. One view is that this is because they have come so near to extinction in the past that all current cheetah descend from very few ancestors.

Avoiding competition

Voles provide dramatic evidence of another compelling force favouring dispersal: competition. Where fences are erected around communities of voles, blocking any opportunity to disperse, their numbers increase to such an extent that the food supply is exhausted and the population crashes. Quite apart from competition for food, individuals may be forced into exile through competition for mates. Dwarf Mongooses, for example, live in packs of up to 20 individuals, averaging eight adults, only one pair of which breeds. Individuals of this East African species are more likely to disperse if they find themselves in the company of elders of their own sex (which presumably block their promotion up the reproductive ladder). Of course, it is all very well saying somebody must go, but what if there is nowhere to go? Often the answer is doom, but some species, for example beavers and jackals, will accept some failed emigrants back into the bosom of the family.

Who disperses?

If somebody has to go, who should it be? There is some indirect evidence, from three species of North American vole, to support the theory that dispersal is in their blood. That is, some individuals differ genetically from others by having a penchant for dispersal. The idea is that dispersing genes may become more common in crowded populations. Dispersal is commonest in microtine rodents during the increasing phase of a population cycle (rather than at the same population density during the downhill phase of the cycle). A genetic predisposition to disperse may prevail under these periods of population growth. In Scandinavia, Meadow Voles from northern, cycling populations react differently to crowding than those from southern, non-cycling populations. This suggests that there are genetic differences in the tendency to disperse between separate populations of the same species.

However, in several other species of vole there is no evidence of such a genetic mechanism. In these cases, aggression may be the sole trigger. There is debate as to whether it makes most sense for dominants, subordinates or middling individuals to disperse (and some evidence for each view), but the general consensus is that dominants stay at the expense of subordinates. (It is also widely believed that dispersing is inherently more dangerous than biding, and thus often an unwelcome option for the individuals forced into it.) Aggression appears to trigger dispersal in wolves, where most dispersers are deposed dominants or aspiring low-rankers. However, although it is often assumed that dispersal in mammals arises because dominant adults actively expel subordinate juveniles, in fact there is scant evidence that this is the general rule. It is equally plausible, if not more so, that dispersers volunteer to emigrate.

A case study of wolves illustrates the complexity of the topic. One adult female wolf roamed over 4,000 km^2 alone for 14 months before meeting a lone male with which she established a 69 km^2 territory. The following year the male was killed and his place (and pups) adopted by a lone male that had previously travelled a range of 300 km^2. Two of the three pups dispersed, but one female stayed to usurp her mother as the breeding female, a role she held for the next eight years. Some of that pair's offspring dispersed far afield (as far as 190 km away), others settled nearby. Two females that settled in nearby territories abandoned their mates when their pups died, and returned to their parents' pack. One of these daughters remained at home indefinitely, the other moved on again after a few weeks. This wolf family was tracked in America, but there is no reason to assume that the lives of their European counterparts are any less involved.

Both competition and inbreeding tend to cause one sex to be more likely to disperse than the other. In the case of competition this is because rivalry between individuals of the same sex is likely to be greater between one sex than the other. This is because members of the same sex are likely to be competing for partners of the opposite sex (and perhaps competing for the most similar food). In the case of inbreeding, the simplest way to avoid inbreeding is for one sex to leave home and the other to stay. But which sex should go? The costs and benefits of dispersal are very different for the two sexes. Inbreeding may be much more expensive for females – in polygynous species they invest more heavily in each young than its father does, and so females might be expected to disperse to avoid the risk of inbreeding. However, in polygynous mammals (most mammals, that is) females are the sex over which males compete, with the result that most reproductive losers are male, and they have to leave town. The fact is that among mammals males are almost always the dispersing sex, but the reverse applies to birds. This paradox may arise because male mammals tend to defend their mates (which in turn defend food resources) whereas male birds tend to defend their territories (to which females are attracted either by the quality of the male or by the quality of his territory). If the general rule were that the sex which defends breeding resources, such as food, does not disperse (because that sex stakes its success directly on those resources), then female mammals and male birds would be the stay-at-home sexes. This seems to be the case. In monogamous mammals both sexes disperse, although males tend to go further.

Avoiding hardship

Migration

When the going gets so rough that individuals of species cannot cope, evolution has provided them with two options: to hibernate or to migrate. Migration is a term beset with sloppy usage, largely because it involves long-distance movements and is thus sufficiently similar to dispersal that the two are often confused. Migration is distinguished from dispersal by involving a return journey, being directional and often by recurring on an annual basis during which animals travel *en masse*; dispersal is generally a one-off, one-way ticket to an unknown destination.

Among European mammals, migration is especially common within the marine species. Blue Whale, Fin Whale, Sei Whale, Humpback Whale, Northern Right Whale, Sperm Whale, Minke Whale, Northern Bottle-nosed Whale, Pygmy Sperm Whale, Narwhal, Beluga, Long-finned Pilot Whale and White-beaked Dolphin all go south in the summer. Hooded, Harp, Ringed and Grey Seals, and Walruses, move large distances in response to the shifting distribution of ice. Bats, too, commonly migrate from a summer range to winter hibernacula. Among terrestrial mammals, at least some populations or some individuals of prey species, ranging from lemmings to Bison, and including Elk, Musk Ox and Wild Boar, migrate, as do predators such as Arctic Foxes, Wolverines, Polar Bears and Steppe Polecats.

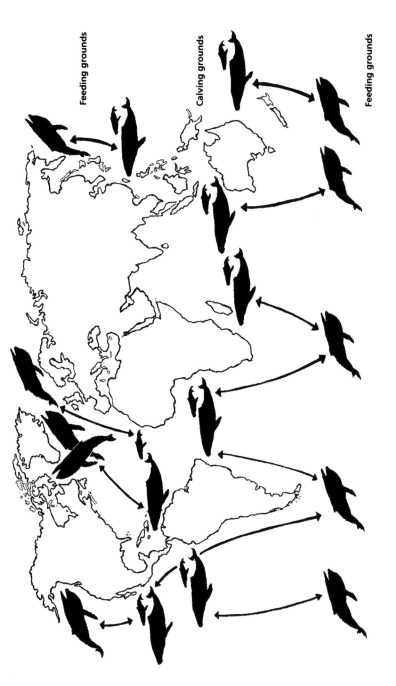

Feeding grounds

Calving grounds

Feeding grounds

Generally hidden from view, the Humpback Whale undertakes immense annual migrations from polar feeding grounds in spring to equatorial calving grounds in winter.

Food, or the lack of it, is the reason for some migrations. The epic migrations of antelope across African grasslands take them from dry-season retreats close to water supplies, to lush but short-term wet-season pastures. This scenario may apply to Reindeer which migrate north in spring, having their calves en route to the nutritious, snow-free vegetation that sprouts during the short growing season of the tundra. In autumn they retreat south, to taiga woodland, where it is warmer and the snow through which they must dig for food is less deep. Elk in north-east Europe migrate up to 300 km between summer and winter feeding grounds. They give birth half-way between the sheltered winter range and more exposed summer range. Migrants travel to find the places offering the best, most predictable, food supply for breeding or preparing to breed. The Humpback Whale, and other mysticete (baleen) whales, spend the summer in polar regions where they put on 50–70% of their body weight in blubber as they gorge on an explosive proliferation of krill. Krill, a mixture of plankton, tiny crustaceans and small fish, are most abundant in cold waters because more oxygen can dissolve in water at low temperatures. At the beginning of the winter, the Humpback migrates some 7,000 km to subtropical waters where food is often scarce, to give birth, suckle and mate. Why do whales travel so far? Travelling such vast distances seems less of an undertaking in the watery world of whales than it might to a land mammal: for example, a Fin Whale tagged off the coast of Iceland was found 1,700 km away ten days later. It may be that what the whales lose in food by moving south they gain in heat conservation. Although the warm waters may not offer enough food to sustain whales throughout the year, they are much less punishing for the newborn whales whose small bodies lose heat faster than those of their giant parents (see p. 60). While the youngsters live on milk they are buffered from local food shortage and can devote more of their energy to growth rather than keeping warm. Smaller cetaceans undertake shorter migrations. The Harbour Porpoïse, whose fish prey is less seasonal than krill, builds up 40% of its body weight in blubber, makes a short migration south to give birth and then returns to icy waters. Its young are born relatively large, at 30% of adult body weight, and grow rapidly to near adult weight.

A harsh climate may drive the tiny Common Pipistrelle and the Whiskered Bat over 1,500 km in eastern Europe. These bats must travel to winter hibernacula that are sufficiently warm to save their small bodies from freezing to death. Noctules migrate many hundreds of kilometres, and the Greater Mouse-eared Bat, Schreiber's Bat and Barbastelle Bat have all been recorded migrating over more than 100 km.

The migrations of prey are wrapped in a complex web with those of their predators. Wolves follow the movements of Reindeer (which in Canada are called Caribou). In spring wolves travel ahead of their prey, find a den and give birth to coincide with arrival of the herds and the birth of the young Caribou.

The question of how migrating mammals find their way has been largely ignored, although masses of research has been conducted on migrating birds (which are known to use sun-compasses, the stars and the earth's magnetic field). However, in one experiment Wood Mice were transported some distance from home in a darkened box subjected to an artificial magnetic field. These mice set off to navigate home, travelling in a different direction from that taken by other Wood Mice that had been transported without the distorted magnetic field. This study suggests that at least one species of mammal uses magnetic field orientation in navigation. However, methods of navigation in other species are largely unknown.

Hibernation and dormancy

Migration is one way out of a tight corner, hibernation is another. Hibernation is a deep sleep during which the body's metabolic processes slow to a tick-over rate in order to save energy. A hibernator's body temperature drops to just above air temperature and can go as low as 2 °C. The result is that energy costs fall to as little as 10% of their normal level. This trick of switching off has evolved independently in six mammalian orders: the monotremes, the marsupials, the insectivores, bats, rodents and primates. European hibernators include the Eastern and Western Hedgehog, Alpine Marmot, Spotted and European Souslik, Edible, Forest, Garden and Common Dormice, hamster, the Pygmy White-toothed Shrew and all European bats.

Hibernation is the prerogative of small mammals. Large mammals do not need to hibernate because they can store sufficient fat to survive food shortages, or they can migrate a sufficient distance to evade the hardship. Also, their larger size means that they cool down and warm up more slowly, making the entering and exiting of hibernation prohibitively costly and slow. However, larger species may enter a less profoundly deep sleep called dormancy. Bears, Eurasian Badgers, Raccoons and Raccoon Dogs can all become dormant (a state known as carnivorean lethargy), during which their temperatures drop by about 10 °C to about 29 °C, and their metabolic rate falls by about a half (a true hibernator's pulse may drop to 3% of its normal rate). The winter denning of bears may last for more than 100 days during which they do not feed, urinate or defecate (the rectum is stoppered with a

Winter is a tough time for mammals, and amongst Carnivores those in the north have developed various ways of coping. The options open to them depend partly on their size and hence their energy demands (see p. 62). The largest is the corpulent Eurasian Badger (1) which lays down an abundant layer of fat and retreats for protracted lethargy in cosy underground chambers. The smallest is the weasel (2) which is simply too small to accommodate such a layer of fat; indeed, weasels must be trim at all times to squeeze through burrows in pursuit of prey. Nonetheless, operating under the snow they can keep warm, as if in an igloo. The Red Fox (3), in thick winter coat can withstand the most brutal cold, and provisions refrigerated stores for the winter (this fox is digging up a food cache made weeks before). The Pine Marten (4), being medium sized, finds itself in a predicament between that of its relatives the Badger and the Weasel: it continues to hunt, but when inactive it returns to a cosy lair.

faecal plug). The sole source of energy and water is fat. The bear's horny foot pads are shed during dormancy, and the bears lick their tender feet when they awaken; this explains the legend in North America and China that bears survive the winter by sucking nourishment from their feet. Badgers can also remain underground continuously for 70 days. During this period they enter bouts of torpor lasting more than a day, during which their temperature falls to 29 °C, and their pulse falls from 55 to 25 beats per minute. Dormant carnivores are capable of coordinated actions – bears, for example, give birth while dormant.

True hibernators, like hedgehogs, put on weight dramatically as winter approaches (hamsters store food instead). When the temperature falls below a critical threshold (16 °C for hedgehogs) they fall into a sleep with slow breathing and a heart rate of only a few beats per minute. This requires changes in the blood plasma to prevent blood from clotting as it chugs slowly round the bloodstream. Hibernators lay down deposits of special brown fat, the primary function of which is to generate heat, especially during the difficult process of awakening. Hibernators wake up every so often, sometimes to eat (e.g. hamsters) or drink, and sometimes to check the day length which determines their breeding cycle (e.g. Turkish Hamster, see p. 205).

The big risks of hibernation are dehydration and being caught napping by a predator. Both these risks put a premium on finding a secluded retreat. The Northern Birch Mouse will die if forced to hibernate in a dry atmosphere. Burrows are suitably humid places to hibernate. The shortage of oxygen and build up of carbon dioxide in a burrow might normally narcotise a sleeping inmate, but hibernating birch mice are adapted to awaken if the carbon dioxide concentration gets dangerously high, whereupon the occupant ventilates the burrow before going back to sleep. Clusters of Horseshoe Bats generally hibernate in damp caves, and huddle together to conserve heat. Because their numbers are dwindling, their clusters tend to be smaller and have a larger surface area to volume ratio, which loses heat faster than would a larger cluster. This chilling adds yet another threat to their survival. Serotine Bats wake every few days, not to eat but to drink.

Winter remains a dangerous time, even for hibernating mammals. Alpine Marmots lose weight over winter, and many die. Marmots live in social groups of a pair and up to 18 lower ranking members, and all of them huddle throughout the winter in a shared hibernaculum. Members of larger groups generally lose less weight over winter than do those in smaller groups and infant mortality in larger groups is lower over winter in larger groups, apparently because the adults act as hot-water bottles for the youngsters. Indeed, amongst the lower ranking group members, those that lose most weight are closely related to the youngsters, whereas those with no kinship to the youngsters lose little or no weight. Therefore, it seems that the life-saving role of acting as a hot-water bottle is expensive, and it is a burden borne only by individuals with a genetic stake in the young. In groups where potential snuggling companions are not closely related to the youngsters, infant mortality is not diminished by larger group size. Clearly this provides a motive for parents to tolerate the prolonged presence of their adult offspring, whose warming influence not only keeps the whole family in better condition, but can be a lifeline to their younger brothers and sisters. These advantages of staying at home are further enhanced because almost a quarter of those that stay eventually inherit either their parents' territory or a neighbouring one, whereas those that disperse suffer higher mortality. Indeed, to judge by the fact that those which lose most weight over winter are the most likely to disperse subsequently, it seems that there is competition to stay at home, with the weakest competitors being ousted.

Perhaps the most remarkable idea about mammalian reproduction in particular, and sexual reproduction in general, is that its purpose is to produce an offspring that is different from its parent (see p. 201). That the parents have survived raises the spectre that generations of parasites have had time to evolve towards the means of bringing about their downfall. To keep ahead of the parasites and to protect their descendants, parents need to shift the evolutionary goal posts at each generation. The success of genes in one generation becomes their liability in the next. By the time that next generation comes around the parasites will surely be on the verge of defeating the defence that hitherto worked well. It is a remarkable insight into the intricacy of evolutionary forces that all the myriad nuances of courtship, sex and parenthood most probably arose from the need of animals to defend themselves from viruses.

PART FOUR

MAMMAL CONSERVATION

Chapter fourteen

Rarities and resources

Little Red Riding Hood has a lot to answer for; her story can be traced back to the Middle Ages when Europe was thickly forested and Grey Wolves were found nearly everywhere. Now, through an unhappy blend of misplaced fear, thoughtlessness and a sometimes brutal determination, this once abundant species is restricted, within western Europe, to a few mountainous refuges in Portugal, Spain, Italy and Scandinavia. In Norway and Sweden, individual wolves number less than ten. Nowadays when, each year, one or two wolves cross from Finland to Sweden, the result is a national furore, with jubilation from some quarters and cries of dismay from others. In 1964 and 1978 pairs survived for long enough to breed in Lapland, but the result has always been the same: relentless tracking by snow-mobile until the immigrants are dead. To be fair, part of the animosity stems from fear on behalf of the Lapps for their reindeer. But it is stretching a point to invoke a similar agricultural excuse to vindicate the persecutors of the famed Varmland Wolves in southern Sweden.

In 1984, following a century when no wolves had bred below the Arctic Circle in Sweden or Norway, a pair bred in the spruce woodlands in Varmland, midway between Stockholm and Oslo. They were apparently a magnificent pair, approaching 50 kg in weight and each regularly killing healthy adult elk single-handedly (see p. 148). Against all the odds, their scattered and beleaguered descendants produced a litter in four of the ensuing five years. But the existence of these wolves has shown that the Little Red Riding Hood complex still flourishes, and has prompted furious debate. Despite legal protection, wolves are being killed one by one. The Varmland Wolves were estimated to kill up to 200 sheep in a year (in a region where every year about 95,000 sheep die of natural causes before coming to market) and to kill too many elk (where 125,000 are shot each year by hunters). More to the point, perhaps, is hatred for wolves which is derived from fabulous notions of wolves threatening man. In fact, excepting those crazed by rabies, recorded history can provide no documented account of a European wolf spontaneously attacking anybody.

The wolves' European strongholds are in the east (they are quite common, and still hunted under bounty in some parts of the former USSR), but in western Europe, Italy provides the best illustration of their plight. Wolves were exterminated from the Alps late in the 19th century, and from Sicily in the 1950s. A few stragglers survive in the Apennine mountains, amounting to about 100 animals in an area of 8,500 km². This fragmented population lives as isolated packs of between two and four (to a maximum of seven) animals, travelling territories of 200–400 km². More than two-thirds of their food comes from scavenging at refuse dumps. However, since Red and Roe Deer were exterminated from these mountains during the 19th century, only sheep remain as suitable prey. For traditional shepherds this was a bearable burden: by restricting their flocks to about 300, penning them at night, and deploying guard dogs, the sheep were generally safe. Modern shepherds may tend, but not pen, as many as 2,000 sheep, are often strangers to the region and have no guard dogs. The result is frequent pilfering by wolves, and the occasional devastating 'surplus kill' (of up to 200 sheep; see p. 103). Even so, shepherds have not been the biggest threat; rather the wolves have fallen victim to both a chemical and a genetic onslaught. In the first place, hunters were profligate in their use of poisons – but this was banned in Italy in 1977. Secondly, some lone she-wolves mated with shepherd dogs, although the liaison appears to be unstable; after all they are effectively the same species despite 10,000 years of domestication. The practice of referring to them as a distinct species is really only a matter of convenience. While such cross-breeding has doubtless been happening since time immemorial, it takes on a sinister aspect when wolves are so very scarce: they face extinction by genetic dilution. The pernicious problem of the dog within is illustrated by two litters born to what appeared to be she-wolves in the Abruzzo National Park in Italy. Both litters contained two black and two wolf-coloured (agouti) pups. Both litters probably had dog fathers, but the motley offspring unveiled grandparental indiscretions. The gene for black fur is recessive, so to show itself in the pups it must be inherited from both parents. Thus, the mothers must have been hybrids as well as the fathers being dogs. The agouti colour of wolves is usually a dominant genetic trait, so first generation hybrids generally look very wolfish (see p. 37).

It seems that wolves have survived in Italy by dodging extinction: a pair establishes itself, breeds, and after three or four years has built a pack that attracts attention. Most are killed, but some slip through the net (perhaps dispersing over up to 80 km – see p. 264) to establish a new pack elsewhere. The ban on poisons hugely improved wolves' prospects, and in the meantime new areas have been colonised and the population may have trebled. Some Red Deer have been reintroduced to the Abruzzi Mountains in Italy, in an attempt to rebuild a natural predator–prey system (see p. 107), but the wolf's predicament is frail at best.

The high population density of modern Europeans has been generally incompatible with the survival of large predatory mammals. The Brown Bear survives in a few fragmented populations, their small numbers and isolation making it highly likely, irrespective of persecution, that they will go extinct. A directive of the European Community in 1992 requires member states to investigate the feasibility of reintroducing species that have been driven to recent extinction, but the reintroduction of predators is inevitably fraught with socio-economic difficulties.

Wolves are not alone amongst Europe's carnivores in trying to finding space in the modern world. For the dispersing youngsters of all large mammals, the problems of finding a territory have increased in the modern world as wilderness has dwindled. The problem is especially acute for such giants as the Brown Bear. Human persecution of these massive carnivores has continued since prehistoric times. In Europe, about a dozen Brown Bears cling on in Italy's Abruzzi Mountains, where farmers are fully compensated for any damage they cause. In the Pyrénées two populations total 20–30 individuals, and 40–50 more live in two populations in the Cordillera Cantabrica of northern Spain. Their crumbling foothold on the planet is all too typical of the predicament of Europe's Brown Bears, and illustrates the precarious situation of all large carnivores, which, ravaged by constant hunting, were few and far between by the mid-19th century. Sweden, where bears almost went extinct in 1925, now has about 600, enough to allow controlled hunting of those raiding domestic livestock. In Sweden and Norway, the governments compensate for damage by bears. The former Yugoslavia has around 300. Having been down to 1,000 Brown Bears in 1940, Romania now has 4,000 – more Brown Bears than any other central European country – due to state protection and limited shooting. Yet in Russia, where there were 32,000 European Brown Bears at the last count,

The few remnant Brown Bears that survive in western Europe amidst alpine human settlements must find winter retreats in which to hibernate once they have gorged on autumnal berries. The widespread development of tourism and ski resorts has shattered the tranquility of the bears' mountainous strongholds.

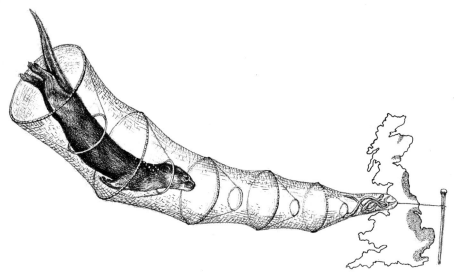

Eel fyke nets are used principally on the eastern waterways of Britain (in the shaded areas) and can be modified with guards to prevent the drowning of otters. The one shown does not have such a guard.

hunting is permitted throughout the year. All in all, however, there is some room for optimism: the 1991 estimate of 35,000–40,000 European Brown Bears is a 35% increase from 1979's figures.

Wolves and bears have been victim to direct onslaughts by people, but other species have been threatened indirectly by human activities. As European Otters began to recover from the effects of pollution by pesticides (see p. 286), their recovery was impeded by the fyke net. This is a device used by fishermen to catch eels in Britain and Continental Europe. The fyke is rather like a sock fitted with one-way valves, into which eels swim and accumulate where the toe of the sock would be (called the cod end). In the old days these nets were made of cotton and otters attracted by the concentration of eels could, and irritatingly did, chew through the cod end to loot the traps. With modern mono-filament netting, too tough to chew, the otters are thwarted, and instead pursue the eels into the net, become entangled and drown. Between 1975 and 1984, when otters were scrabbling back from the verge of extinction in England, 89 were reported drowned in underwater traps, and these reports are probably only a quarter of the true casualties. At a very practical level, conservationists tested the design of various guards that could fit over the entrance to the next, excluding otters but allowing eels free access. A design was found which had no detectable effect on the number of eels of saleable size (over 100 g) captured, but which successfully excluded otters. The result of this simple but important work is that various parts of Britain are passing by-laws to enforce the use of guards on fyke nets.

Reintroduction

Reintroduction has been the salvation of the European Bison. Once widespread, this species was exterminated from Sweden in the 11th century, Britain in the 12th century and France in the 14th century. Eventually, its only stronghold was Poland, and there it was protected as royal game (Aurochs enjoyed the same protection, but sadly the last of them succumbed in 1627). The ravages of the Napoleonic wars left only 300 bison in 1812, but it was the lawlessness following World War I that led to a poacher killing the last wild bison in 1919. The bison's final refuge had been the Bialowiecza Forest and it was to there in 1929 that three captive bison, from zoos around Europe, were brought. After a captive breeding programme the first bison were released into the wild in 1952. Now the Bialowiecza herd numbers some 250 adults, and populations have been established in three other Polish forests.

The European Beaver's hold on survival has been a similar case of brinkmanship. Having invaded Sweden in about 6000 BC (via a landbridge then linking Sweden and Denmark), beavers spread across the region. While they were numerous in the 14th century, the toll of hunting for their flesh, pelts and the gooey scent castoreum (as medicine) began to deplete their numbers. By the 17th century they were in trouble and the last Swedish beaver was killed in 1871. There is an eerie poignancy to the thought that

beavers, more than any mammal (save man), have shaped parts of the Swedish landscape; the boggy spruce woodlands are an epitaph to millennia of beaver dams. However, these landscape architects have had a reprieve: between 1922 and 1940 about 80 beavers were reintroduced to Sweden (from Norway where they had fared rather better), and within 20 years they had dispersed down river systems, allowing their numbers to rise to more than 2,000. Today the beaver population numbers 100,000. In Finland, following the near-extinction of the Euro-

Poland

The European Bison is confined to only three forests (shaded), all of them in Poland.

pean Beaver, the Canadian Beaver was introduced. Now Finland is home to about 6,000 Canadian Beaver and only 200 European Beaver, and the fear is that spreading, immigrant Canadian Beavers from Finland will compete with the European species in Sweden. In 1992 the European Community passed a directive instructing member states to evaluate reintroductions that would restore their former fauna. Although reintroduction is certainly a difficult issue there are some promising candidates. For example, in Great Britain the last recorded supposed beaver sighting was in Scotland near Loch Ness in 1527; beavers might be reintroduced at minimal inconvenience. Another candidate for Scotland would be the Wild Boar, although their capacity to damage crops makes this problematic. Furthermore, so long as sheep farming remains a significant factor on the Scottish mainland, the frequent calls for reintroducing wolves are likely to fall on deaf ears.

Reintroductions require careful planning, and often raise perplexing questions about the provenance of the animals to be released. Aside from trying to assure that the translocees are of an appropriate genetic constitution, it is also important to consider the vexatious issue of whether the most suitable stock is captive bred or wild caught and, in either case, how they are to be acclimatised to their new surroundings. For example, due to loss of habitat because of a decline in coppicing as a management tool in broad-leaved woodlands, the so-called Common Dormouse has become very uncommon in Britain. In an attempt to bolster their numbers, both wild-caught (translocated) and captive-bred dormice were released. Some 45% of the former survived, but only 22% of the latter did so. This was apparently because the captive-bred dormice were more inclined to travel on the ground, perhaps a little nonchalantly, when crossing clearings. In contrast, their wild-born counterparts tended to keep to the branches and when forced to they scuttled apprehensively across clearings. Clearly, captive breeders need to devise ingenious conditions that promote in their stock whatever behaviour patterns most promote their survival when released.

Habitat change

The Greater Horseshoe Bat, whose range spans from Britain to Japan, has suffered drastic declines recently (98% of the British population has disappeared within one century). It is now extinct in parts of northern Europe. These bats forage for beetles and cockchafers over woodland and pasture, and they require a mosaic of these habitats to ensure that they can find suitable hunting grounds whatever the conditions. For example, during the windy chill of early spring, woodland is better for foraging, while pasture seems more bountiful in summer when moths and beetles are abundant. Both these habitats have shrunk with the modernisation of agriculture. Within a patchwork of habitats the movements of members of one colony may span 700–2,500 km^2, and in autumn the breeding males each occupy a separate roost, at which oestrous females visit them. Females roost communally and during pregnancy their sociability is vital: by huddling together to generate a fug of some 30 °C they ensure a high temperature for the development of their embryos. The roofs of caves seldom exceed 10 °C, so the necessary warmth in roosts was, in times gone by, generated by thousands of clustered bodies. Nowadays, Greater Horseshoe breeding roosts are almost always in buildings, where the heat of the sun often raises the temperature nearer to that needed by the pregnant females. Selecting warm buildings is necessary because the bats are so few that shared body heat is insufficient to generate the level of heat required.

Problems brought about by agricultural change may have triggered the decline in numbers of Greater Horseshoe Bats, but they were exacerbated by disturbance of traditional hibernation roosts in caves, and fatally worsened when roof timbers were treated with insecticidal wood preservatives. In Britain, for example, where single roosts once numbered thousands of Greater Horseshoe Bats, the total population is now scarcely 2,000. However, practical ideas are under test in an attempt to create new roosts: for example, wet blankets are hung in suitable lofts to create the humid atmosphere that minimises the problems of water loss through evaporation during hibernation. Most importantly, the major roost sites have been purchased by a conservation trust to protect them from development.

Pollution

Another species decimated by pesticides is the European Otter. Since the end of the 19th century otters have declined in Britain, Finland, Holland, Italy, Sweden and Switzerland, and a number of explanations have been mooted. Some people blamed hunters, others blamed hard winters, others disturbance (such as that caused by the massive popularity of angling) and others competition with American Mink (see p. 144). However, no one idea seemed sufficient until one study in Britain showed that the numbers of otters took a sudden dive throughout the whole country in 1957. This was suspiciously soon (two years) after the introduction of two insecticidal seed dressings – dieldrin and aldrin. These insecticides dissolve in animal fats and therefore accumulate in bodily tissues. When these fats are called upon, for example during food shortage, large concentrations of the chemicals may be released into the bloodstream with fatal results. By 1956 there were reports of pigeons dropping dead in mid-flight and in the early 1960s Red Foxes were dropping like flies. It seems certain that it was these toxic chemicals that precipitated the otter's downfall. But both chemicals were banned in Britain in 1962, so why did the otters not recover? The short-term answer is doubtless that the half-life (the time taken for half of a sample to lose its toxicity) of dieldrin is estimated at four to seven years (for DDT it is 57 years!). In the longer term, while other victims such as birds of prey began to recover, otters continued to decline. Perhaps other agricultural chemicals were involved such as heavy metals (e.g. cadmium and lead), and perhaps subsequent habitat disturbance (or even competition with American Mink), although inadequate explanations for triggering the decline, are implicated in prohibiting a recovery.

The idea that the American Mink might be implicated in the decline of the otter in the UK is one of several charges levelled against this introduced species. Having been trapped for their pelts by native Americans for at least 11,000 years, in the 1870s mink were found to be one of the easiest fur-bearers to farm. During a boom in fur prices in the 1920s American Mink farms proliferated in Europe and inevitably there were many escapes.

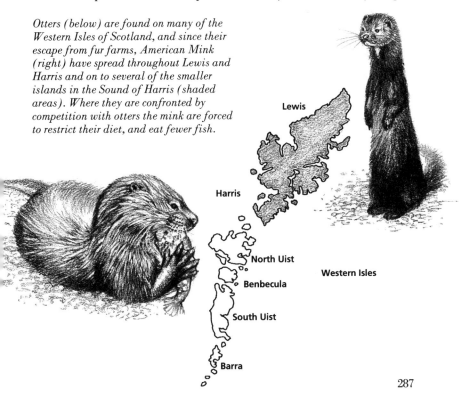

Otters (below) are found on many of the Western Isles of Scotland, and since their escape from fur farms, American Mink (right) have spread throughout Lewis and Harris and on to several of the smaller islands in the Sound of Harris (shaded areas). Where they are confronted by competition with otters the mink are forced to restrict their diet, and eat fewer fish.

Lewis

Harris

North Uist

Benbecula

Western Isles

South Uist

Barra

287

In Russia mink were released deliberately to provide a stock for trapping. In Iceland mink farming began in 1931, by 1937 escapees were established in the wild and by 1965 they had colonised all suitable habitats throughout the island and were blamed for the local extinction of ducks and waders, and in particular for declining numbers of Black Guillimot. They were also accused of damaging Iceland's eiderdown industry. These ducks normally nest (and thus produce their down) on small islands off the coast and out of reach of Arctic Foxes. However, their colonies were easily raided by the semi-aquatic mink, whose reputation was worsened by a tendency to make surplus kills (see p. 103) – some 700 eider ducklings were found cached in one mink den! However, the decline of the eiderdown harvest preceded the spread of mink in Iceland, just as the decline of the otter preceded the American Mink's rapid expansion between 1960 and 1980 in Britain (in contrast, there is evidence that the arrival of mink is associated with the decline of some populations of water vole in England).

The catastrophic decline of European Mink, now confined to a few pockets in the Baltic states, Russia and western Europe, was also blamed on the arrival of the more robust American species, but began before the invader arrived. Although introduced species generally ferment conservation problems, the American Mink has often been a scapegoat when accused of causing the decline of endemic species, although it may well now hinder the recovery of smaller would-be competitors, such as polecats in Wales or European Mink on the Continent. Observations on the Scottish Hebridean islands have shed some light on whether the American Mink is also likely to impede the recovery of otters in Britain. This archipelago is the nesting ground of a large proportion of the 77,000 pairs of Arctic Tern breeding in British waters, along with many other ground-nesting sea-birds. The prospect of invading mink island-hopping from one colony to the next was a chilling one for bird conservationists. Escapes from three mink farms established on the island of Lewis in the 1950s resulted in the discovery in 1969 of a population of American Mink which is currently thriving throughout Lewis and Harris and in some of the smaller islands in the Sound of Harris. So far there is no evidence that these mink have affected the distribution of tern colonies, although adult terns on islands occupied by mink are more inclined to flee from a stuffed mink than are those on mink-free islands, so it seems they have learnt the perils of cohabiting with the new-arrivals. However, on these Hebridean islands otters and mink did compete. On islands inhabited by only one of these species, both fed largely on fish, supplemented with crustaceans, birds and mammals. In contrast, where mink and otter shared an island in the Sound of Harris, the otter's diet remained largely piscivorous whereas the mink turned to less preferred prey.

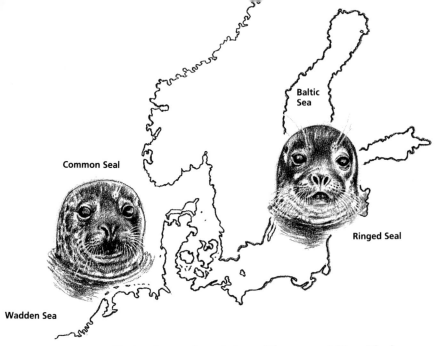

Pollution with PCBs has damaged populations of Common and Ringed Seals.

Being seven-fold heavier, and a fish specialist, the most likely explanation is that the otter can generally force the mink to eat more terrestrial prey, assuming these are available. If they are not, it seems likely that otters could oust mink altogether. The recovery of otters is, therefore, unlikely to be hindered by mink.

A noxious family of pollutants, the PCBs (polychlorinated biphenyls), have affected otters in some other European countries, notably Sweden. Recently PCBs have hit Ringed Seals in the Baltic Sea too. Fertility of Ringed Seals has declined, and so too has their age at first breeding. This precocity is the result of a decline in the Ringed Seal population – the result is that more food is left for the survivors which consequently grow fast and mature more rapidly than they would have done in a more crowded population (see p. 120). In the 1940s Ringed Seals in the Baltic reached sexual maturity at five years, whereas now they breed at three years of age. Things are just as bleak where the waters of the Wadden Sea lap the Dutch coast: between 1950 and 1975 the populations of Common Seal resident in the area plummeted from 3,000 to 500. This decline is linked with a failure in pup production in the western, but not the northern section of the sea. The reason is that the Rhine disgorges its load of PCBs into the western Wadden Sea, where these pollutants contaminate fish and are eventually concentrated in the seals that eat them. Mermaids may soon be extinct in the Mediterranean Sea, at least insofar as these mystical nymphs were illusory glimpses of monk seals. The plight of the Mediterranean Monk Seal appears to arise simply through its intolerance of disturbance by people. Barely 500 of these seals survive, principally on the Aegean and Turkish coasts. Female monk seals cannot tolerate disturbance while they are nursing, and so the blossoming tourist industry in the Mediterranean is anathema to them.

Finally, rarity can mean many different things, and although there are all too many reasons for jumping to the conclusion that rarity is a bad thing brought about by people, it is worth remembering that it can be natural. For example, for so long as it is stuck on Orkney, the Orkney Vole is destined to remain a rarity in that it has only ever been found on one tiny speck on the map. Equally, wolves in the high Arctic will always be rare in comparison to Norway Lemmings in the same region, due to both their lofty position in the food pyramid and their size.

Genetic Pollution

Throughout the world, mammalian species shift their distribution with the result that their relationships with other species are altered. Sometimes these shifts are natural, such as the ebb and flow of Red versus Arctic Foxes with the coming and going of Ice Ages (see p. 139). Some of these changes bring closely related, but formerly separated, species into contact with the result that they cross-breed. There is, for example, a hybrid zone where Wolves and Coyotes meet. Whether two species can produce viable off-spring, or even fertile offspring, depends on their genetic similarity. Even between separated populations there are distinct genetic differences – for example the world's total population of Killer Whales is actually divided into five genetically dissimilar entities, although the dissimilarities are not so great as to prevent them breeding. There are other sets of closely related species that do not interbreed, because they are geographically isolated, but would do so if the opportunity arose. All too frequently such opportunities have arisen because of meddling by people.

1800

In Europe there are examples of two distinct types of genetic pollution of wild mammals caused by human tinkering, the first type involves wild species, the second involves domestic species. Both threaten the genetic integrity of wild mammals and raise the risk that a blending of two species into one will result in a loss of biodiversity. Maintaining biodiversity is just about the only quantifiable consensus goal of conservation.

Although the encounter between Brown and Mountain Hares is the result of human intervention, the deed was done so long ago that this almost escapes notice. The Romans appear to have been great meddlers, moving wildlife around from one part of their empire to another. They brought Brown Hares to Britain for coursing, which had been homeland for Mountain Hares for the previous 70,000 years or so (the Normans subsequently brought rabbits, but they did not spread widely until about 1750). The state of affairs in Ireland suggests that the introduced Brown Hares had a radical effect on the fortunes of Mountain Hares on the British mainland. Mountain Hares took up residence in Ireland before that island was separated from the British mainland, perhaps about 8,000 years ago, and well before the Romans came on the scene. In Britain Mountain Hares are confined to uplands, whereas Brown Hares flourish at lower altitudes. There are a few localised pockets of Irish Brown Hares, but they were introduced within the last hundred years or so and have not spread far. The fact that Irish Mountain Hares occupy habitats that would be typical of British Brown Hares suggests that British Mountain Hares would be more widespread were it not for Brown rivals. The fact that Brown Hares have made such small inroads in

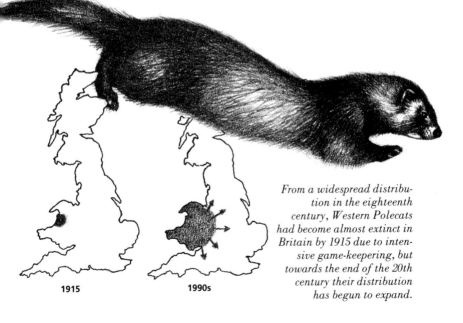

From a widespread distribution in the eighteenth century, Western Polecats had become almost extinct in Britain by 1915 due to intensive game-keeping, but towards the end of the 20th century their distribution has begun to expand.

1915   1990s

291

Ireland in the last century suggests that their conquest of Britain may have been a slow process. It seems likely that one reason that the Mountain Hares retain an upland stronghold is that their guts are specially adapted to detoxify toxins in the birch twigs on which they browse during winter, a digestive feat that Brown Hares are not capable of. The fact that the two species have established a contemporary status quo disguises the fact that the introduced Brown Hares have precipitated a reshuffle of the mammalian grazing community to the disadvantage of Mountain Hares.

At least it seems that where they meet the two species of hare do not generally interbreed. However, that they are capable of producing fertile hybrids is known because they are deliberately crossed in Sweden to produce hunting quarry. Therefore, something other than genetics must maintain their separate identities in Britain; perhaps their courtship behaviour, or social odours are incompatible. In stark contrast, Red Deer and Sika Deer are all too compatible. Two types of Sika Deer have been introduced to Europe, those from Japan, and those from the Asian mainland which are themselves thought already to have resulted from hybridisation between Japanese Sika and Chinese Red Deer (which are confusingly known as Wapiti). In England and Ireland between 1860 and 1930 some 30 shooting estates were deliberately stocked with Sika Deer which have subsequently spread far and wide. They have met Red Deer, a native species but one whose genetic complexion has already been flushed with imports of American and Continental Reds. The Reds and Sika have now interbred in many places – in one area of Argyll in Scotland, almost a quarter of the deer are hybrids (hybrids are also numerous in the Czech Republic, where similar introductions were made). Worse still, from the point of view of maintaining the integrity of the native Red Deer, Sika appear to have a greater potential for population growth, and so appear set to proliferate. The only practical suggestion to forestall the Sika infiltration of the Red Deer stock, is to avoid siting conifer plantations in places that would provide the invaders with corridors through which to reach pristine populations of Reds.

Two domestic species in Great Britain, the ferret and the cat, now pose threats to the survival of their wild ancestors. Ferrets may have been another Roman import, and were originally domesticated, according to Aristotle, in the 4th century BC. They are used for hunting rabbits and rats, which are natural quarry of the ferret's wild ancestors: either or both of the Steppe Polecat of Russia or the more western European Polecat. Modern domestic ferrets can hybridise with both these wild species to produce fertile cross-bred offspring. European Polecats were widespread throughout England, Scotland and Wales until, in the late 19th century, they were largely annihilated by game keepers seeking to protect sporting game such as pheasants and partridges. By 1915 they were confined to a few pockets in Wales. By the late 20th century, however, European Polecats were staging a comeback, and have spread out of Wales to recolonise the English Midlands. Meanwhile, however, feral ferrets have become well established in the wild on several islands (e.g. Arran and the Isle of Man) and parts of the north of England. The extent to which the new wave of European Polecats has been contaminated by cross-breeding with ferrets is unknown. Also unknown is whether the recovery of the polecat will be hindered by the now widespread American Mink which has been introduced in the meantime. The mink is somewhat larger than the polecat, but similar enough that competition between them seems plausible. Although the American Mink is not seen as a threat to British European Polecats through hybridisation, this is precisely the charge levelled against it in the context of the precipitous decline of the European Mink. When male American Mink mate with female European Mink the embryos are not viable. However, they are not resorbed

To distinguish the Scottish Wildcat from a domestic cat purely on the basis of its outward appearance is effectively impossible despite the wild type appearance and thick tail tip of the mother. The domestic tabby markings of the kitten on the right, and the white blaze on the face of the other kitten are clues to the frequent cross-breeding between domestic and wild cats. However, some populations of the wildcat may be genetically less tainted with recent interbreeding with their domestic cousins, and may also have behavioural and anatomical distinctions (for example, a population in the Cairngorm Mountains has larger bodies and shorter guts than commonly found elsewhere).

until after the period of delayed implantation. Therefore, mating with an American male effectively takes the European female out of circulation for an entire breeding season. Doubtless such cross-mating is a disadvantage to the already very rare European Mink, but it cannot have been responsible for their initial decline which began before American Mink were introduced. On the other hand, European Polecats can produce viable hybrid offspring when they mate with European Mink, and although its frequency in the wild is unknown, the possibility of such interbreeding further emphasises the genetic similarity between these various members of the weasel family.

Interbreeding between the Scottish Wildcat and domestic cats is potentially catastrophic. The two are actually subspecific variants of the same species, domestic cats having been domesticated some 4,000 years ago from the North African subspecies of Wildcat. The history of Wildcats in Britain has been woeful since the Middle Ages when habitat loss and increasing persecution led to their extinction in England and Wales by 1880. By 1915 they were virtually extinct south of the Caledonian Canal but, as with the European Polecats, the waning of fanatical predator control by gamekeepers has seen a resurgence in Wildcats which are now spreading again in southern Scotland. There is some evidence that domestic cats began to be common in Britain only after the Norman conquest in the 11th century. The result of the unhappy coincidence of a decline in Wildcats and an increase in domestic ones has been an ever greater potential for hybridisation. Worse still, as the Wildcats have recovered and spread southwards, they have entered a world where the overwhelming majority of potential mates are domestic cats. Wildcats have relatively shorter guts than domestic cats, and subtly different skull shapes. Studies of century-old Wildcat skulls in museums reveal that modern Wildcat skulls are depressingly similar to domestic cat skulls, suggesting that interbreeding has already had a big effect. It is thus urgent, using genetic techniques, to find any remaining enclaves of relatively isolated Scottish Wildcat stock and to seek ways of protecting them. One possibility would be an incentive scheme to neuter farmyard tomcats in such enclaves. The case of the Scottish Wildcat raises perplexing philosophical questions for conservation. After all, the wild and domestic cat are essentially the same species, so does it matter if an increasing proportion of so-called Scottish Wildcats are splattered with exotic colours rather than their original striped tabby design? Aesthetically, the answer to this question is clearly yes for many people, and such unconventional coats may have serious implications in terms of the cat's camouflage while hunting. It certainly has legal implications, as Scottish Wildcats cur-

The success of Raccoon Dogs in Finland, without apparent detriment to native predators, may indicate that they occupy a formerly vacant niche.

rently enjoy the highest tier of legislative protection, whereas hybrids (and feral domestic cats) are pests. There may also be deeper reasons why pollution of the Wildcat with domestic genes matters. For example, domestication may have changed other aspects of the ancestral cat in addition to their colour scheme; one study of African Wildcats in Saudi Arabia revealed that they visited a rubbish tip to scavenge alone, whereas domestic cats congregated there as a colony, perhaps suggesting that domestication has increased the tendency of cats to be sociable. Such a change in sociality, or possible changes in hunting behaviour, could make a hybrid fundamentally different to a true Wildcat.

Most introductions of alien species cause disruption in the community they join. This is because in most habitats most 'professions' or niches are filled. The fact that the Raccoon Dog has been introduced to Europe without obvious disadvantage to resident predators is therefore intriguing. Raccoon dogs come from south-east China and Japan (although the Japanese form probably deserves to be considered as a separate species). Continental Raccoon Dogs were released in eastern Europe between 1929 and 1955. This was done methodically, to create a harvest of fur bearers, and the introduction of 9,100 individuals was recorded. By the mid-1970s Raccoon Dogs were very common in the Baltic States, and occurred in Finland, Sweden, Norway, France, Germany, the Netherlands and Switzerland. Their occupation of Finland has been particularly revealing: 818 were shot there during the 1970/71 hunting season, and 75,000 during the 1990/91 season. The Raccoon Dog in Finland is a committed omnivore, just like the Red Fox, and enthusiastically consumes bilberries and lingonberries in autumn, before falling into prolonged winter lethargy, just like Eurasian Badgers. The potential for intense competition with the existing professions of fox and badger would seem a recipe for strife when Raccoon Dogs move into an area. Yet, remarkably, the huge increase in Raccoon Dogs in Finland has not been accompanied by any decrease in other species, indeed fox and badger numbers increased slightly during the early 1980s. The arrival of the Raccoon Dog was a conservation crisis that did not happen.

The ability of the Raccoon Dog to practice its profession alongside foxes and badgers in Finland may arise from its particular combination of diet and winter lethargy. First, they are amazingly fecund: litters average nine (with a maximum of 16) and represent 24% of the mother's body weight (more than twice the average for canids of similar size). Second, by gorging on the glut of autumn fruit, Raccoon Dogs escape the punishing conditions of winter when food is scarce – indeed, their short legs and neat paws would make them ill-equipped for foraging in snow. Thus, for Raccoon Dogs, everything depends on the yield of the fruit crop and the summer growing period. The later the thaw, the later the Raccoon Dogs breed, the less time there is available for their cubs to put on weight before the next winter, and thus the less likely the yearling females are to emerge the following spring in a fit state to breed. The result is that almost 90% of females breed where the snow thaws early, whereas closer to 65% breed where it thaws late, and litter sizes are larger when the winter is less protracted. Furthermore, juvenile mortality is closely linked to the quality of the fruit crop from year to year. This link between climate and the reproductive lives of Raccoon Dogs explains why they have not spread further north into Lapland where, with snow cover lasting for around 175 days a year, the growing season is simply not long enough for them to put on enough fat to last the winter. Similar limitations apply to badgers, although they take a greater proportion of invertebrates than do Raccoon Dogs, and both species absent themselves from competition for the lean pickings of winter, which are left for the Red Fox. Remarkably, it seems Raccoon Dogs have found a vacant niche in western Europe.

In contrast, the spread of the Reeves' Muntjac in England has brought problems. These small Asiatic deer were first introduced to the Woburn Estate in the English Midlands by the 11th Duke of Beaufort in 1894. Supplemented by additional releases and translocations, these little deer have spread through much of England, in some places reaching an astonishing population density of 100 per km². It seems likely that they compete with the native Roe Deer, and certain that their heavy browsing affects the woodland ecosystem. For example, in one wood heavily populated by Reeves' Muntjac 98% of the Bluebells had been eaten before they could produce seed, and the egg-laying sites of the White Admiral butterflies had shifted upwards because lower leaves had been browsed off. Thus the impact of an introduced species may not be confined to similar types of animal (in this case, other species of deer), but may be far reaching.

Mammals as resources

Massive antlers in pride of place on the drawing-room wall, a large hare on the butcher's hook, a moleskin waistcoat, a carved walrus tusk, the Red Fox in flight ahead of a pack of hounds, the whale oil greasing the parts of a space rocket or seal blubber burning in a rustic lamp. All these have two things in common: they are products originating from mammals and they provide something that people want. The fact is that mammals have provided valuable resources to mankind since time immemorial and it does not really matter whether the product is fun, food or fuel; the principles of exploitation are the same and the risk we run is of killing the goose that laid the golden egg.

The killing of whales provides stark graphic illustration of the misman-agement of a natural resource. The relationship between whales and man is very ancient: whale bones abound in the 3,500-year-old middens of Eskimo villages, and almost as long ago dolphins were featured in the frescoes of Minoan temples on Crete. By AD 1000 Norsemen were hunting Northern Right Whales and Bowhead Whales, and by the 12th century Basques had joined the hunt. These early whalers hunted from canoes, using hand-held harpoons. Until recently, some traditional whalers off the Azores used six-oared boats called *canoas* to row after whales. Early whalers selected Bowheads and Right Whales because these species are so buoyant with oil that their corpses float (hence the name 'right' as in self-righting). With advances in boat building, 17th-century Dutch and British fleets pursued whales around Spitzbergen and Jan Mayen Island in Arctic waters with such vigour that stocks collapsed by the end of the century. The American Yankee whalers exploited Sperm Whales (which also float when they are killed) globally opening up new grounds as old ones became exhausted. But the discovery of new hunting grounds and new technology has repeatedly rejuvenated the industry. Critical dates in this history are: 1868 – the invention of the explosive harpoon gun by a Norwegian, Sven Foyn, which together with the use of compressed air to keep carcasses afloat, initiated the final phase of modern whaling; 1905 – the discov-ery of Antarctic whaling grounds around South Georgia; 1925 – the invention of factory ships allowing the processing of carcasses far from land. Now the fast swimming baleen whales, including the great Blue and Fin Whale stocks of the Antarctic were open to exploitation.

The value of whales was largely for the oil rendered from their blubber and which was used in margarine amongst a variety of products. Sperm Whale oil is a high-quality lubricant, especially the spermaceti oil from the head (see p. 170). The importance of the oil is that it maintains constant viscosity over a wide range of temperatures, a peculiar property not found in any petroleum or mineral oil. A subsidiary product is ambergris, a mysterious excretory material harvested from the intestines of Sperm Whales (a record-breaking 421 kg lump was extracted from the guts of one 15 m long male). This material, continuing the tradition of unwholesome origins for seductive products, was used as a fixative for perfumes and cosmetics.

In all, some nine species of baleen (mysticete) whale and one toothed (odontocete) whale – the Sperm Whale – are economically important. The largest whale, the Blue Whale, was most commercially attractive when it was abundant. In the 1920s the total world annual catch peaked at about 30,000, but by the 1950s their numbers had been so reduced that attention turned to the next largest, the Fin Whale. Fin Whale populations in the southern oceans collapsed in the early 1960s, whereupon it was the Sei Whale's turn. As far as golden eggs were concerned, the goose, if not killed, had been badly put off laying. As the Sei Whale also became scarce, attention shifted to the relatively tiny Minke Whale.

The dilemma facing whalers is fundamentally the same as that facing those wanting to kill foxes for fur, elk for antlers, porcupines for quills, hares for food or even rabbits for bounty (because, of course, if the bounty hunter kills too many of his quarry he destroys his income for the next year). The question is, how many individuals should be killed to produce the maximum profit without exhausting the resource? Most businesses cannot afford to cut and run, so the profit should be sustainable (of course, in addition to sound business reasons, there are also vital ecological and conservation motives for demanding that management of natural resources is sustainable). This gives rise to the notion of the maximum sustainable yield (MSY): that is the greatest number (or weight) of individuals that can reliably be harvested without taking so many as to endanger the population, and without taking so few that potential profit is thrown away. The concept of MSY can only function when exploitation is controlled by a single set of regulations. Other-wise, the laws of scramble competition apply. This was the problem of control-

As the whaling industry has over-exploited its quarry, whalers have turned to smaller and smaller species, focusing in turn on (from bottom to top) Blue, Fin, Sei and Minke Whales.

ling whalers since it was in none of their interests to hold back, as long as nothing held back their competition. Under the conditions of scramble competition, the best economic strategy for the individual harvester in the short-term is to exploit now and bank the money to earn interest.

Bits of whales were used in all sorts of odd places (e.g. corsets), and for unexpected functions (such as stringing racquets with their tendons) for which there were usually alternative materials; it was Sperm Whale oil, protested the whalers during the debates of the 1980s, that was apparently irreplaceable. One alternative, the oil from the seeds of the jojoba shrub, came into use. This oil was first used by the Indians of Arizona and is now used in intercontinental ballistic missiles amongst other things. The problem is that jojoba is slow to grow, so genetic engineering is afoot to produce a high-yielding variety. By 1990 the main remaining whale product was the meat of Minke Whales killed during 'scientific whaling' by the Japanese. (The concept of scientific whaling is that some whales have to be killed to discover the basic information required in order to manage them prudently; e.g. the age-composition of the stock, which is assessed from plugs that form in their ears.)

Today it is the meat of the small Minke Whale, which can command a high price as a delicacy in Japan, which is the most valuable commercial product from whales. In 1986 a moratorium on commercial whaling came into effect. During the moratorium the management procedures used to determine catches and to enforce quotas are being fundamentally revised and estimates of important populations are being reassessed. The whaling fleets of various nations, in particular Japan and Norway, have exploited a loophole to continue catching Minke Whales. They claim that whales are being hunted for scientific reasons even though their products are sold commercially and the International Whaling Commission's Scientific Committee has consistently criticised these research programmes. In 1994 the whole of the Southern Ocean was declared a sanctuary for whales by the IWC. This has not stopped Japan continuing to make its 'scientific' catches there. In 1993 Norway resumed commercial whaling on the protected stock of Minke Whales in the north-east Atlantic. It was allowed to do this under IWC laws because it had registered objections to key decisions including the moratorium and it sets its own quotas.

Harvesting

Remembering that stable populations produce a surplus of individuals each year (see p. 120), one might jump to the conclusion that the best way to maximise yield would simply be to harvest these doomed individuals before they starved or succumbed to disease or predators. However, things are not that simple, because when populations are reduced below the number that can be supported by their habitat (i.e. below carrying capacity), they compensate by increasing production (see p. 120). The central relevance of this fact to wildlife management becomes clear if one pictures the way in which a population increases when occupying a new area. The principle applies to most species, but let us take the Roe Deer as an example. This species has tremendous potential to increase by large mammal standards because all females can conceive from the age of one year and can produce two or three fawns per litter. This they do in low-density populations or in high-quality habitat. However, as their population density increases, the age of first reproduction rises to two years or older and only a proportion of this mature age group conceives in any given year, producing litters which fall in size to singletons or twins. If such a stable population is harvested, releasing the density-dependent brake on their reproduction, they revert to high productivity. During this sequence the production of young per head of the population is lowest when population density is highest. In consequence, the maximum sustainable yield can be harvested from populations whose numbers are less than the carrying capacity of their habitat. Indeed, an often quoted, although probably unreliable, generalisation is that maximum sustainable yields are obtained from populations maintained at half their carrying capacity. This bonus productivity from individuals in populations below carrying capacity may not apply to some Antarctic whales like the Blue Whale and Fin Whale. They do not aggregate at breeding grounds and there are fears that they have become so rare that individuals are unlikely to find a suitable mate. Certainly attempts to manage whales using simple maximum sustainable yield levels have not succeeded and have now been abandoned.

The case of the Roe Deer illustrates that the practice of deciding how many to kill is even more complicated than the theory. The difficulty is deciding upon what to maximise, a difficulty that arises because the deer (like many other species) mean different things to different people. If the sole object was the production of venison then maximising the weight of carcasses might be the solution. If the idea was to maximise the number of bucks with large antlers available to sportsmen, then a different harvest policy might apply. Yet another policy might be necessary if minimisation of damage to forestry and surrounding crops was the goal. Clearly, in formulating such policies, a detailed knowledge of the species' biology is necessary. As it happens, Roe Deer are polygynous, and so the harvest could safely remove many more bucks than does (drifting, two- to three-year-old bucks will probably die anyway if they fail to secure a territory of their own), but the same would not apply to a more monogamous species, such as muntjac deer. The point is that balanced management has to integrate many aims, so that a compromise in the form of an optimal, rather than maximal, sustainable yield ensues.

This point has been made eloquently by studies of Red Deer on the Scottish Isle of Rhum, where the first decade of a moratorium on culling saw an increase in population from 15 deer per km^2 to 25 deer per km^2. This increase in density resulted in a fall in the hinds' reproductive output from 45 to 25 calves per 100 hinds. Similarly, as population density increased, so the antler size of stags declined. Both changes were doubtless due to competition for resources (see p. 116). Less well-fed stags grew less ornate antlers. Two vital points emerge from these observations. First, the deer numbers seemed to stabilise at the new, higher density, without catastrophic mortality and a population crash; second, the ideal population size is shown to be quite different for the different objectives of harvesting trophy antlers or venison. The antler sizes were most magnificent before the population increase, but the sustainable yield of carcasses was greatest when there were 20 deer per km^2. True, at higher densities the average deer was in slightly more ropy condition, but this was much more than compensated, in terms of venison production, by the greater number of individuals that could be harvested. The behaviour of these Red Deer, as well as their weights and measures, had implications for the slaughtering strategy. Killing old hinds was imprudent because their demise removed a barrier to matrilineal groups coalescing, which is disadvantageous in that reproductive performance is lower in larger groups of females.

Where does the idea of a sustainable yield leave the whale story? If a population is harvested more heavily than can be compensated by increased birth rate and lowered death rate among the survivors, then it will be driven to extinction. This was what was happening to the whales. Numbers of Northern Right Whales fell from 100,000 to 3,000. Certainly, production per capita went up as whale numbers dwindled (the pregnancy rate among female Sei Whales rose over 30 years from 25% to 60%, the age of sexual maturity among Fin Whales fell from ten years in the 1930s to six years in 1950), but these compensations could not keep pace with the losses. Interestingly, whaling also shifted the balance between species, for example, the pregnancy rate of Sei Whales began to increase before the full force of whaling fell upon them, possibly because they enjoyed respite from competition for krill due to the decline in numbers of Blue and Fin Whales. Similarly, the Antarctic Fur Seal, having been harvested at rates of 112,000 pelts annually from South Georgia in the 19th century, appeared to be extinct between 1907 and 1916. From a few hidden survivors, a population of one million has since blossomed at an astonishing speed (increasing at 16% per annum), a revival that has probably been facilitated by the reduced competition for krill between these fur seals and the baleen whales. Such shifts as these illustrate that, although commercial deep-sea whaling was banned in 1986, the whales will be recovering in a different world to that from which they had so nearly been toppled. Depletion of the great whales of the southern oceans freed as much as 150 million tonnes per year of uneaten krill, but this surplus may already have been taken up by seals, birds and squid. We now harvest formerly uncommercial fish, such as sand eels (for fish meal and fertiliser) and krill, so this competition may make it harder for the great whales to recover.

The major problem of whaling in a free market was anticipated by Shakespeare in the Merchant of Venice. Shylock saw little point in breeding ewes and rams when, once converted to silver and gold, he could make their value breed faster in his bank. Whales also breed more slowly than money (in terms of the interest earned on their capital value), so if the aim is to maximise profit, the most profitable strategy for a private company (but not necessarily for humanity and definitely not for the whales) is to harvest relentlessly up to the point that whales are so rare it is more lucrative to devote the time to another venture. This is one of several reasons that economics alone is an inadequate basis for conservation planning.

Endangered mammals of Europe

Many European bats are threatened including (clockwise from top left) Whiskered, Brandt's, Bechstein's, Mouse-eared, Grey Long-eared, Leisler's and Barbastelle.

Although hitherto subjective, modern proposals give a quantitive basis for very rare mammals such as:

> V = vulnerable. The species has a 10% probability of becoming extinct in 100 years.
>
> E = endangered (shaded on chart). The species has a 20% probability of becoming extinct within 20 years or ten generations, whichever is the larger.

These definitions are used in the chart overleaf. There are various classifications and lists that include individual species that are imperilled; the IUCN prepares a definitive list in the *Red List of Threatened Animals*.

Species	Scientific name	Status
Pyrenean Desman	*Galemys pyrenaicus*	V
Lesser Horseshoe Bat	*Rhinolophus hipposideros*	E
Mediterranean Horseshoe Bat	*Rhinolophus euryale*	V
Blasius' Horseshoe Bat	*Rhinolophus blasii*	E
Greater Horseshoe Bat	*Rhinolophus ferrumequinum*	E
Whiskered Bat	*Myotis mystacinus*	V
Brandt's Bat	*Myotis brandtii*	V
Long-fingered Bat	*Myotis capaccinii*	V
Pond Bat	*Myotis dasycneme*	E
Natterer's Bat	*Myotis nattereri*	V
Geoffroy's Bat	*Myotis emarginatus*	E
Greater Mouse-eared Bat	*Myotis myotis*	E
Lesser Mouse-eared Bat	*Myotis blythi*	E
Common Pipistrelle	*Pipistrellus pipistrellus*	V
Nathusius's Pipistrelle	*Pipistrellus nathusii*	V
Kuhl's Pipistrelle	*Pipistrellus khulii*	V
Savi's Pipistrelle	*Pipistrellus savii*	V
Leisler's Bat	*Nyctalus leisleri*	V
Noctule	*Nyctalus noctula*	V

Species	Scientific name	Status
Barbastelle Bat	*Barbastella barbastellus*	V
Grey Long-eared Bat	*Plecotus austriacus*	V
Brown Long-eared Bat	*Plecotus auritus*	V
Schreiber's Bat	*Miniopterus schreibersii*	E
European Free-tailed Bat	*Tadarida teniotis*	V
Barbary Ape	*Macaca sylvanus*	E
Wolf	*Canus lupus*	V
Polar Bear	*Ursus maritimus*	V
European Mink	*Mustela lutreola*	V
Wolverine	*Gulo gulo*	V
European Otter	*Lutra lutra*	E
Lynx	*Lynx lynx*	V
Pardel Lynx	*Lynx pardina*	E
Walrus	*Odobenus rosmarus*	V
Ringed Seal	*Phoca hispida*	V
Harbour Porpoise	*Phocoena phocoena*	V
Northern Bottle-nosed Whale	*Hyperoodon ampullatus*	V
Blue Whale	*Balaenoptera musculus*	E
Fin Whale	*Balaenoptera physalus*	V

Species	Scientific name	Status
Bowhead Whale	*Balaena mysticetus*	E
Northern Right Whale	*Enbalaena (Balaena) glacialis*	V
Sika Deer	*Cervus nippon*	E
Bison	*Bison bonasus*	V
European Souslik	*Spermophilus citellus*	V

The exact number of mammalian species currently resident in Europe is a matter of some debate, but one recent list included 217 species. Of these, the Council for Europe concluded that 44% were threatened (endangered, vulnerable or rare) and 24% were known to be not merely uncommon but also declining.

Chapter fifteen

Competitors

Humans versus squirrels

Foresters maintain, with understandable chagrin, that Grey Squirrels selectively vandalise the very best quality trees. This charge arises because, especially in summer, squirrels strip bark from valuable hardwoods, such as sycamore, beech or oak, and destroy the lining of soft tissue within. The wounded tree is thus exposed to damage by disease and insects which, even if the tree survives, may leave scars which diminish the value of the timber. If the stripped bark girdles the trunk, then the tree will die, because the tissues within the bark are the vascular system that carries nutrients up and down in the sap. Ring-barking the tree is, in effect, cutting its throat. Of course, squirrels are not alone in this murderous activity. Dormice do much the same thing, while deer and rabbits eat bark (which squirrels discard) to obtain rare nutrients such as zinc. But why do squirrels inflict this damage?

Many and varied explanations have been proposed to explain the squirrels' behaviour, but most flounder in failing to accommodate the facts that squirrels only strip bark from some trees in certain years, and then they do so only from young trees (of less than 40 years, and diameter smaller than 20 cm). They cannot, as a common fallacy suggests, merely be looking for material on which to blunt their continuously growing incisors at a time when nuts are scarce, partly because they eat the tissue, and largely because their teeth are sharpened by grinding against each other rather than by gnawing on hard materials. Equally, it is hard to see the sap as a major source of food between the flush of spring buds and the autumn nut crop, because they eat so little of it. They do not appear to be seeking water, in that they will strip bark even beside ponds. The weeping wounds are not conventional territorial markers because Grey Squirrels are not territorial, but rather have a pecking order among individuals that share overlapping ranges. It seems, however, that squirrels are connoisseurs of sap: the volume of sappy tissue varies greatly in trees, and squirrels strip bark in districts where, and in years when, sap tissue is most succulent. So foresters are not prey to a persecution complex – the squirrels really do attack the best trees (those with the thickest sap have the most abundant circulating nutrients and thus the best growth). The thickness of sappy tissue gives a fair indication of the amount of circulating sugars within; indeed, a squirrel with a mathematical bent and a sweet tooth could, by assessing the thickness of this tissue, estimate its likely sugar content with a 75% accuracy. Damaged trees often compensate with increased growth (mobilising nutrients from the roots). It may be that elk recurrently browse some trees to hasten their regeneration, but perhaps this habit is no more than coincidence.

Squirrels and people are thus thrown into competition for the same resource albeit for different reasons, and competition, in a broad sense, typifies many unhappy relations between wild mammals and man. In the case of the squirrels, what can be done? In the short-term, nothing much more imaginative than killing the squirrels comes to mind, although a humane proposal might be to offer them sugar solution in feeders, in the hope that this would distract them from real sap. In the longer term, planting strategies (such as deliberate overcrowding and thus under-nourishing of saplings) might minimise the availability of sap until the trees were sufficiently old that their bark was tough enough to discourage squirrel-attack. Facing a similar problem with elk, a foresters' solution might be to plant saplings so densely that elk cannot squeeze between the standing trunks. The advantages of elk exclusion would have to be weighed against the consequences for the growth rate of the trees. Another idea to deter squirrels rests in genetic engineering: to produce tree varieties with distasteful sap!

Canadian Red Squirrels (similar to European species of the same name) have actually been set to work by foresters. Where natural regeneration of forests is too slow, foresters grow conifers such as Scots Pine in seed orchards, where they harvest seeds as a cash crop. The problem is that Red Squirrels may beat them to it, filching as much as 85% of the pine cones

In Britain Grey Squirrels can cause serious economic damage to forestry by bark-stripping, although this is not a problem in their native North America.

before the foresters get to them. The squirrels do not eat all the seeds on the spot, but hoard them as a source of food for the winter. Two obvious solutions to this theft are to kill the squirrels, or to harvest the cones before the squirrels get them. Both solutions fail, the first because new squirrels reinvade immediately, the second because the squirrels harvest the seeds at exactly the right time in September – most seeds collected even a few weeks earlier fail to germinate. However, there is another extremely elegant solution: to pay the squirrels to work for the foresters.

These Red Squirrels often carry food to be eaten at favourite perches beneath which, on the ground below, uneaten debris collects and rots. These squirrel refuse tips accumulate to form mounds a metre high – conspicuous landmarks to both squirrels and foresters. When the squirrels begin to stockpile their winter larders they scatter about half the cones, one by one, in many hideaways, but the remainder they cache *en masse* in big larders. These larders are in the piles of debris – each contains at least ten cones and may contain 2,000! All the forester has to do is search for these middens and gather the cones from them. Better still, the squirrels have an eye to quality control too, rejecting cones badly infested with insects. In young plantations, where traditional squirrel-middens have not yet accumulated, and where the hidden cones are hard to find, foresters can rake up piles of debris, which the squirrels soon stock with 200–400 cones. Paying foresters to raid squirrels' larders is cheaper than the only alternative: paying them to climb trees in competition with the squirrels. Every time the forester empties the larder, the squirrels do their best to replenish it. However, if the foresters do not leave some cones, the squirrels will starve over winter. To avoid this they are paid in peanuts, which is cost effective because peanuts are much less valuable than the cones. The contract is strictly enforced – if the foresters renege on their payments of peanuts, the starving squirrels turn to stripping bark which kills the trees.

Humans versus moles

Competition does not necessarily involve face to face contest. The effect is just the same if the presence of one species devalues the habitat of another, even if the two never meet (see p. 116). In this sense, the charge that Common Moles damage farmland implies that they are in competition with farmers. Molehills certainly can be plentiful: one record-breaking field sported 7,380 molehills per hectare, representing 64,500 kg of displaced soil amounting to 40 m^3. These molehills covered about 7% of the surface and had been excavated from an estimated 25 km of tunnels! Fear of earthworks on this scale prompts widespread mole control, and the conventional method in Britain is to sprinkle 1 g of strychnine into a can of 100 worms and to drop the worms into mole tunnels at a density of about 25 per hectare. What follows from the liberation of this unwholesome can of worms is a horribly slow death, as moles eating the dosed bait asphyxiate over a period of 15 minutes to two hours (strychnine paralyses the respiratory muscles). If the moles were not so discreet as to die underground and out of sight, this cruelty would surely cause a public outcry.

But what damage do molehills cause? Complaints include loss of pasture, the provision of fresh soil that can be colonised by weeds, and damage to agricultural cutting machinery striking the molehills. But it seems that much the most serious agricultural problem is that soil from the hills contaminates silage. As the silage ferments, the soil bacteria from molehills cause a build-up of butyric acid. Unlike the lactic acid that should be there as a result of the fermentation cycle, this does not lower the pH sufficiently to preserve the silage properly and it thus putrefies. Worse still, the soil may contaminate the silage with a bacterium called *Listerella* which is dangerous to the stock that eventually eats it. However, it seems that additives may be found to counteract these problems in silage-making, thereby letting moles off the hook. Furthermore, moles can do good: they stir leaf litter into the soil, facilitate penetration by roots and enhancing drainage and aeration. Moles may even throw up, for the benefit of archaeologists, flints and Roman tesserae. Rarely, however, have moles been so directly beneficial as when causing King William of Orange's horse to stumble, leading to the death of the monarch in 1702, and thereby ending his attempt to subjugate the Scottish clans!

Humans versus predators

The most obvious conflict between humans and wildlife arises when both parties seek to harvest the same crop. Foxes and shepherds, for example, share an interest in lambs although the extent of this particular competition may be greatly exaggerated in the public mind. The critical question is not whether foxes eat lambs (they undoubtedly do, although there is some evidence that they do not especially relish them). Rather, if the fox had not eaten the lambs in question, would the shepherd have been able to rear them to market? Like many apparently straightforward questions, this one is wildly and intriguingly difficult to answer and requires consideration not just of fox and sheep behaviour, but of regional differences in economics and farming practice. However, one important point is that dead lambs found at fox earths (or in their droppings) do not constitute evidence that the fox killed the lamb. For example, in bleak hill farms in Scotland, sheep constituted the bulk of Red Fox diet, and lamb remains were found outside most breeding dens. However, field signs revealed that the foxes had probably killed less than 3% of the lambs they ate, and this loss to the farmer paled in significance in the context of 25% lamb mortality due to poor weather and malnutrition. However, and importantly, in favoured lowland farms lamb mortality is much lower and shepherds can nurse even the weediest lamb to adulthood. In such circumstances the loss of even one lamb to foxes would be more serious economically, although at the same time the intensive nature of the shepherding minimises the risk of any such loss.

Even if foxes killed rather than scavenged lambs, to get a true picture of events it is necessary to know whether these lambs were on their last legs. Predators are known, not surprisingly, to select enfeebled prey. In one flock of merino sheep studied in Australia, overall lamb losses stood at 25% and there were signs that Red Foxes had killed a quarter of these. But half of the lambs that the foxes had killed were so thin and weak looking that they were dismissed as irrelevant – they would have died anyway. The conclusion of this study was that three more lambs in every 100 might have survived in the absence of foxes. As expected, Red Foxes were about four times more likely to kill an ailing lamb than a healthy one. Many other factors, fascinating in their intricacy, may influence fox predation on lambs: gimmers (first-year mothers) suffer higher losses of lambs (including still births which foxes then eat) than older ewes; twin lambs may be at greater risk because the ewe cannot protect her first-born while delivering the second (although in some hill areas the survival of twins, having to share their mother's limited milk, is so poor that the fox taking one of them might actually increase overall survival). Equally, the habit of mating a small ewe with a large ram (to secure a larger fat lamb) prolongs birth and therefore may further increase the risk of predation on the first-born of twins. All this, however, must be viewed in the context of two crucial questions: does fox control diminish lamb losses, and if so, is it cost effective? While the evidence is poor, and circumstances vary regionally, it is likely that the answer is very often no.

So far there has been only one systematic European study of the impact of foxes and their control on lamb losses. This was conducted in the west Highlands of Scotland against the background of a deep-seated hatred of foxes. In Scotland some 29 Fox Destruction Clubs operate under a government subsidy. For example, in 1986/87 1,904 adult and 848 cubs were killed by these clubs at a cost to the taxpayer of £30,365. Did this reduce lamb mortality? To find the answer for at least one locality, fox control was stopped for four years on the Loch Eriboll estate. The result was no obvious difference between the periods with and without attempted fox control in fox predation on lambs (estimated at 0.6–1.8%), nor in the numbers of foxes (estimated at five or six adults on the estate). In this case, winter food (sheep and deer carrion) limited the number of foxes, and the foxes were of minimal importance to lamb survival.

A similar experiment investigated the effect of predators (Red Foxes, stoats, crows and magpies) on game species on Salisbury Plain in southern England. The game bag on two sites was compared over six years. For the first three years these predators were killed by a gamekeeper on one site but not the other, and for the following three years the treatments were reversed. The numbers of partridges, pheasants and hares were reduced where there was no gamekeeper. More importantly it looked as if the combined effect of all the predators also reduced the productivity of game, with pheasant broods 30% smaller in the absence of predator control. This result indicates

The mother Roe Deer stamps to register defiance of the Red Fox scavenging afterbirths. Her still-born fawn will make a good meal for the fox, who is more than likely to be blamed for its death if seen in the vicinity. Proving that a predator has eaten a particular prey is quite different from proving that it killed the prey.

that Red Foxes contribute to the general effect of predation in limiting prey populations (see p. 107), which makes it potentially counterproductive that the British Forestry Commission has for years spent taxpayers' money on killing foxes (1,682 adults and 794 cubs in 1988/89) which feed largely on small mammals that are pests of young plantations.

Although the opportunistic Red Fox has prospered, the impact of intensive predator control in the British countryside had a devastating effect on carnivores in the early 20th century. The distributions of European Polecats, Scottish Wildcats, Otters and Pine Marten all shrank to enclaves. In 1800 the Pine Marten, for example, was found throughout most of Britain, but by 1915 it was confined to the northwest Highlands of Scotland, a tiny area of North Wales, and the English Lake District. Its numbers recovered slightly while peoples' attention was distracted by World War I, and thereafter social changes reduced the pressure of gamekeepers on the land (a workforce of 23,056 gamekeepers in 1911 fell to 4,391 in 1951). Subsequently, outside their stronghold in the Scottish Highlands, Pine Marten have probably suffered from strychnine (aimed at foxes), organochlorine seed dressings (making scavenged birds toxic) and rat poison. There may now be as many as four enclaves of martens in the north of England, but if so they are so rare as almost never to be seen, and those in north Wales are

1800

1915

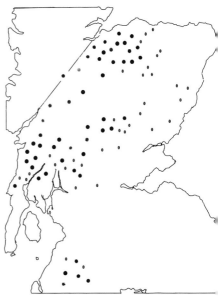

Scottish distribution in 1994

By 1982 most of the wooded areas north and west of the Great Glen were thought to contain pine marten. The results of a 1994 marten survey, based on the collection of scats, suggest that marten are now established in the areas represented by a black dot, are dispersing into areas represented by a grey dot, and are not present in areas represented by a '0'.

so elusive that they are probably extinct. It seems that, unlike Polecats (see p. 291), the martens cannot regain lost ground without assistance.

Humans versus rats

Competition for domestic crops is fearsome: rats of various types are estimated to consume (or spoil) grain worldwide to a value equivalent to the entire gross national product of the ten poorest countries in the world. House Mice can also cause damage of spectacular proportions when populations mass on arable land. The obstacle to rat control used to be the rat's flair for aversive learning, in other words the capacity to put two and two together when, having nibbled a suspicious looking food, the rat subsequently felt queasy. Somehow, rats manage to associate such cause and effect as long as twelve hours after sampling a sub-lethal dose of poison, and have the uncanny ability to do so even if they have eaten lots of other things in the meantime. This, together with their extreme distrust of unfamiliar foods (see p. 151) made them exceptionally difficult to poison before the invention, in the 1940s, of slow-acting anti-coagulants such as Warfarin. These poisons do not take effect until some five or six days after they have been eaten, thereby lulling the rat into a false sense of security. However, after thirty years of intensive selective pressure (see p. 31), evolution has found two solutions to these anti-coagulants. Rats in some populations have developed both bodily and behavioural resistance to them.

Physiologically resistant rats have a dominant gene that alters their blood clotting time. However, everything has its price, and in the case of Warfarin resistance, survival has to be paid for in vitamin K. The resistant rats survive because they metabolise vitamin K differently from normal rats, and vitamin K is an important ingredient of the blood-clotting process. Resistant rats need much more vitamin K, and satisfying this requirement puts a great strain on them. A male Welsh rat that carries a double copy of the resistant gene (homozygous) needs twenty times more vitamin K than a normal rat, and a male that carries a mixture of resistant and susceptible genes (heterozygous) needs three times more vitamin K than normal. One consequence of this burden on resistant rats is that they generally grow slowly and, if they survive, become small adults. The result is that populations subjected to Warfarin-like poisons develop an intriguing state of affairs called a balanced polymorphism; that is, a case of swings and roundabouts, where the costs of both susceptibility and resistance are so punishing that neither prevails. Instead, a stable compromise is reached with a mixture of rats, some with and some without the protective but burdensome gene.

Warfarin poisoning has exerted such immense pressure on Brown Rat populations that physiological resistance to it has evolved several times, involving slightly different genetic varieties in different regions. The single dominant gene that controls resistance is different in Welsh, Scottish and Danish rats, for example. Furthermore, there are populations in southern England where resistant rats have a four-fold greater vitamin K requirement than do their Welsh counterparts. Nonetheless, in most cases a balanced polymorphism has arisen because resistance almost invariably brings both benefits and costs.

However, rats in two populations in southern England have been found to display a much more worrying combination of traits. Contrary to the general rule, the Warfarin resistant rats in these populations were the biggest. Large size is not only a general advantage in rat society, it is also indicative that these rats incurred minimal costs by being resistant. In this case, even when they bred in a Warfarin-free environment, these rats remained physically robust and resistant to the poison (whereas usually, the costs of resistance are so great that its bearers are enfeebled and the trait is quickly bred out of populations not exposed to poison). The fact that Warfarin resistance seems to be advantageous to these rats even in the absence of poison is ominous for the future of rat control. Normally, when a population gets too resistant, leaving them alone for a while leads to resistance dying out and the rats once again become susceptible to control. This tactic would not work where Warfarin resistance was linked to qualities that are advantageous even in the absence of poison.

The second protection against poison, behavioural resistance, is a more recent joker in the pack. Rats in some regions, for example Hampshire in England (and House Mice in Birmingham, England) seem to be exceptionally unwilling to eat poison bait. These rats, when confronted with poisoned bait, may sniff it, walk on it, dig in it or defecate on it, but the one thing they rarely do is eat it in lethal doses. On farms with behaviourally resistant rats, more than half of them may survive a control operation by avoiding the poison. Several factors may contribute to the rats unwillingness to eat poison. First, caution is a luxury that they are better able to afford when there is abundant alternative food, such as a grain store. Second, wild rats are exceedingly neophobic – and this fear extends to novel food. Some Brown Rats will not eat even familiar food if it is tainted with human odour, and some will reject familiar food in an unfamiliar container (and unfamiliar food in a familiar container) for at least a month. Within a population there are great, and unexplained, differences between individual rats in the intensity of their neophobia (although some of this can be attributed to their health, see p. 35). Between populations, there is evidence that the average rat becomes a bit blasé to novelty if its environment is bombarded with change: for example, rats accustomed to the ever-changing circumstances of a busy farmyard may be less neophobic than those living a more secluded existence. This great caution is potentially an enormous problem for rat control, but it must cause the rats difficulties too. Straight-laced, conservative rats must forego many opportunities that their more adventurous ancestors could have grasped. Ironically, besieged by attempts to poison them, modern Brown Rats prosper by restraining the opportunism that has hitherto been the key to their species' success.

The competition for food

In most European countries the losses of foodstuffs to House Mice by spoiling (mice leave some 50 droppings a day) and incidental damage (gnawing) are economically serious. But there is also competition for wild harvests: seals are seen as competitors of fishermen, for instance. In particular, Grey Seals in the North Sea are accused on three counts. First for damaging salmon nets and the fish caught in them, second for eating into the fish stock (although this is difficult to prove), and third for playing host to parasites of fish. The cod-worm is a nematode parasite which lives as a youngster in the muscles and intestines of cod, and as an adult graduates to the more salubrious surroundings of seal stomachs. The problem is that heavily infested cod are unsaleable. In the 1970s Grey Seal populations increased, and so too did the cod-worm problem. This provoked fishermen to kill seals in the hope of breaking the parasite's life cycle. However, the 1980s saw a continuing increase in seal numbers (until disease struck Common Seals, see p. 322) without a corresponding increase in the parasite problem, so the link remains uncertain. Meanwhile, some light has been shed on the supposed competition with fishermen: diet studies reveal that up to 60% of the seals' diet is sand eels, and that the majority of commercially important species make up less than 2% of their diet. Actually, this calculation says nothing about the impact of seals on fish (on which there is minimal evidence) as there are no numbers involved, but it was useful in putting the fishermen's claims in perspective.

Perhaps the most widespread battle between wild mammals and people rages over predation on game. Game rearing is very big business, and often the reality is more closely akin to farming than traditional hunting. In Britain, for example, during the 1980s half a million people shot 12 million pheasants annually, having released a total of some 21 million incubator-reared birds – loosely speaking, this is the poultry equivalent of pick-your-own fruit farming. Mammalian predators blamed for losses in game crops include Brown Rats, Western Hedgehogs, Weasels, Stoats, Pine Martens, Eurasian Badgers and Red Foxes. It seems certain that predators such as Red Foxes can diminish the bag of game; more hares, pheasants and partridges are shot where rabies or mange has decimated fox numbers. Indeed, following a mange epidemic in Sweden there is some evidence that not only has the autumn bag of Brown Hares quadrupled, but also the spring breeding stock may have doubled. This last finding suggests that foxes had not only been eating the doomed surplus of hares, but also reducing the breeding population below that which the food supply could have supported (see p. 120).

The competition between wildlife and humans, as illustrated most vividly by the conflict between game sportsmen and predators, emphasises that market forces determine the nature of the countryside. After all, about 70% of European countryside is actually farmland, and almost none is beyond the influence of people. There will always be different factions, and management of the countryside will thus always be a compromise. We may hope that it will increasingly be a conscious and informed compromise. We may want more game, or more predators, or some balance of the two, but either way, as custodians of nature, we should not be deluded by notions of 'naturalness' in a landscape where the choice is, in fact, largely in our hands.

Chapter sixteen

Diseases

Rabies

The Greek goddess Diana was bathing naked with her nymphs when Actaeon the hunter, fascinated by their beauty, crept up to watch. Perhaps Actaeon's fieldcraft was not up to much, or perhaps it was goddess' intuition, but Diana spotted him and in her rage turned mad all the hounds in his hunting pack. So it was, according to one version of an ancient Greek myth, that rabies was created. Certainly, whether or not you believe this version of events, rabies has been an important disease in Europe throughout recorded history. During the 20th century, the impact of rabies, combined with the impact of people trying to control it, has made it the most important disease of wild mammals in Europe.

Rabies is a viral disease and it can be contracted by all species of mammal. In practice, species differ in their susceptibility and in the symptoms they show (the terror of water – hydrophobia – is a symptom seemingly unique to humans). Raccoons and some mongooses, for example, are among those that can survive the disease and become immune, whereas both Red and Arctic Foxes are extremely susceptible and once infected probably have little or no chance of survival. The transmission of the disease from one species to another is vastly complicated by the fact that there are various strains of the virus, each more or less specific to a given type of mammal (for example, fox rabies is a subtly different disease from bat rabies, and while cats are highly susceptible to the dog strain they are much less susceptible to the fox strain). In Europe, wildlife rabies is largely of the vulpine strain, except that wolves in the former Yugoslavia and Turkey are apparently smitten by the dog variety. These subtle differences between strains of virus may explain why foxes in Denmark and Holland have been free of rabies during periods when rabies was affecting Serotine Bats (but hardly any other bats) in these countries.

Outbreaks of rabies have swept across Europe periodically throughout history, but the recent outbreak began in Poland in 1939 and has subsequently spread in Red Foxes at a rate of between 20 km and 60 km annually. In 1986, having spread westwards some 1,400 km, the epidemic (or epizootic, as animal epidemics are called) petered out close to the English Channel. Throughout the 1980s some 10,000 to 15,000 European Red Foxes (plus many badgers, martens and even deer) were diagnosed annually as rabid. Since most foxes die discreetly, the true vulpine death toll during the 1980s was probably well in excess of a million. Rabies hits foxes hard; when the virus spreads to a healthy population as many as 80% of the foxes perish. Their numbers fall so dramatically that the disease burns its own boats – with insufficient survivors to pass on infection, the disease burns itself out. However, each time fox numbers build up sufficiently to sustain the disease there will be a fresh outbreak, and in Europe this occurs every three or four years, resulting in a cycle in fox numbers. Such cycles are out of synchrony with each other in different regions, depending on when rabies first arrived in each region.

The disease affects the nervous system. Rabid foxes may behave, broadly speaking, in two ways. A minority of them exhibit 'furious' symptoms (more commonly shown by domestic dogs) and travel widely, apparently losing their normal fear of man, and may bite wildlife and domestic stock indiscriminately (the virus is 'injected' along with saliva). This behaviour can spread the disease far and wide. Much more commonly, foxes suffer 'paralytic' symptoms, in which they move within their normal range but become increasingly paralysed. In the latter case, they are more likely to spread the disease locally, biting creatures that approach them. Both symptoms can suit the virus' nefarious purposes – a fact which illustrates the evolutionary games that viruses play. Often the symptoms of disease are no accident, but the carefully engineered result of a pathogen manipulating the victim to ensure its own spread. Either way, the social behaviour of infectious foxes is the key to disease transmission. For example, the footloose, adversarial lifestyle of a dispersing fox may spread the disease much further than a resident one. Just 1 cm^3 of salivary gland extract of one fox sheds enough virus to infect 34 million others – an admittedly abstract calculation, but one that emphasises the potential of the disease.

What can be done about rabies? The traditional European approach has pivoted on the principle that the disease would die out if enough foxes could be killed, so that numbers among the survivors were so low that the average infectious individual died before it infected a susceptible one. The approach has been pursued by armies of game and forest rangers across Europe, who have gassed foxes in their earths. As a result, very many thousands of foxes have been killed annually but, although it may have protected humans, this slaughter has conspicuously failed to eradicate rabies or even slow its progress (with the notable exception of peninsular Denmark). This may be because the killing strategy works against, rather than with, the foxes' behaviour. Killing resident foxes may attract newcomers into the blitzed area (by a 'vacuum' effect), it probably produces a compensatory increase in the reproduction of survivors and, most important, it certainly provokes turmoil in fox society (thereby probably increasing social contact and thus opportunities to spread the disease).

A very exciting alternative to the killing policy is to persuade the foxes to immunise themselves against rabies. This is done by offering them baits loaded with oral vaccine – sometimes delivered from helicopters by the entertaining method of bombing the countryside with vaccine-dosed chickens' heads (appropriately, French foxes receive a pâté bait, whereas in Germany a bait more reminiscent of sausage is favoured). Recent triumphs in the production of two different sorts of vaccine have made this dream a reality. First, a so-called 'live attenuated virus' (known by the inauspicious acronym SAD ERA) was first tested in 1978 in Y-shaped Swiss valleys. Foxes were killed in one limb of the Y, and fed vaccine in the other. Rabies progressed as normal through the slaughter zone, but was stopped by the vaccine. Subsequently, field trials in Switzerland, West Germany, Italy, Austria, Luxemburg, Belgium and France have virtually eliminated wildlife rabies from large tracts of land. About 70% of foxes immunise themselves, and this is about the same proportion as an effective slaughter campaign might kill. This indicates that the difference in the success of the two approaches lies in their contrasting consequences for fox social behaviour. The second advance has been the production in 1986 by French scientists of a completely new type of 'recombinant' vaccine through genetic engineering. (A relatively innocuous virus, Vaccinia, has its genetic composition manipulated to incorporate sufficient elements of the rabies virus to fool the recipient's immune system into thinking it has rabies, and thereby into making antibodies to combat the disease.)

Between late 1989 and 1993 some 750,000 baits dosed with recombinant vaccine were airdropped over 10,000 km^2 of Belgium, and these were eaten by 81% of the local foxes. Numbers of rabid foxes have plummeted in Belgium, the cases in domestic livestock reached zero in 1993, and people seeking post-exposure vaccination following bites by suspected rabid animals fell from 1,214 in 1989 to 71 in 1993. So far, recombinant Vaccinia has been delivered to the foxes in bait, but the ideal would be to engineer a form that spread from fox to fox – the dream of contagious immunity! In Continental Europe, the future for the rabies virus looks rather bleak and, with this burden removed, the population dynamics of both foxes and their prey will operate in a new world.

Phocine distemper virus

Vaccination may eventually be a useful tool in the management of a new virus affecting marine mammals. In April 1988 an epidemic disease erupted in Common (i.e. Harbour) Seals, and over the next six months 14,000 of them were washed up dead around Europe's coasts. Ailing seals were lethargic, short of breath and had streaming noses – all symptoms reminiscent of canine distemper. Subsequently, it emerged that although the virus belonged to the morbilli family (which does include canine distemper, as well as rinderpest and measles) these Common Seals were victim to a new disease, named Phocine Distemper Virus (PDV). By 1990, over 17,000 dead seals had been washed up on the shores round the North Sea. Along the Wadden coastline (where seals form large groups), more seals were found dead than had been thought to exist in that area. Only about 200 Grey Seals have been found dead, so it seems that they are more resistant to the disease than the Common Seals. By 1990 probably at least half of the North Sea's Common Seals had succumbed. By this time it also seemed that organochloride pollutants were involved. In the Wadden Sea, an area heavily laced with these pollutants, seal numbers fell by at least 60% between 1988 and 1989. Off the Scottish coast, where waters are less tainted with organochlorides, seal numbers were stable. Pollutants don't cause PDV, but may increase the susceptibility of individuals to infection. Since organochlorides impair breeding, these figures may mean that pollutants are hampering the recovery of some populations.

The pattern of disease outbreaks in seals with foci around the British coast, the Dutch Wadden Sea, the Skagerrak and the Baltic Sea raised the question of how the virus spread between populations of seals (within populations it spread rapidly between neighbours at shoreline haul-outs). Then, late in 1988, two Harbour Porpoises and a Bottle-nosed Dolphin were found on the coast of Northern Ireland – all three were victims of PDV. This immediately focused attention on the coincidence between the spread of the virus and the annual migration route of porpoises from the Baltic to the North Sea and English Channel. Porpoises and dolphins could have relayed the virus between seal populations. Indeed, the decline in porpoises and dolphins in European waters in recent years may indicate that PDV has been leading some of them, unnoticed, to watery graves. However, this is only speculation, and may distract attention from a definite threat to porpoises, namely that they are at high risk from accidental capture in fishing nets. The virus *Phoca sibirica* which had caused a similar disease among the seals of Lake Baikal in the previous year (1987) also had much in common with canine distemper, so it may well be that the disease of marine mammals originally developed in dogs.

The seals' plight may be worsened by pollutants. Because seals are at the top of a food chain their bodies accumulate toxins, initially packaged in countless tiny doses within the bodies of plankton, then passed upwards by smaller fish to bigger fish and, ultimately, to seals. Worse still, these products of industrial and agricultural waste (e.g. polychlorinated biphenyls, dioxins etc.) do not flush through the seal's system, but accumulate in the fats of their blubber, reaching high concentrations. Already, in the Baltic and Wadden Seas, these pollutants have caused infertility in seals on a massive scale, and they are known to suppress the body's defence (the immune system) against disease. Although those seals dying of distemper do not appear to be more heavily contaminated with PCBs than others, the possible involvement of pollution hangs like a spectre over the whole story.

Dead and dying Striped Dolphins began appearing on Spanish Mediterranean beaches in 1990. A morbillivirus similar to the phocine distemper virus was soon identified as the cause of death. The epizootic spread east with hundreds of dead dolphins appearing along French, Italian and North African coasts. By 1991 mortalities were appearing in Greece and new outbreaks were reported in southern Italy in 1992. Over 1,000 dead dolphins were recovered, but this represents only a small proportion of the total mortality as most carcasses of this offshore species would be lost at sea. Again this epizootic occurred in an area well known for its high pollutant levels. Damaged immune systems may have made the animals vulnerable to infection and the long-term effects of pollution on many aspects of fitness including reproduction would hinder the recovery of populations.

The existence of a disease so similar to PDV so close to the remnants of the monk seal population in Greece gave rise to concerns that this critically endangered species might be infected and driven to extinction.

Bovine tuberculosis

Much less dramatic, but important nonetheless, is the relationship between Eurasian Badgers in Great Britain and the bacterium named *Mycobacterium bovis*. These bacteria cause bovine tuberculosis, a disease which (along with its more damaging partner, human tuberculosis) was a major killer of people and cattle before the advent of antibiotics and pasteurisation. In the 1930s, 20% of slaughtered cattle were infected, but 30 years of tight legislation reduced this alarming incidence to only 0.04% of slaughtered cattle in Britain. However, just as the tubercle bacillus seemed to be vanquished it fired one stinging Parthian shot. The incidence in cattle stubbornly remained at five to ten times the national average in certain areas of south-west England. In April 1971, in the heart of the problem zone, a badger was found dead and riddled with TB. Since then, while the disease has smouldered, public debate has flamed. Between 1975 and 1982 the occupants of some 4,000 badger setts thought to be infected were killed with poison gas. Subsequently, the gassing policy was replaced by cage-trapping (the trapped badgers being shot). But the critical question remained equally unanswered whatever the method: was killing badgers actually making any difference to the prevalence of disease in cattle? Nobody knows, and hence the debate still rages as to whether it is legitimate to continue the attempt at control. The problem is that, despite sharing the same stagnant air in their underground setts, badgers are only slightly susceptible to TB (infection rates in the troubled area range between about 3% and 30%). Furthermore, cattle are not prone to infection by badgers (the infection probably occurs when either cattle inhale bacilli during an encounter with a badger, or graze or sniff grass contaminated with infected badger urine or sputum). Because the disease merely chugs through badgers, rather than ripping through them as might rabies, controlling it becomes, paradoxically, more difficult. Catching the infected badgers is a problem because only a minority of individuals are infected and the diagnostic test is sufficiently insensitive that it only detects about 40% of those affected. So far, it is not obvious that the disease is any less prevalent among badgers (or cattle) where attempts have been made to control them than if they are left alone.

The effect of previous attempts to control TB in cattle by killing badgers has been studied by comparing the time interval between a first and second

Black Rats are becoming very rare in western Europe. In colder climates they are dependent on buildings for warmth. They were once responsible for transmitting bubonic plague carried by fleas and in the Middle Ages they may thus have been indirectly responsible for limiting human populations.

outbreak of TB in cattle on farms during two periods: firstly before any badger control began (1966–72) and secondly during the period in which a recent control strategy had been operative (1986–93). The results of this comparison seemed to suggest that badger control had some effect in reducing the transmission of TB from badgers to cattle, but this conclusion was greatly weakened because the two samples were separated by more than a decade and thus not strictly comparable as other factors might have changed in the meantime. In any event, by 1995 the number of herds of cattle suffering TB outbreaks was on the increase despite 20 years of controversial attempted badger control.

An intriguing complication of the badger story is that *Mycobacterium bovis* is far from being the only bug of its ilk. On the contrary, the soil is heavy with mycobacteria of one sort or another, but most of them are harmless. Furthermore, it seems that the strains of soil mycobacteria vary from one locality to another. This raises an extraordinary possibility regarding the odd distribution of tuberculosis in badgers. It is just possible that in some areas the badgers, which are forever in contact with the soil as they forage for earthworms, are effectively inoculated against TB by exposure to particular strains of soil mycobacteria. In other words, challenged by the soil bacteria, the badgers' immune system produces protective antibodies that ward off not only the harmless bacteria, but also protect the badger against their dangerous cousin that causes tuberculosis. This is one line of thought that gives hope to the idea that it may be possible to provide badgers in south-west England with an oral vaccine against bovine tuberculosis. However, estimates made in 1995 suggest that it will take at least a decade to develop such a vaccine. In the meantime, in 1990 British scientists produced a test that will allow live badgers to be screened in the field for infection with TB, and this should allow not only detailed study of the spread of the disease, but also somewhat selective removal of tuberculous badgers.

In 1995 application of this live test began. On one proportion of farms where an outbreak of TB was blamed on badgers, an attempt was made to catch the badgers and test them for TB. The plan is that if any occupant of a sett is positive then an attempt is made to kill all occupants of that sett, whereas occupants of uninfected setts are all released. The goal is to evaluate whether selective removal of infected animals is more effective than previous attempted control strategies. However, this evaluation will be difficult and take at least five years, because the test (called an ELISA test) for TB in live badgers gives lots of 'false negatives' because it detects disease in only 41% of the infected badgers (although at least it rarely gives 'false positives'). The hope is to reduce the problem of these false negatives by killing all the badgers in those setts from which any positives are found; this strategy is expected to detect three out of four infected setts. Another problem with this programme is that trapping is not very efficient (it is almost inevitable that quite a few animals will not be tested) and because neither this strategy, nor any of its predecessors can be compared with doing nothing about the badgers – as that crucial option has never been tried.

A major worry about all attempts to control TB in cattle by killing badgers is that the death of these badgers may so unsettle and stress the surviving badgers that the net effect is to enhance the spread of the disease. With this potentially counter-productive effect in mind, it may be time to consider alternative approaches. For example, fertility control of badgers seems ethically preferable to killing them, and may also have a less disturbing effect on the social behaviour of survivors. Computer models suggest that there is a critical badger population density, below which the disease cannot persist amongst them, although the relationship between prevalence of disease and badger numbers is not always straightforward in reality. If there is such a density-dependent disease prevalence, the repeated delivery of a contraceptive to the badgers (perhaps via a bait) might be a humane way of reducing their numbers in a specified locality to a level at which tuberculosis was limited. The danger would be, however, that in order to achieve a significant reduction in disease prevalence, badger numbers would have to be so drastically reduced that they were not viable in the long term. The fact is that tuberculosis smoulders so effectively in badgers, making them almost ideal in the role of what epidemiologists call maintenance hosts, that the disease may persist even when badgers numbers are precariously low. Thus although it may be possible to diminish the problem of TB in dairy cattle, the perplexing reality is that it is unlikely that vaccination, fertility control or any other strategy will ever eradicate this disease from badgers.

New epidemics

The threat of new diseases hangs like the sword of Democles over all mammalian populations, including our own. For example, in 1984 in China a new disease was reported amongst rabbits: Viral Haemorrhagic Disease (VHD). This is an acute and highly infectious form of hepatitis and by moving through the domestic and fancy rabbit trade it arrived in Italy in 1986 and England in 1992. An outbreak in wild rabbits in Spain killed 95% of local rabbits so, when in 1994 VHD appeared in wild rabbits in the south-west of England, similar devastation seemed inevitable. Considering that in Britain rabbits do an estimated £120 million of damage to crops each year (one rabbit consumes roughly 1% of the yield of wheat per hectare of wheat crops), a superficial reaction to their apparent doom might well have been delight in the farming community. Yet, despite being an introduced species to Britain, rabbits are now the mainstay of much of the island's predator community so their demise would be catastrophic for wildlife (and would probably destroy the recent recoveries of species such as polecats and buzzards). Indeed, following the arrival of myxomatosis – the last scourge of rabbits – many butterflies and plants depending on the 'mown' grasslands created by rabbits were disadvantaged. The greatest fear was that widespread disease in rabbits would herald the end of habitats such as breklands and chalk grasslands that are maintained by rabbits grazing. Thus the impending demise of the rabbit threatened to be not only a boom to farming but also a catastrophe for conservation. The extraordinary infectiousness of VHD indicated that it would spread fast: cases emerged that suggested the virus had travelled to England on car tyres from France, and been relayed from the Continent on gulls' feet to the Swedish island of Gotland. But then it emerged that, in contrast to their Spanish cousins, many British wild rabbits (10–100% varying between populations, but fewer in the south) were immune to the disease. The origin of this immunity is a mystery – British rabbits that have never been exposed to the disease have antibodies against it. A clue may lie in the presence of a suspiciously similar epidemic: European Brown Hare Syndrome. Perhaps rabbits challenged by the hare disease have survived and developed antibodies that protect them from VHD. Whatever the explanation, it seems likely that this new disease is unlikely to wipe out Britain's rabbits after all, although it may yet prove locally serious. However, the idea has been mooted to introduce it to Australia where the local rabbits have no immunity.

Some diseases of wild mammals threaten people too. Leptospirosis, a bacterium always held to be widespread in Brown Rats, has been vaunted as just such a threat to humans and responsible for Weil's Disease. However, a recent survey revealed that this longstanding motive for fearing rats was at least partly the result of 'Chinese whispers' in the scientific literature. Early records of a high prevalence of *Leptospira* were based on precariously small samples and unreliable diagnostic tests, but had become uncritically incorporated into subsequent generations of text books which suggested that up to 90% of Brown Rats carried the strain of bacterium causing Weil's Disease (which can be fatal). However, a recent survey of English farmyard rats suggest that either things have changed or, more probably, the role of rats has been exaggerated (a maximum of 14% of rats were infected with *Leptospira* and only half of those with the strain that causes Weil's Disease). This raises the interesting question of whether other reservoirs might be important for the disease. However, far from vindicating the Brown Rat as a health hazard, the same study also discovered that these English farmyard rats were rife with the pathogens causing five diseases previously unknown in British rats: Listeriosis, Yersinosis, Cryptosporidiosis, Q-fever and Hantaan Fever. The last is a particularly nasty disease which killed some 5–10% of the UN troops contracting it in Korea in the early 1950s and is now spreading in Europe and North America. Thus, the close association between Brown Rats and people remains a health hazard, even if in a somewhat different guise to that traditionally supposed.

Field study

Las Margaritas was a wolf, and her story a true one. With two toes missing from her front paw, she left distinct spoor as she travelled the badlands of New Mexico. Las Margaritas was among the last wolves in the southern states of the USA, and she travelled far and wide. There was a bounty on her head, and a governmental edict to annihilate wolves. Las Margaritas' movements were dogged by a handful of men, determined to claim the bounty. Such was their skill that they could recognise her deformed paw print and track her over literally thousands of kilometres, and such was their determination that they did so for years. By eluding them, she followed the tradition of such famous predecessors as Three Toes of South Dakota, who was killed in 1925 after evading an estimated 150 trappers for 13 years. But then one man, Roy McBride, devoted himself to Las Margaritas. Her two toes had been lost to the jaws of a steel gin trap, and the wolf had learnt her lesson. With uncanny skill she avoided traps set by the best woodsmen of their generation, and she often emphasised her point by exposing the trap and urinating upon it. At last, having discovered that Las Margaritas was fascinated by cinders, McBride set his traps, built a fire over the top of them, and let the embers burn down. Several days later, as she pawed the ashes, Las Margaritas made her second and last mistake. She was probably the last wolf in New Mexico. McBride had spent 11 months on horseback to catch her. The wolf's skill at eluding her persecutors for so long is awesome, but two other painfully contradictory things emerge from this story. First, and shockingly, it was 1970 when society demanded and claimed the death of this last wolf; the recentness makes humanity's disgrace more vivid. Second, we can marvel at the fieldcraft which led lone men to trail a lone wolf, using skills that doubtless decided the life and death of our ancestors; skills that today we might more properly employ for study and prudent management.

It is true that most mammals are elusive, and many conduct their affairs under cover of darkness, so the mammalogist faces different challenges to the ornithologist, whose subjects often flaunt themselves so brazenly. But it is by no means an impossible challenge. Generations of woodsmen have read a daily paper of events written in field sign, and the modern naturalist can acquire this fieldcraft and learn much from it. Of course, the northern countries have a wonderful advantage in their reliable covering of snow on which some mammals cannot fail to write their story, but even snow does not register the detail stamped into mud. Attention to wind direction, stealth and a sharp eye come with practice, and this book cannot teach fieldcraft, although I hope it might kindle a desire to learn. However, there are a few techniques to consider.

For example, even the clearest paw prints are sadly ephemeral, but can be preserved with plaster casts. To make plaster casts you need plaster of

FIELD SIGNS (RIGHT)
The modern mammalogist still relies on traditional fieldcraft. Feeding signs are especially helpful, as depicted in the top half of the page. Browse line of tree, chewed by deer (1), the height of the line depends on the deer's height. Norway Spruce cones are more ragged (2) if opened by a squirrel than by a Wood Mouse (3). Hazelnuts may be split open by any rodent – their lower jaws are not fused and so the distance between the lower incisor teeth marks is variable. Rodents may gnaw into hazelnuts, leaving characteristic signs: Squirrel (4), Wood Mouse (5), Bank Vole (6), water vole (7), Common Dormouse (8). Carnivores tend to chew through feathers (rather than plucking them as do birds of prey). These feathers have been chewed through at the quill by a stoat (9). A Red Fox has peeled back the skin from a Rabbit's foot (10).
Droppings are also vital to the naturalist's sleuthing. The Red Fox often leaves its scats on tussocks or boulders, and following a meal of rabbit they may have a characteristic twirly end (11). Vole droppings (12) are rather nondescript and seed-like, whereas those of a Brown Hare (13) are spherical. Muntjac droppings (14) are black dimpled pellets.
Mammals leave tracks in soft mud, such as the indistinct Roe Deer tracks (15) leading across the edge of an arable field to a grassy tunnel (16) that might be used also by hares, Red Foxes, badgers and many others. The best chance of identifying those who use a particular path is to find tufts of fur snagged on a barbed wire fence (17).
Nest material can also give clues to the local mammals: Harvest Mice shred grasses (18) to make nest material.

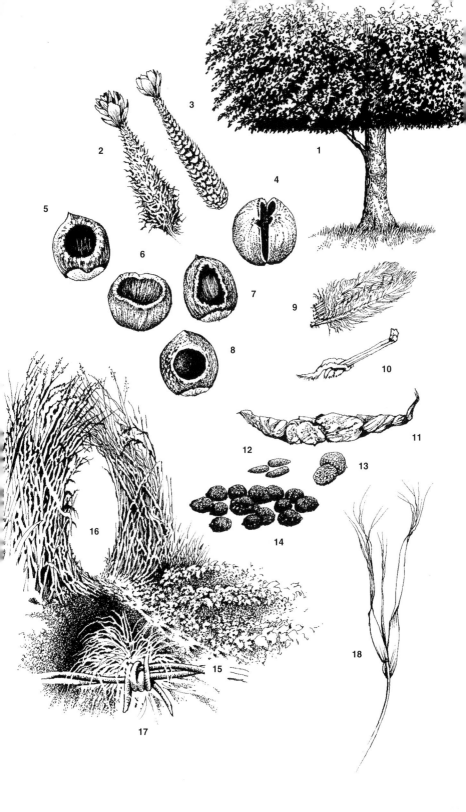

Paris (bought from a chemist), a mixing bowl and a frame to be placed around the track in order to contain the plaster while it sets. The powdered plaster is stirred into the water (not vice versa, to avoid lumps) very thoroughly, and the mixture rocked gently in an attempt to remove air bubbles, until it is the consistency of creamy milk. Once poured into the footprint it will take about a quarter of an hour to set. The end product can be carefully brushed clean, and the footprint itself highlighted with paint.

The comings and goings of small mammals can be monitored by using smoked paper. Tunnels, for example made of ceramic drainpiping, seem to attract small mammals even without any bait, and if the floor of the tunnel is covered in smoked paper the pattering footfalls displace the smoke particles and leave a record of passers-by.

Hair-tubes involve a similar approach. Short lengths (say 10 cm) of plastic piping of a diameter through which appropriately sized small mammals can squeeze are positioned in likely spots (such as hedgerow bottoms). Strips of Velcro, or reversed sticky tape, are stuck within the tube, so as the mammals pass through bits of hair are snagged. With a collected reference set of hairs, one can identify many on sight. However, a more elaborate (and actually rather tricky) method of identifying hairs is to make moulds of the pattern of their cuticular scales in nail-varnish. Hairs are covered in scales which tessellate in patterns that are often species- (or at least genus-) specific. Simply looking at the hair through a microscope will not suffice, because the hair is so thick that it merely appears as a black tree-trunk. To try this technique, smear clear nail-varnish on a microscope slide and place the hair on it to dry. Alternatively, set the hair in some gelatin (just like making a jelly, but using rather less water than suggested in the instructions to ensure a slightly more rigid end product). Once the nail-varnish has set, remove the hair with tweezers and a cast of the scale pattern is left. This can be examined under a high-power (x 100) microscope.

Hairs of larger mammals are often snagged on barbed-wire fences, at places where a trail runs beneath the fence. However, the most abundant source of hair remains are in the droppings of predators. These excreta are a wonderful source of information. The positioning of droppings (or scats – *skatos* is Greek for dung) often says a lot about the lifestyle of their depositor, not least due to their role in scent marking (see p. 185). Their contents can unravel the diet in great detail. There are, broadly, two approaches: the wet and the dry. In the former, the dropping is washed through a series of progressively finer sieves, and the undigested remains collected. A less time-consuming, and less detailed, approach is to dry the dropping so that it can simply be crumbled up and the large items separated from the dusty powder. The undigested remains can then be sorted under a binocular microscope. Predators' droppings contain bone chips, teeth, and hair (to be identified by the nail-varnish method), while fruit pips, beetle carapaces, and earthworm chaetae are among the host of indigestible remains that can be identified. Ungulates pose a more taxing problem: it is possible to identify plants by the shape of the cells on the cuticle of undigested fragments, but this is difficult and tedious. It is also important to remember that mammal faeces carry parasites and disease, so they should only be handled with plastic gloves and with a keen eye to hygiene (they should be dried at 110 °C, or stored in 70% formalin bought from a pharmacy). Increasingly there are health and safety regulations which dictate how biological material is handled or stored.

Sometimes you may come by a freshly dead mammal, and want to preserve parts of it. This requires more detailed advice than can be given here, but the general idea is to prepare a study skin as follows: make a lengthways slit in the underside, from the anus to below the sternum, and gently peel the skin away from the carcass, over the hips and tail. Snip through the tail and ankle bones, and then, as if it were a pullover, pull the skin over the shoulders and head, snipping off at the wrists, ears, eyes, lips and, finally, nose. Rub borax (bought from a pharmacy) into the skin to dry and preserve it and, for mammals of squirrel-size or larger, inject the paws with 5–10% formalin. Stuff the skin with cotton wool, replace the tail bone with wire, sew up the original cut, and label clearly. Pelts from which the fur can easily be pulled are clearly too rotten to preserve. Skulls and bones can be cleaned by leaving them in a nest of wood ants (in a perforated container, or else the teeth will be mislaid), or by soaking in very dilute hydrogen peroxide (at less than a tenth of the concentration sold at pharmacists' shops). Alternatively, having removed the skin, the skull can be boiled in water and then the flesh picked off.

For those with a more advanced interest in mammals there are a variety of ingenious techniques, but be alerted that many require licences from government authorities. Much of what is known about small mammals comes from trapping studies. For example, the Longworth trap consists of a nest chamber and tunnel with a trap door. Grids of these traps, provided with hay bedding, are laid out in an area where a small mammal population is to be censused, and baited with appropriate food (for example, wheat for mice and voles, or blowfly pupae, which can be bought as 'casters' from fishing-tackle shops, for shrews). The traps are inspected several times a day and any captives marked (for example, by snipping a coded pattern on their fur), measured and released. In principle it is then possible to estimate the population size by what is known as a mark-release-recapture index. The idea is that if, say, 10 wood mice are marked and released over a few days and then, on the last day of trapping half the captives are found to carry these marks, then one would estimate that the whole population numbered 20 (i.e. that half of them had been marked). However, in practice this simple extrapolation is based on many assumptions, and interpreting the resulting numbers is fraught with difficulty.

Although an animal may be caught in several different places, live-trapping provides little insight into its movements ('snap-trapping', using back-breaking traps to collect museum specimens, provides even less).

A simple technique is to feed mammals marked food and then recover the markers from their droppings. This has worked rather well on species varying from mice to badgers (badgers use latrines, which makes the markers particularly easy to find – p. 192). In these cases tiny chips of coloured plastic are mixed with suitable bait. Similar thinking has employed baits laden with coloured or luminous dyes which show up in faeces or urine marks. An even more complete record can be gleaned from spool-and-line tracking. This technique has been applied successfully to Western Hedgehogs, among other species. The hedgehog is fitted with a small (1 cm) plastic base-plate glued to its spines about 2 cm above the tail. A re-usable container is stuck to this plate, within which is coiled about 1,000 m of nearly frictionless thread. The end of the spool is secured at the hedgehog's release point, and thereafter a gossamer thread is trailed behind its every move (but readily snaps off if it becomes entangled). The idea is that as the thread snags on vegetation, so tracing the animal's route, so more thread pays out from the container.

Most sophisticated of all, as a method of studying animal movements remotely, is radio-tracking. The mammal to be tracked is caught and fitted with a miniature radio-transmitter (often attached to a collar or harness). These transmitters can weigh as little as 0.6 g and have been used successfully on creatures as small as Wood Mice and Greater Horseshoe Bats. The signal, inaudible to its bearer, is picked up on a radio-receiver (sometimes many kilometres away). The receiving antenna fitted to the receiver is directionally sensitive, and discloses the direction of the radio-tagged subject. By taking cross-bearings, or by triangulation (i.e. plotting where two, or three, bearings cross) the subject's location is disclosed. The marvel of this technique is that it banishes the fear of the snapped twig or gust of wind that cruelly gives away the observer's position: rather, the animal goes about its business undisturbed while the tracker plots its movements remotely. Furthermore, radio-telemetry can encode additional information: for example, on the heart rate or body temperature of the subject, and transmit these, too, across the airwaves. The accuracy of radio-tracking varies with circumstances, but even from long distances animals can often be pinpointed to within 50 m. Perhaps the most remarkable development of all is the advent of satellite tracking – a technique suitable for studying species, such as Polar Bears or even whales, which travel across large areas in inaccessible places. The satellite transmitter is interrogated several times a day by a satellite orbiting the earth, which then beams the map coordinates of the animal's location back to a computer at base, information which is instantly relayed to the naturalist's computer whilst he snoozes in an armchair.

No electronic wizardry or ingenious sleuthing really matches up to watching mammals, but so many species are shy to the point of invisibility. Worse still, many are nocturnal. However, with the advent of night-vision equipment it is possible to see in the dark. These gadgets fall into two categories, the traditional infra-red binoculars and the more modern image intensifiers. The former work by casting a beam of infra-red light (invisible to the mammalian eye) and then converting it to a visible image; the latter use optic fibres to intensify starlight. By removing the cloak of darkness these night scopes revolutionise mammalogy, but they are prohibitively expensive for the amateur. Happily, with practice, even a good pair of conventional binoculars allows one to see surprisingly well on moonlit nights. In the end, patience and stealth are the mammalogist's greatest assets.

Fieldsign quiz

The fieldsigns in a country scene can be read like a newspaper, if you know what clues to look for. Test yourself as a mammal detective by searching the picture for clues (answers overleaf).

(1) How many live animals can you see in this picture?

(2) Which mammals' paw prints can you see?

(3) What type of deer shed the antler lying at A?

(4) What is the nest called at B, and what lives there?

(5) What is the name given to the fox cubs' den at C, and what else uses it?

(6) Whose skull is at E?

(7) What are the foxes playing with, and why do they not eat it?

(8) What type of mouse built the nest which is at D?

(9) Name three mammals which might lie-up in the tree roots by the river.

(10) What signs of deer can you see?

(11) Which mammals have been eating the hazelnuts scattered beside the tree?

(12) What type of animal has eaten the bird whose feathers are scattered beside and do you know how?

(13) What has been happening at F, G, H and I?

(14) Which mammal droppings and/or scent marks can you see in this picture?

(15) Look for nest and den sites, and name the mammals that might use them.

(16) List all the signs you can see of mammals feeding, and name the animals that made them.

(17) Find as many signs of rodent activity as you can, and name the animals responsible for each.

(18) List all the tell-tale signs left by the fox as you follow it from the stream to the foreground of the picture.

Fieldsign Quiz

Fieldsign quiz answers

(1)   There are six live mammals (three foxes, a squirrel and two Fallow deer)

(2)   There are paw prints of deer, badger, fox and hedgehog.

(3)   The antler is from a Roe Deer.

(4)   The nest at the end of the branch is a Grey Squirrel's drey.

(5)   A Red Fox's den is called an earth, and it may be shared by a badger.

(6)   The skull is that of a rabbit.

(7)   The fox cubs are playing with a Common Shrew; they would not eat it as it is unpalatable.

(8)   The nest of grass is that of a Harvest Mouse.

(9)   Otter, American Mink and water vole might lie-up in the tree root by the river.

(10) The signs of deer are: browse line in field, lowered upper strand of fence, hair on barb of upper strand, tracks, bitten shoots, and frayed and broken sapling (right hand side), cast antler, fewmet (droppings of Fallow Deer).

(11) The animals that had eaten the hazelnuts were, from left to right, Wood Mouse, Bank Vole and Grey Squirrel.

(12) The feathers have been bitten off by a carnivore, not plucked by a raptor.

(13) (F) Mole hills indicate tunnelling by moles; (G) fraying of the bark of the sapling tree by deer; (H) smear caused by grease from Brown Rat's fur; (I) scratching on tree-trunk by badger.

(14) There are droppings or scent marks of Fallow Deer, Eurasian Badger, Stoat, Red Fox and rabbit.

(15) Bank Voles, Wood and Yellow-necked Mice and Common Weasels might nest in holes in the ground; Field Vole runway (bottom left-hand corner) might lead to the nest. In the picture there are: Grey Squirrel's drey, Harvest Mouse's nest, Red Fox's earth also used by badger, rabbit's warren, Brown Hare's form, Otter's holt; Stoats and weasels might nest between stones in the wall, and mink in reeds by the stream. The old hut could be used as a den site for Brown Rats, House Mice and bats. The tree hole could be used as a hibernation site for Grey Squirrels, Common Dormice and bats. It might just be big enough to accommodate a Pine Marten.

(16) Signs of mammals feeding: browse line – deer; short lawns around warren – rabbits; spruce cones – Grey Squirrel (left), Wood Mouse (right); rabbit skull and pigeon feathers– Red Fox, badger or Stoat;

shoots bitten – rabbit, Brown Hare or deer; insect remains – bat; hazelnuts – Wood Mouse, Bank Vole and Grey Squirrel; egg – Stoat or Weasel; bark of tree root – vole.

(17) Signs of rodent activity: nest – Harvest Mouse; run – Field Vole; root de-barked – vole; nuts – mouse, vole and Grey Squirrel; cones – squirrel, mouse.

(18) Sign left by Red Fox: muddy wire and fur on barb; dropping on stone; skull, feathers and shrew, earth and track.

Suggested further reading

Much information about mammals can be found in technical papers published in scientific journals, and these are beyond the scope of this list. However, the following good books provide a start for those wanting to explore details mentioned in this book. Readers should refer first to this book's companion volume, in which you will learn about individual European mammal species.

Macdonald, D.W. and Barrett, P. (1993) Collins Field Guide to Mammals of Britain and Europe. HarperCollins, London.

Readable, non-technical but informative accounts of mammals, along with many illustrations, can be found in:
Macdonald, D.W. (ed.) (1984) The Encyclopaedia of Mammals, 2 vols. George, Allen and Unwin, London.

Similarly general books, but organised by species, include:
Boyle, C. (1981) The RSPCA Book of Mammals. Collins, London.
Bjarvall, A. and Ullström, S. (1986) The Mammals of Britain and Europe. Croom Helm, London.

More technical books include the excellent:
Corbet, G.B. and Harris, S. (eds) (1990) The Handbook of British Mammals (3rd edn). Blackwell Scientific Publications, Oxford
And its four volume continental equivalent:
Niethammer, J., and Krapp, F. (1978, 1982) Handbuch der Säugetiere Europeas. Akademische Verlagsgesellschaft, Wiesbaden.

Definitive lists of mammals can also be found in:
Nowak, R.M. and Paradiso, J.L. (eds) (1983) Walker's Mammals of the World (4th edn) 2 vols. John Hopkins University Press, Baltimore and London.
Honacki, J.H., Kinman, K.E. and Koeppl, J.W. (1982) Mammal Species of the World: a Taxonomic and Geographical Reference. Allen Press, Inc. and Association of Systematics Collections, Laurence, Kansas, USA.
Corbet, G.B. and Hill, J.E. (1991) A World List of Mammalian Species (3rd edn). Natural History Museum Publications/Oxford University Press, London and Oxford.

Three books will provide the enthusiast with first class, clear yet scholarly accounts of the crucial topics of evolution, ecology and behaviour:

Dawkins, R. (1976) The Selfish Gene. Oxford University Press, Oxford.

Begon, M., Harper, J.L. and Townsend, C.R. (1990) Ecology: Individuals, Populations and Communities. Blackwell Scientific Publications, Oxford.

Krebs, J.R. and Davies, N.B. (1987) An Introduction to Behavioural Ecology (2nd edn). Blackwell Scientific Publications, Oxford.

Index